Progress to Higher Mathematics

Mary Teresa Fyfe
Andrew Jobbings
Kitty Kilday

Shipley, United Kingdom

Progress to Higher Mathematics

Published by Arbelos.

PO Box 203, Shipley, BD17 5WT, United Kingdom
http://www.arbelos.co.uk

First published 2007.

Cover illustration and typographic design by Andrew Jobbings.
Typeset with LaTeX.
Printed in the UK for Arbelos.

ISBN 978-0-9555477-0-6

Contents

Preface

We have written this book in response to the experience of teachers in Scotland who are familiar with the difficulties students face as they make the transition from Standard Grade or Intermediate 2 to Higher Mathematics: specifically a lack of mathematical skills which makes some concepts inaccessible. *Progress to Higher Mathematics* aims to make the transition smoother and more motivating.

Every year SQA examiners and the Inspectorate comment on the need to improve skills among Higher Mathematics candidates. In many schools, the relaxation of the age and stage regulations makes it possible to teach the Mathematics curriculum with greater flexibility and provide the time to consolidate the essential skills necessary for Higher Mathematics. For teachers in these schools, this book should be a welcome resource.

Progress to Higher Mathematics provides a series of exercises which can be used either as a precursor to the Higher syllabus or as introductory material throughout the course. The approach emphasises graphicacy since it is recognised that graphics play a key role for the modern learner. Basic algebraic skills are also stressed. Collectively the exercises will help students gain a thorough grounding in the essential skills required for success at Higher Mathematics.

We have designed the units to suit students with any starting level of competence, from basic to well beyond Intermediate. The range of exercises should enable students of all abilities to practise the techniques essential to improving their performance at Higher. Each exercise has clearly defined learning outcomes, allowing it to be used individually or as part of a complete unit. Within each exercise the questions are graded and cross-referenced to related material elsewhere in the book. Extension materials are indicated by a snowflake symbol ❄.

We would like to thank all those who have given us advice and encouragement during the preparation of this book. In particular we would like to thank Sharon Frisher, Bob Gomersall, Michael Raw and Dennis Ward for their support. We also thank Michael and Dennis for their assistance with copy-editing which helped to improve the quality of the content. Pupils and colleagues, past and present, have always been an inspiration—in some cases probably unknowingly—and we hope that this book helps future generations enjoy teaching and learning mathematics.

1 Preliminaries

1.1 Expanding brackets

In this exercise you will learn how to:

- ❏ rewrite an expression with brackets, by expanding the brackets and collecting like terms

1 Expand the brackets and collect like terms:

(a) $3(x+2)+4(x-1)$

(b) $5(p+2)-3(2p+1)$

(c) $3(m-2)+2(m+6)$

(d) $6(2q-1)-3(q-4)$

(e) $6(y-1)-(2y+4)$

(f) $3p(p+2)+p(2p-1)$

(g) $4x(x-1)-x(2x+2)$

(h) $6t-2t(t+4)$

(i) $4-3(n-1)$

(j) $4x(x-1)-2x(x-3)$

2 Expand the brackets and collect like terms:

(a) $(3x+1)(x+2)$

(b) $(4p+3)(p-1)$

(c) $(6x-1)(x+2)$

(d) $(2x-1)(3x-2)$

(e) $(2q+1)^2$

(f) $(3m-2)^2$

(g) $3(x-1)^2$

(h) $4(p+2)^2$

(i) $(x+1)(x-2)+(x-3)^2$

(j) $(x+1)^2-(x-2)^2$

(k) $3y(y-2)+(y+1)(2y-5)$

(l) $4-2(x+2)(x-1)$

3 Expand the brackets:

(a) $(x+1)\left(x^2+2\right)$

(b) $(y-4)\left(y^2-3\right)$

(c) $(z+2)\left(z^2+2z-1\right)$

(d) $(t-3)\left(t^2-5t+2\right)$

(e) $(w-1)\left(w^2+2w+9\right)$

(f) $\left(m^2+4\right)\left(m^2+1\right)$

(g) $\left(n^2+6\right)\left(n^2-2\right)$

(h) $(a+4)^3$

(i) $(b-5)^3$

(j) $(2c+1)^3$

1.2 Linear equations

In this exercise you will learn how to:

- solve linear equations with brackets, by expanding the brackets and then collecting terms together on one side of the equation
- solve linear equations with fractions, by multiplying each term by the same expression and then collecting terms together on one side of the equation

1 Solve the equation:

(a) $3(4 - n) = 5(3 - n)$

(b) $3(x + 2) - 2(3x - 4) = -10$

(c) $5(3y - 2) = 23 - 6(7 - 2y)$

(d) $2(5z + 1) - 4(3z + 2) = 5 + 8(z + 3)$

(e) $t(t + 2) = (t + 5)(t - 2)$

(f) $(2w + 1)(3w - 1) = (w + 1)(6w - 7)$

2 Solve the equation:

(a) $\frac{3p}{5} - 2 = \frac{p}{3} + \frac{2}{5}$

(b) $\frac{q-2}{4} = \frac{q-4}{5}$

(c) $\frac{x+2}{4} - x = -4$

(d) $\frac{y+1}{5} + \frac{2y+3}{7} = y - 4$

(e) $\frac{9}{z} = 2 - \frac{1}{z}$

(f) $\frac{3}{2t} + 5 = 7 + \frac{4}{3t}$

1.3 Simultaneous equations

In this exercise you will learn how to:

- solve simultaneous equations given in various formats, using the method of substitution *or* the method of elimination

1 Solve the simultaneous equations:

(a) $y = 2x + 3$
$y = x + 4$

(b) $y = x - 5$
$y = 2x - 7$

(c) $b = 3a - 12$
$b = -a$

(d) $2d = c + 1$
$d = c - 3$

(e) $3n = 2m - 7$
$n = m - 5$

(f) $2q = p - 5$
$q = p - 2$

(g) $5t = s + 4$
$2t = s + 1$

2 Solve the simultaneous equations:

(a) $x + y + 3 = 0$
$x + 3y - 5 = 0$

(b) $2u - v - 4 = 0$
$u + 4v - 11 = 0$

(c) $2a + 3b - 8 = 0$
$5a + 7b - 21 = 0$

(d) $7p - 5q + 1 = 0$
$4p - 3q = 0$

3 Solve the simultaneous equations:

(a) $3x + 2y = 14$
$x - y = 8$

(b) $y = 2x - 7$
$x - 5y + 1 = 0$

(c) $y = 2x + 7$
$2x + 3y = 5$

(d) $a + b + 1 = 0$
$4a + 3b = 0$

(e) $3x + 2y = 6$
$y = x + 3$

(f) $u = 3v + 7$
$u + 3v = 1$

(g) $p + q = 5$
$p - 4q = 5$

(h) $a + b = 0$
$a = b + 6$

(i) $x = 4y - 2$
$x = 2y$

(j) $5y - x = 1$
$x = 2y + 2$

1.4 Expressions with fractions

In this exercise you will learn how to:

- ❑ rewrite an expression with fractional terms in brackets, by expanding the brackets and collecting like terms
- ❑ rewrite a compound fractional expression as a simple fraction, by multiplying every term in the numerator and the denominator by the same expression

1 Expand and simplify:

(a) $\left(2 + \frac{1}{x}\right)^2$

(b) $\left(p - \frac{1}{p}\right)^2$

(c) $\left(k^2 + \frac{1}{k}\right)^2$

(d) $\left(x + \frac{5}{x}\right)\left(x - \frac{5}{x}\right)$

(e) $\left(2t + \frac{1}{t}\right)\left(t - \frac{2}{t}\right)$

(f) $(2a + 3)\left(\frac{5}{a} + 1\right)$

2 Write as a simple fraction:

(a) $\dfrac{1 + \frac{1}{x}}{3 - \frac{1}{x}}$

(b) $\dfrac{2 - \frac{3}{r}}{4 + \frac{1}{r}}$

(c) $\dfrac{\frac{1}{a}}{a - \frac{5}{a}}$

(d) $\dfrac{\frac{1}{y+2} + 1}{1 - \frac{4}{y+2}}$

(e) $\dfrac{\frac{2}{p} - \frac{3}{p+1}}{\frac{5}{p+1} + \frac{4}{p}}$

1.5 Surds

In this exercise you will learn how to:

- simplify expressions containing surds using

$$\sqrt{ab} \equiv \sqrt{a} \times \sqrt{b} \text{ and } \sqrt{\frac{a}{b}} \equiv \frac{\sqrt{a}}{\sqrt{b}}, \text{ provided } a, b > 0$$

- simplify an expression by division or by rationalising the denominator

Harder questions on surds appear in Exercise 9.4 on page 80.

1 Simplify:

(a) $\sqrt{8}$ (b) $\sqrt{12}$ (c) $\sqrt{18}$ (d) $\sqrt{24}$

(e) $\sqrt{27}$ (f) $\sqrt{32}$ (g) $\sqrt{48}$ (h) $\sqrt{75}$

(i) $\sqrt{98}$ (j) $\sqrt{\frac{1}{128}}$ (k) $\sqrt{\frac{8}{49}}$ (l) $\sqrt{\frac{18}{125}}$

(m) $\sqrt{\frac{147}{50}}$ (n) $\sqrt{\frac{100}{121}}$

2 Expand the brackets and simplify:

(a) $\sqrt{2}\left(\sqrt{2}-1\right)$ (b) $\sqrt{5}\left(3-\sqrt{5}\right)$

(c) $\sqrt{3}\left(4\sqrt{3}-5\right)$ (d) $\sqrt{7}\left(\sqrt{14}-3\sqrt{7}\right)$

(e) $\left(\sqrt{2}-1\right)\left(\sqrt{2}+3\right)$ (f) $\left(\sqrt{5}-2\right)\left(3\sqrt{5}+4\right)$

(g) $\left(5\sqrt{2}+3\right)\left(\sqrt{2}-1\right)$ (h) $\left(6-\sqrt{5}\right)\left(2+\sqrt{5}\right)$

(i) $\left(4-\sqrt{3}\right)\left(4+\sqrt{3}\right)$ (j) $\left(\sqrt{3}-2\right)\left(\sqrt{3}+2\right)$

3 Simplify into a form with a rational denominator:

(a) $\frac{2}{\sqrt{2}}$ (b) $\frac{10}{\sqrt{5}}$ (c) $\frac{6}{\sqrt{3}}$

(d) $\frac{21}{\sqrt{7}}$ (e) $\frac{12}{\sqrt{3}}$ (f) $\frac{18}{\sqrt{2}}$

(g) $\frac{2+\sqrt{2}}{\sqrt{2}}$ (h) $\frac{3\sqrt{5}+5}{\sqrt{5}}$ (i) $\frac{5\sqrt{3}+\sqrt{6}}{\sqrt{3}}$

(j) $\frac{\sqrt{7}+14}{\sqrt{7}}$ (k) $\frac{5\sqrt{2}+2\sqrt{3}}{\sqrt{6}}$ (l) $\frac{\sqrt{2}+4}{5\sqrt{2}}$

1.6 Indices

In this exercise you will learn how to:

- ❑ evaluate fractional and negative indices using

$$a^{\frac{m}{n}} \equiv \left(\sqrt[n]{a}\right)^m \equiv \sqrt[n]{a^m} \text{ and } a^{-p} \equiv \frac{1}{a^p}$$

- ❑ simplify expressions containing indices using

$$(a^p)^q \equiv a^{pq}, \; a^p \times a^q \equiv a^{p+q} \text{ and } \frac{a^p}{a^q} \equiv a^{p-q}$$

Harder questions on indices appear in Exercise 9.4 on page 80.

1 Evaluate:

(a) $16^{\frac{1}{4}}$ (b) $125^{\frac{1}{3}}$ (c) $400^{\frac{1}{2}}$ (d) $27^{\frac{1}{3}}$

(e) $64^{\frac{2}{3}}$ (f) $81^{\frac{3}{4}}$ (g) $343^{\frac{2}{3}}$ (h) $625^{\frac{3}{4}}$

(i) $32^{\frac{3}{5}}$ (j) 6^{-1} (k) 5^{-1} (l) $4^{-\frac{1}{2}}$

(m) $16^{-\frac{3}{4}}$ (n) $125^{-\frac{2}{3}}$ (o) $32^{-\frac{2}{5}}$ (p) $\left(\frac{8}{27}\right)^{\frac{2}{3}}$

(q) $\left(\frac{64}{49}\right)^{\frac{1}{2}}$ (r) $\left(\frac{36}{25}\right)^{-\frac{3}{2}}$

2 Simplify:

(a) $\left(x^6\right)^{\frac{1}{2}}$ (b) $\left(y^4\right)^{\frac{3}{2}}$ (c) $\left(a^8\right)^{\frac{3}{4}}$ (d) $\left(z^2\right)^{-\frac{1}{2}}$

(e) $\left(b^{12}\right)^{-\frac{5}{6}}$ (f) $\left(t^{\frac{3}{2}}\right)^4$

3 Simplify:

(a) $\dfrac{a^3 \times a^6}{a^4}$ (b) $\dfrac{2b^3 \times b^5}{b^4}$ (c) $\dfrac{7h \times h^4}{h^5}$

(d) $\dfrac{6p^2 \times p^2}{3p^5}$ (e) $\dfrac{15c^4 \times c}{5c^7}$ (f) $\dfrac{16r^2 \times r^2}{2r^5}$

(g) $\dfrac{d^3 \times d^2}{d^2}$ (h) $\dfrac{6s^9 \times s^6}{2s^4}$ (i) $\dfrac{12g^4 \times g}{3g^2}$

(j) $3t^{-1} \times 4t^3$ (k) $w^{-2} \times 3w^7$ (l) $12a^{-1} \times 2a^3$

(m) $5p^{-2} \times 2p^{-3}$ (n) $2k \times 3k^{-1}$ (o) $8z^2 \times 3z^{-2}$

1.7 The angles 30°, 45° and 60°

In this exercise you will learn how to:

- ❑ find exact values for the sine, cosine and tangent of 30°, 45° and 60°
- ❑ use exact values in simple problems
- ❑ find the exact value of the area of a triangle using area of triangle = $\frac{1}{2}ab\sin C$

This is a non-calculator exercise.

1 The diagram shows an isosceles triangle ABC with $BC = 1$ unit.

(a) Write down the length of AB.

(b) Calculate the length of AC, leaving your answer as an exact value.

(c) State the size of angle ACB.

(d) Write down the exact values of $\sin 45°$, $\cos 45°$ and $\tan 45°$.

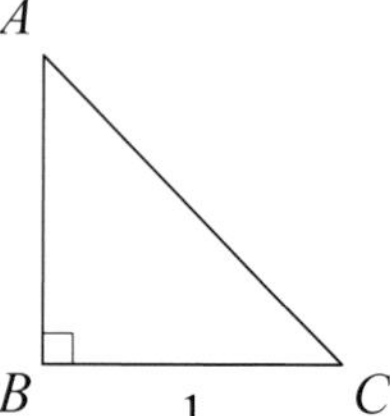

2 The diagram shows an equilateral triangle PQR with $PR = 2$ units.

(a) Write down the length of PQ and QR.

An axis of symmetry is drawn from P to QR meeting QR at T as shown in the diagram.

(b) Write down the length of TR.

(c) Calculate the length of PT, leaving your answer as an exact value.

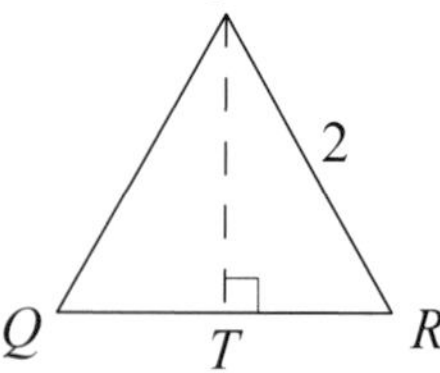

(d) State the size of angle PRT and the size of angle TPR.

(e) Write down the exact values of $\sin 30°$, $\cos 30°$ and $\tan 30°$.

(f) Write down the exact values of $\sin 60°$, $\cos 60°$ and $\tan 60°$.

3 Using your answers from Questions 1 and 2 copy and complete the table:

	30°	45°	60°
sin			
cos			
tan			

In Higher Mathematics, you are required to know the exact values of the sine, cosine and tangent of 30°, 45° and 60°. These are not given on the formula sheet and so need to be memorised *either* by learning the information on the triangles in Questions 1 and 2 *or* by learning the table in Question 3.

4 Find the exact value of x in the triangle:

(a)

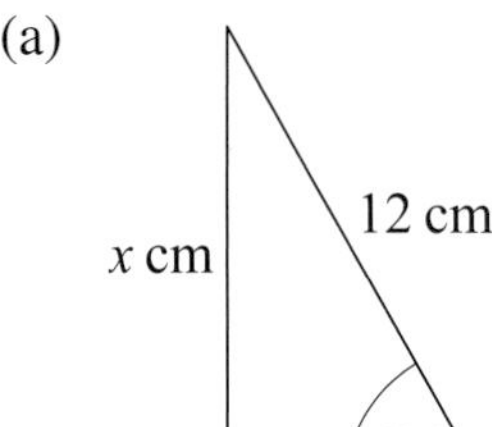

(b)

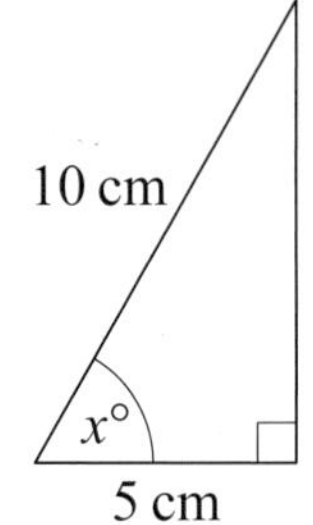

(c)

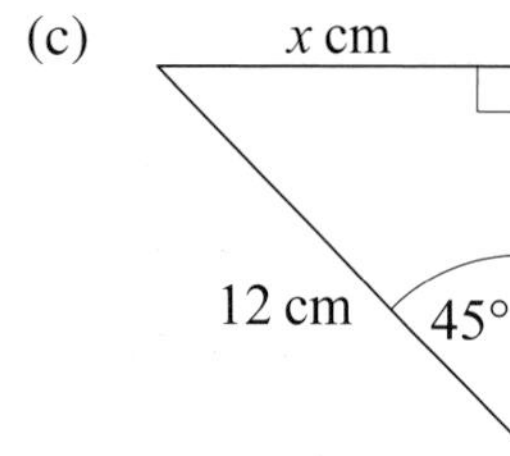

(d)

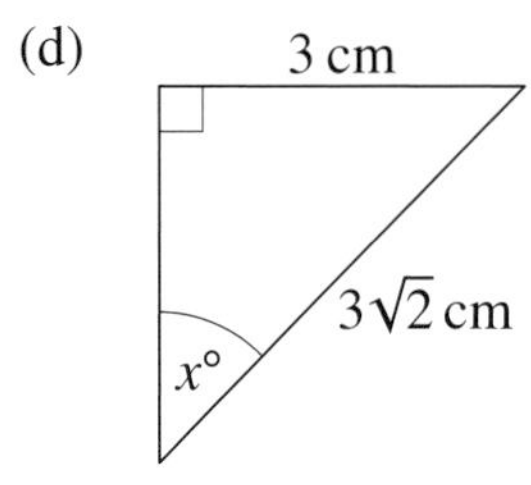

(e)

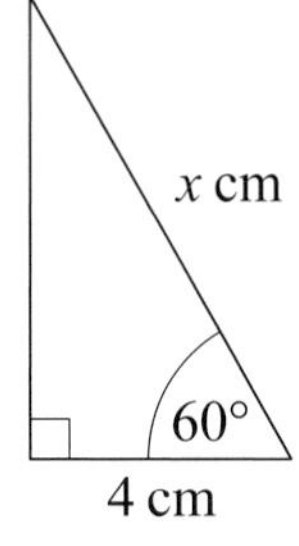

(f)

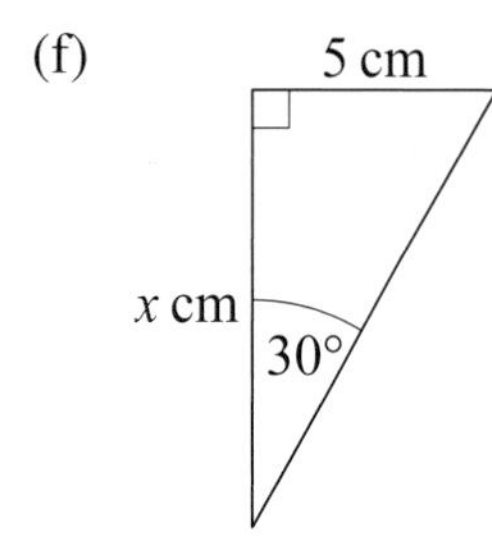

(g)

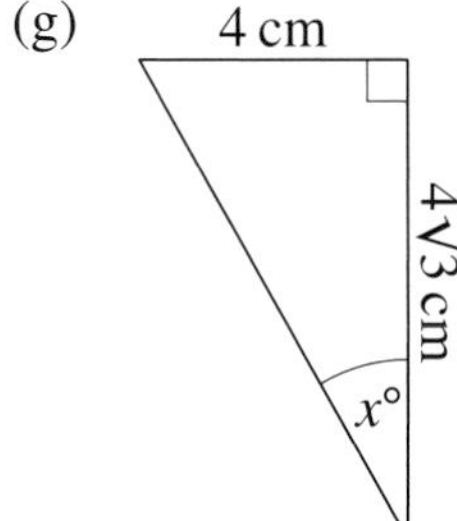

(h)

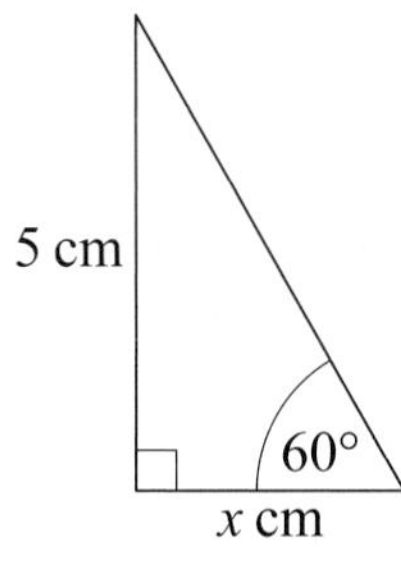

(i)

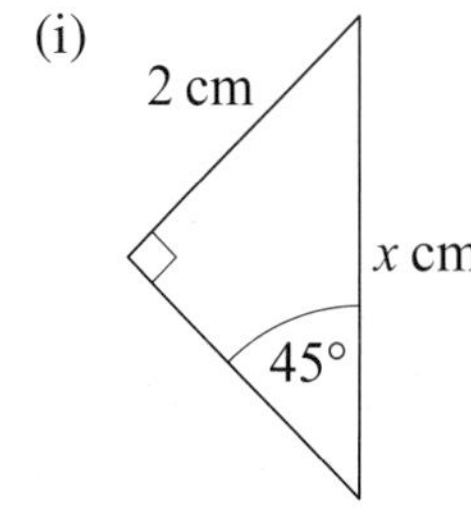

5 Find the exact value of the area of the triangle:

(a)

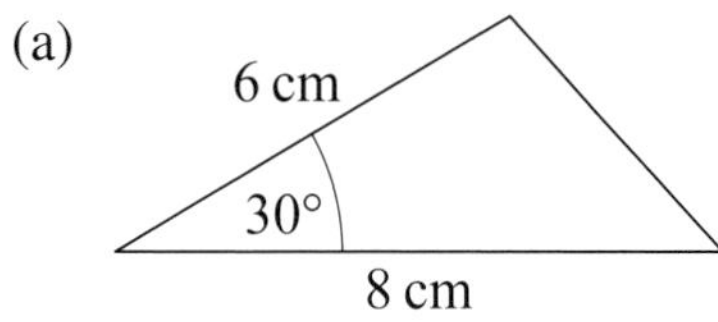

(b)

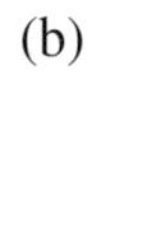

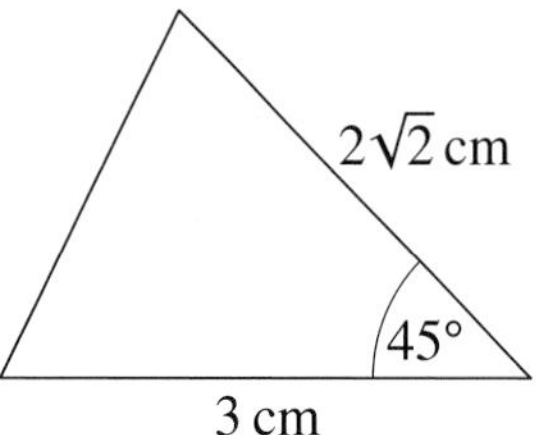

(c)

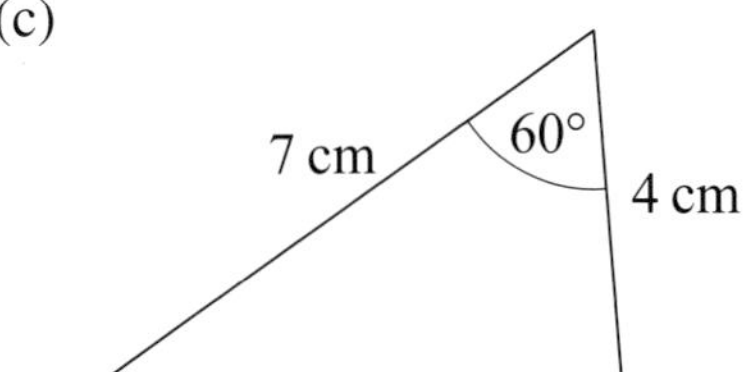

(d)

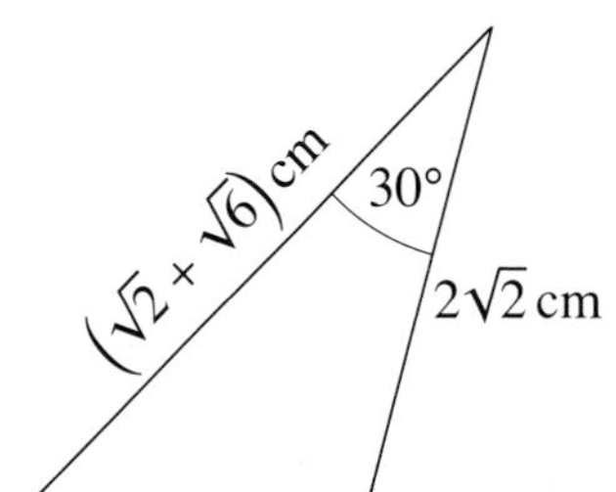

2 Solving equations

2.1 Equations with fractions

In this exercise you will learn how to:

- ❏ solve equations where the unknown occurs in a denominator
- ❏ remove the denominators by multiplying each term by the same expression

1 Solve the equation:

(a) $x^2 = \frac{8}{x}$ (b) $x^2 = -\frac{243}{x^3}$ (c) $a = \frac{1}{a}$

(d) $p^2 = \frac{16}{p^2}$ (e) $t = -\frac{64}{t^2}$

2 Solve the equation:

(a) $3x^2 = \frac{81}{x}$ (b) $\frac{x}{5} = \frac{125}{x}$ (c) $112w^3 = \frac{7}{w}$

(d) $\frac{6}{d} = -\frac{d^2}{36}$

3 Solve the equation:

(a) $\frac{9}{x} - \frac{x^3}{9} = 0$ (b) $x - \frac{49}{x} = 0$ (c) $5h^2 + \frac{40}{h} = 0$

(d) $\frac{49}{2r} - 2r = 0$ (e) $\frac{2}{5t^2} - \frac{25t}{4} = 0$

2.2 Quadratic equations

In this exercise you will learn how to:

- ❏ solve quadratic equations by factorising into the form $(x - a)(x - b)$
- ❏ solve quadratic equations not in standard form by rearranging the terms

1 By factorising, solve the quadratic equation:

(a) $x^2 - x - 6 = 0$ (b) $x^2 - 6x + 5 = 0$ (c) $x^2 + 6x + 8 = 0$

(d) $x^2 - 5x = 0$ (e) $x^2 - 6x - 27 = 0$ (f) $x^2 - 9x + 14 = 0$

(g) $6a - a^2 = 0$ (h) $b^2 + 16b + 64 = 0$ (i) $c^2 + 3c - 10 = 0$

(j) $p^2 - 36 = 0$ (k) $q^2 + 12q + 27 = 0$ (l) $r^2 - r - 72 = 0$

2 Rewrite in standard form and factorise to solve the equation:

(a) $x^2 = 7 - 6x$
(b) $x^2 - 7x = 3x - 21$
(c) $x(x - 4) = 5$
(d) $2x^2 + 7 = x^2 - 8x - 5$
(e) $x(x + 13) = 6(x + 3)$
(f) $3(2d - 1) = d^2 + 2$
(g) $k(k + 7) = 2(k - 3)$
(h) $t(2t + 1) = (t + 2)^2$
(i) $(y + 2)(2y - 1) = (y + 1)(y - 2)$

❄ **3** Remove the denominators and rewrite as a quadratic equation to solve:

(a) $\frac{5}{x+3} - \frac{1}{x} = \frac{1}{2}$
(b) $\frac{2}{x+4} + \frac{3}{x} = 1$
(c) $\frac{x+5}{x} = x - 3$
(d) $p + \frac{3}{p+4} = 0$
(e) $\frac{1}{q+3} + \frac{2}{q+8} = \frac{1}{6}$
(f) $\frac{6}{r+2} - \frac{1}{r-4} = \frac{1}{3}$

2.3 General quadratic equations

In this exercise you will learn how to:

- ❑ solve quadratic equations of the form $ax^2 + bx + c = 0$ by factorising
- ❑ solve quadratic equations not in standard form by rearranging the terms

1 Factorise into the form $(ax \pm 1)(bx \pm 1) = 0$ to solve the equation:

(a) $2x^2 - 3x + 1 = 0$
(b) $5x^2 - 6x + 1 = 0$
(c) $21x^2 - 10x + 1 = 0$
(d) $4x^2 + 4x + 1 = 0$
(e) $2x^2 - x - 1 = 0$
(f) $3x^2 + 2x - 1 = 0$
(g) $14y^2 + 5y - 1 = 0$
(h) $10z^2 + 7z + 1 = 0$
(i) $12t^2 - 4t - 1 = 0$
(j) $24a^2 + 2a - 1 = 0$
(k) $30h^2 + 11h + 1 = 0$
(l) $60d^2 + 7d - 1 = 0$

❄ **2** Solve the equation:

(a) $2x^2 - 7x + 3 = 0$
(b) $3x^2 + 5x + 2 = 0$
(c) $5x^2 - 11x + 2 = 0$
(d) $3x^2 + 4x - 7 = 0$
(e) $5x^2 - 34x - 7 = 0$
(f) $2x^2 + 9x - 11 = 0$
(g) $7y^2 - 36y + 5 = 0$
(h) $3y^2 + 2y - 5 = 0$
(i) $2y^2 + 11y + 5 = 0$
(j) $2z^2 - 13z + 15 = 0$
(k) $3z^2 + 19z - 14 = 0$
(l) $5z^2 - 17z - 12 = 0$
(m) $3t^2 - 20t - 63 = 0$
(n) $2t^2 - 3t - 9 = 0$
(o) $25t^2 + 30t + 9 = 0$
(p) $6a^2 + 11a - 10 = 0$
(q) $6b^2 - 13b - 28 = 0$
(r) $10k^2 + 29k + 10 = 0$

❄ **3** Rewrite in standard form and factorise to solve the equation:

(a) $15x^2 = 1 - 2x$
(b) $5x(2x + 3) = 8x - 1$
(c) $10k(2k + 1) = (2 + k)(1 - k)$
(d) $2x + 1 = \frac{3}{x}$
(e) $\frac{1 + x}{3 - 5x} = 3x$
(f) $\frac{3}{v} = 2 - \frac{2}{v - 1}$

2.4 Quadratic equations resulting from a substitution

In this exercise you will learn how to:

- ❑ use a substitution in order to convert a more general equation into a quadratic equation
- ❑ solve the resulting quadratic equation and hence solve the original equation

1 Solve the equation:

(a) $\cos^2 x + \cos x = 0$ for $\cos x$, by putting $c = \cos x$

(b) $4\sin^2 x - 1 = 0$ for $\sin x$, by putting $s = \sin x$

(c) $5\cos^2 t - 2\cos t = 0$ for $\cos t$, by putting $c = \cos t$

(d) $6\sin^2 t + 5\sin t - 1 = 0$ for $\sin t$, by putting $s = \sin t$

❄ 2 By using the given substitution to form a quadratic equation in x, solve the equation:

(a) $t^4 - 10t^2 + 9 = 0$; $x = t^2$

(b) $k^6 + 7k^3 - 8 = 0$; $x = k^3$

(c) $(y + 3)^2 - 12(y + 3) - 28 = 0$; $x = y + 3$

(d) $A - 11\sqrt{A} + 30 = 0$; $x = \sqrt{A}$

(e) $a^{\frac{2}{3}} - 5a^{\frac{1}{3}} + 4 = 0$; $x = a^{\frac{1}{3}}$

2.5 Equations of the form $k(x - p)^2 = q$

In this exercise you will learn how to:

- ❑ solve equations of the form $k(x - p)^2 = q$ by finding the square root of each side
- ❑ solve similar equations with a higher power by taking the appropriate root of each side

1 Solve the equation:

(a) $(x + 2)^2 = 9$ (b) $(x - 4)^2 = 100$ (c) $(y + 5)^2 = 25$

(d) $4(p + 3)^2 = 81$ (e) $9(q - 1)^2 = 4$ (f) $16(r + 1)^2 = 9$

(g) $(2t + 3)^2 = 1$ (h) $(5b + 2)^2 = 9$ (i) $16(3h + 1)^2 = 25$

❄ 2 Solve the equation, leaving the answer in surd form:

(a) $(x + 3)^2 = 5$ (b) $(x - 1)^2 = 2$ (c) $(y - 7)^2 = 5$

(d) $4(d + 2)^2 = 24$ (e) $(2w - 1)^2 = 3$ (f) $(2z - 5)^2 = 7$

3 Solve the equation:

(a) $(x + 2)^3 = -27$ (b) $(x - 5)^4 = 256$ (c) $(6 - y)^5 = 1$

(d) $(4f + 1)^4 = 625$ (e) $(2t - 7)^3 = -1$ (f) $(5v + 2)^3 = -27$

2.6 Cubic equations

In this exercise you will learn how to:

- ❑ solve a cubic equation given in factorised form
- ❑ solve a cubic equation by factorising
- ❑ solve a cubic equation by rearranging and factorising

❄ **1** Solve the cubic equation:

(a) $(x + 5)(x - 2)(x + 3) = 0$ (b) $(x + 3)(x - 7)(x + 3) = 0$

(c) $(2x + 1)(x - 10)(x + 2) = 0$ (d) $k(k + 1)(k + 3) = 0$

(e) $(m - 2)(m + 4)^2 = 0$ (f) $x^2(x - 8) = 0$

(g) $n(n^2 + 1) = 0$ (h) $d(d^2 - 3) = 0$

❄ **2** Factorise then solve the cubic equation:

(a) $x^3 - 3x^2 - 4x = 0$ (b) $x^3 + 10x^2 + 25x = 0$

(c) $y^3 + 5y^2 + 6y = 0$ (d) $z^3 - 9z = 0$

(e) $q^3 - q^2 - 12q = 0$ (f) $a^3 + 5a = 0$

❄ **3** Solve the equation:

(a) $(x - 1)(x + 3) = x^3 - 3$ (b) $(t^2 + 1)(t + 2) = 2$

3 Lines and circles

3.1 The gradient and equation of a straight line

In this exercise you will learn how to:

- ❑ find the gradient of the line joining two points using $\text{gradient} = \dfrac{\text{change in } y}{\text{change in } x}$ or $\text{gradient} = \dfrac{y_2 - y_1}{x_2 - x_1}$
- ❑ find the gradient m of a line by converting the equation to the form $y = mx + c$
- ❑ find the equation of a line through a given point with a given gradient, or through two given points
- ❑ find the points of intersection of a line with the x- and y-axes
- ❑ convert the equation of a line into a different form

1 Find the gradient of the line joining:

(a) $(2, 5)$ to $(4, 11)$ (b) $(0, 11)$ to $(-2, 1)$ (c) $(4, -2)$ to $(-2, 10)$

(d) $(-5, -3)$ to $(7, 1)$ (e) $(-5, 2)$ to $(0, -1)$ (f) $(5, 7)$ to $(4, 7)$

2 Write down the gradient of the line with equation:

(a) $y = 3x - 4$ (b) $2x + y = 7$ (c) $4y = 8x + 1$

(d) $x - y = 3$ (e) $x - 3y = 9$ (f) $4x + 5y = 20$

(g) $2x + 3y + 8 = 0$

3 Find the equation of the line:

(a) through $(0, 4)$ with gradient 2 (b) through $(0, 2)$ with gradient -1

(c) through $(1, 1)$ with gradient 3 (d) through $(5, -3)$ with gradient -2

(e) through $(0, 6)$ with gradient $\frac{2}{3}$ (f) through $(4, 2)$ with gradient $-\frac{1}{2}$

4 Find the equation of the line:

(a) through $(2, 5)$ and $(-3, 0)$ (b) through $(4, -1)$ and $(3, -3)$

(c) through $(-4, 1)$ and $(8, 7)$ (d) through $(1, -1)$ and $(-3, 15)$

(e) through $(5, -1)$ and $(-10, 2)$ (f) through $(-3, -1)$ and $(9, 7)$

(g) through $(3, -4)$ and $(-9, 12)$

5 The diagram shows four graphs labelled A, B, C or D. On each graph the same scale is used on the x-axis and the y-axis.

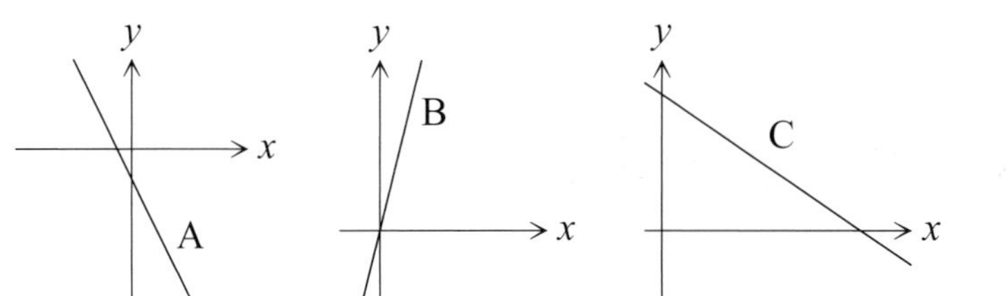

Write down the letter corresponding to the graph with equation:

(a) $y = 4x$ (b) $y = 3 - x$ (c) $2x + 3y = 24$ (d) $2x + y = -1$

6 Find the points of intersection with the x- and y-axes of the line with equation:

(a) $y = 2x + 4$ (b) $y = 12 - 3x$ (c) $y = 3x - 10$
(d) $x + y = 5$ (e) $3x + 5y = 30$ (f) $x - 4y = 4$
(g) $2x + y = 6$ (h) $2x - 3y = 5$ (i) $x + 3y + 15 = 0$
(j) $6x - y - 9 = 0$

7 By converting into a form with no fractions and no negative numbers, rewrite the equation of the line:

(a) $y = \frac{2}{3}x + 5$ (b) $y = x + \frac{1}{9}$ (c) $y = \frac{4}{5}x - \frac{1}{3}$
(d) $y = 6 - \frac{2}{5}x$ (e) $y = -4 - \frac{1}{2}x$ (f) $y = \frac{1}{4}x - \frac{1}{3}$

8 By converting into the form $ax + by + c = 0$, where $a > 0$, rewrite the equation of the line:

(a) $y = x - 4$ (b) $2y = x + 5$ (c) $4y = 6 - 3x$
(d) $y = \frac{2}{3}x - 1$ (e) $y = 2 - \frac{3}{5}x$ (f) $y = \frac{5}{6}x$

3.2 Lines parallel to the axes

In this exercise you will learn how to:

- find and use equations of the form $x = k$ for lines parallel to the y-axis
- find and use equations of the form $y = l$ for lines parallel to the x-axis

1 Write down the equation of the line:

(a) through the point $(2, 3)$ which is parallel to the x-axis
(b) through the point $(1, 4)$ which is perpendicular to the y-axis
(c) through the point $(2, 5)$ which is parallel to $x = 3$
(d) through the point $(7, 1)$ which is perpendicular to $x = -1$
(e) through the point $(3, 4)$ which is parallel to $y = 7$

2 A median of a triangle is a line joining a vertex to the midpoint of the opposite side.

Triangle ABC has vertices $A(7, 4)$, $B(1, 6)$ and $C(1, 2)$. Find the equation of the median AM, where M is the midpoint of BC.

3 Two sides of a rectangle have equations $x = 4$ and $y = -6$. One vertex of the rectangle is $(-3, 8)$.

(a) Write down the equations of the other two sides of the rectangle.

(b) Find the equations of the diagonals of the rectangle.

4 The diagonals of a rhombus have equations $x = -2$ and $y = 5$.

(a) Write down the coordinates of the point of intersection of these diagonals.

The points $(0, 5)$ and $(-2, 8)$ are vertices of this rhombus.

(b) Write down the coordinates of the other two vertices.

5 The diagram shows the first few of a sequence of kites, placed together and extending to the right. The kites are labelled consecutively A, a, B, b, ...

(a) Write down the equations of the diagonals of the kites labelled E and e.

(b) Write down the equations of the diagonals of the kites that will appear later in the sequence with labels G and j.

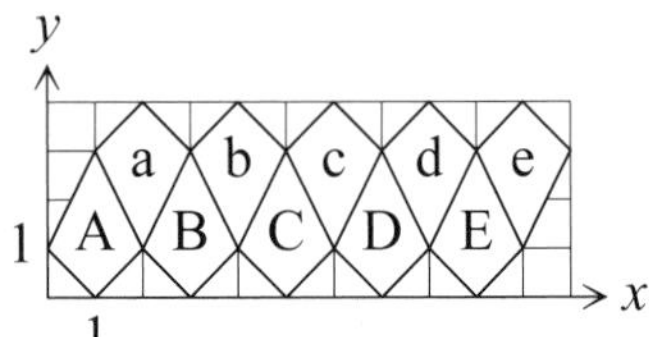

❄ 6 A triangle is formed by the lines PQ with equation $3x + 2y = 12$, QR with equation $y = 6$, and PR with equation $x = 4$. Find the equation of the angle bisector of angle PRQ.

3.3 Parallel lines

In this exercise you will learn how to:

- use the fact that parallel lines have equal gradients *or* that lines with equations of the form $ax + by + c_1 = 0$ and $ax + by + c_2 = 0$ are parallel
- find the equation of a line through a given point parallel to a given line

1 Write down the equation of the line:

(a) through the point $(0, 1)$ and parallel to the line $y = 4x + 5$

(b) through the point $(0, -2)$ and parallel to the line $2x - y = 5$

(c) through the point $(1, 2)$ and parallel to the line $x + y = 8$

(d) through the point $(-2, -3)$ and parallel to the line $3x + 2y - 1 = 0$

(e) through the point $(0, 0)$ and parallel to the line $6x - y = 7$

2 Find the equation of the line through the points $(a, 4)$ and $(7, a)$ which is parallel to the line $y = 2x + 14$.

3 In the rhombus $ABCD$ the side AB has equation $y = 1 - x$ and vertex C is $(1, -6)$. Write down the equation of the side CD.

4 In the rectangle $KLMN$ the side KL has equation $2x + 5y = 17$ and vertex N is $(-1, 3)$. Write down the equation of the side MN.

5 Two of the vertices of parallelogram $ABCD$ are $A(-2,7)$ and $C(5,-1)$.

The side BC has equation $y = -5x + 24$ and the side AB has equation $x + 2y = 12$.

Find the equations of AD and DC.

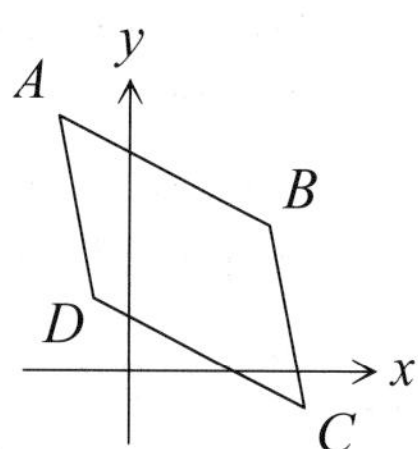

6 In the trapezium $PQRS$ the sides PQ and SR are parallel.

Three of the vertices are $P(3,2)$, $Q(6,1)$ and $R(3,-3)$.

(a) Find the equation of PQ.

(b) Find the equation of RS.

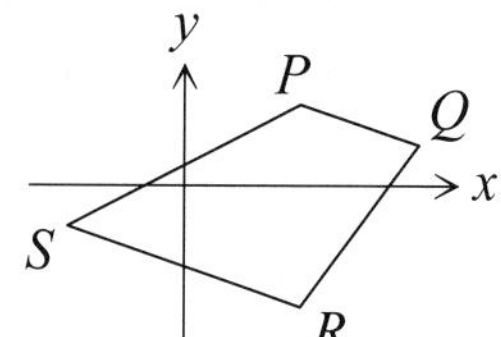

❄ **7** The lines $2x + py = 7$ and $qx - 5y = 4$ are parallel. Show that $pq = -10$.

3.4 Midpoint and length of a line

In this exercise you will learn how to:

- ❑ use the fact that the midpoint is (average x-coordinate, average y-coordinate) or $\left(\frac{1}{2}(x_1 + x_2), \frac{1}{2}(y_1 + y_2)\right)$ to find the midpoint of a line segment
- ❑ find the length of a line segment *either* by drawing an appropriate right-angled triangle *or* by using the fact that length$=\sqrt{(\text{change in } x)^2 + (\text{change in } y)^2}$ or length$=\sqrt{(x_2 - x_1)^2 + (y_2 - y_1)^2}$
- ❑ solve problems involving midpoints and lengths of line segments

1 Find the midpoint of the line joining:

(a) $(2,8)$ to $(14,4)$ (b) $(5,-1)$ to $(-9,3)$ (c) $(7,0)$ to $(1,3)$

2 The parallelogram $PQRS$ has vertices $P(1,5)$, $Q(10,-2)$, $R(7,-3)$ and $S(-2,4)$. Find the coordinates of the point of intersection of the diagonals of $PQRS$.

3 The centre of the square $ABCD$ is at $M(5,-1)$ and $A(-2,3)$ is one end of the diagonal AC. Find the coordinates of C.

4 Show that $(4,7)$ is the midpoint of the line joining $(-1,11)$ to $(9,3)$

5 Write down the coordinates of the midpoint of the line joining $(2a, 5b)$ to $(6a, -b)$.

6 Calculate the length of the line joining:

(a) $(4,2)$ to $(7,6)$ (b) $(-5,3)$ to $(0,15)$ (c) $(3,-6)$ to $(2,1)$

(d) $(-4,2)$ to $(-1,5)$

❄ **7** The length of the line joining $A(1,6)$ and $B(a,9)$ is 5. Calculate the two possible values of a.

❄ **8** Two vertices of triangle PQR are $P(-3,4)$ and $Q(3,-2)$. The vertex R lies on the line $y = 1$ and the length of PR is half the length of PQ. Find the coordinates of the two possible positions of R.

3.5 Collinear points

In this exercise you will learn how to:
- ❑ determine whether given points are collinear
- ❑ use properties of collinear points

1 Show that the point $(4,-1)$ lies on the line with equation $y = 3 - x$.

2 Four points have coordinates $P(4,7)$, $Q(0,1)$, $R(-2,-5)$ and $S(-4,-7)$.
(a) Which of the points P, Q, R and S lie on the line $y = 2x - 1$?
(b) Show that the gradient of PR is 2.

3 Show that:
(a) $A(4,6)$, $B(-2,12)$ and $C(-5,15)$ are collinear
(b) $P(-2,-14)$, $Q(1,1)$ and $R(3,11)$ are collinear
(c) $K(-6,12)$, $L(0,7)$ and $M(3,6)$ are not collinear
(d) $S(9,25)$, $T(5,5)$ and $U(3,-5)$ are collinear

4 Find the value of a for which:
(a) $(2,1)$, $(4,5)$ and $(a,11)$ are collinear
(b) $(-3,-13)$, $(1,7)$ and $(4,a)$ are collinear
(c) $(a,2)$, $(0,4)$ and $(3,6)$ are collinear
(d) $(2,8)$, $(a,-20)$ and $(0,0)$ are collinear
(e) $(10,5)$, $(2,9)$, $(a,6)$ and $(4,a)$ are collinear

5 (a) Does the point $C(3,9)$ lie on the line through the points $A(1,1)$ and $B(7,25)$?
(b) Does the point $F(2,9)$ lie on the line through the points $D(0,1)$ and $E(-2,11)$?
(c) Does the point $J(-3,3)$ lie on the line through the points $G(1,3)$ and $H(-4,6)$?
(d) Does the point $M(4,0)$ lie on the line through the points $K(8,3)$ and $L(0,-3)$?

3.6 The angle between a line and the x-axis

In this exercise you will learn how to:

- use the equation $m = \tan\theta$ connecting the gradient m of a line and the angle θ between the line and the positive x-axis

Where answers are approximate, give angles to one decimal place and gradients to one significant figure.

1 Find the gradient of the line whose graph is:

(a)
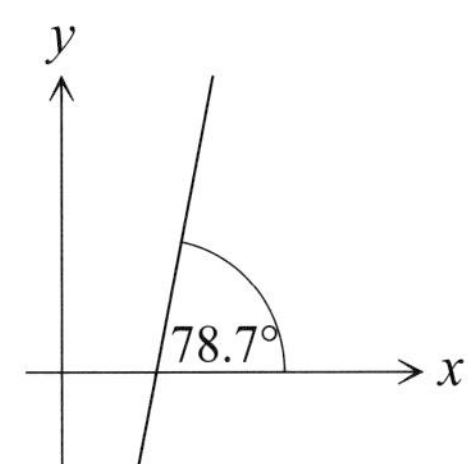

(b)
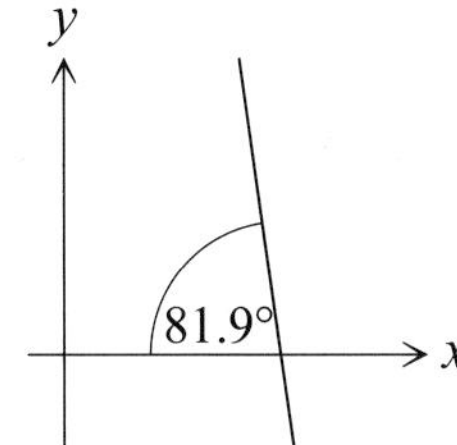

(c)
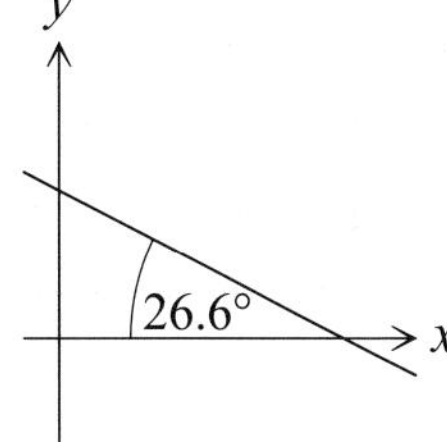

(d)
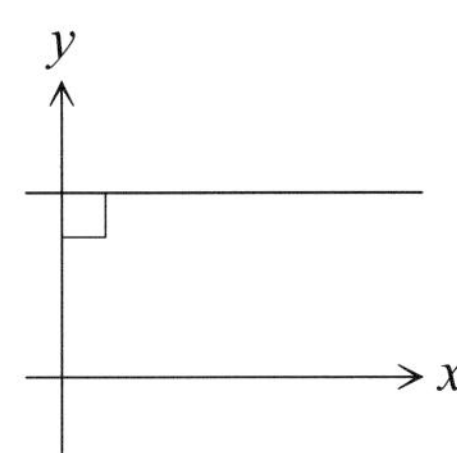

(e)
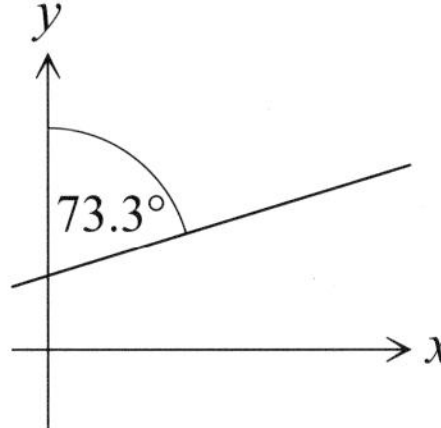

(f)
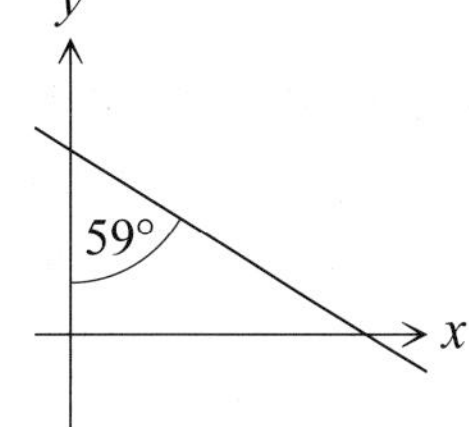

2 Find the value of a in the diagram:

(a)
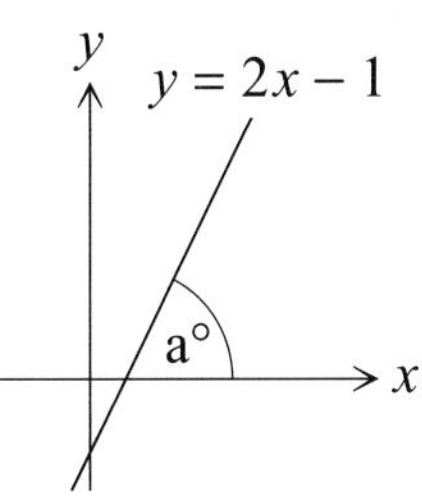

(b)
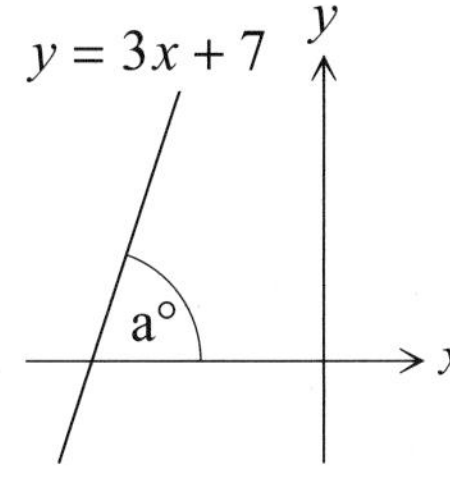

(c)
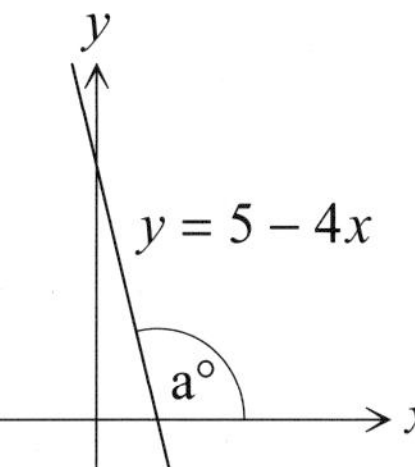

(d)
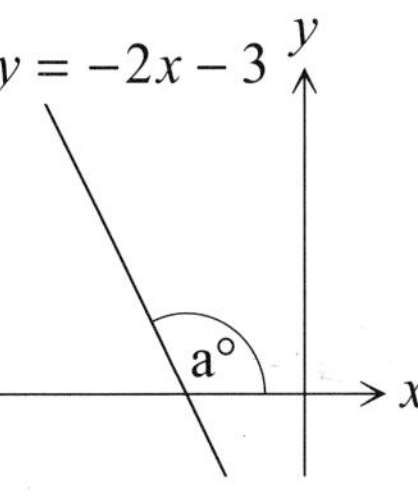

(e)
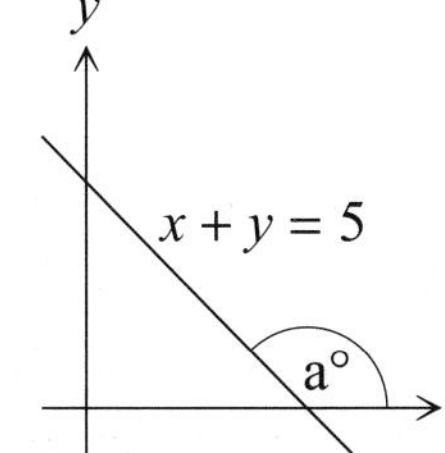

(f)
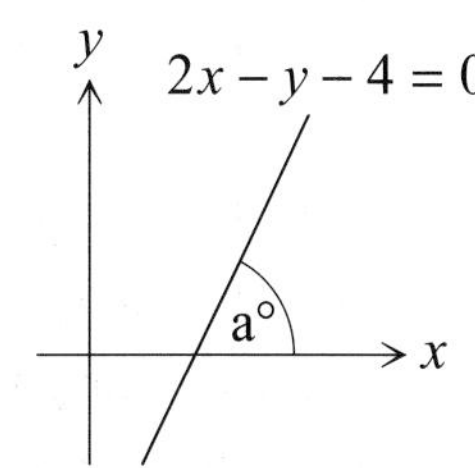

3 Find the angle made with the positive x-axis by the line whose equation is:

(a) $y = x - 2$ (b) $y = 1 - 4x$ (c) $3y = 2x + 4$ (d) $3x + 4y + 2 = 0$

4 Calculate the size of the acute angle between the two lines whose graphs are:

(a)

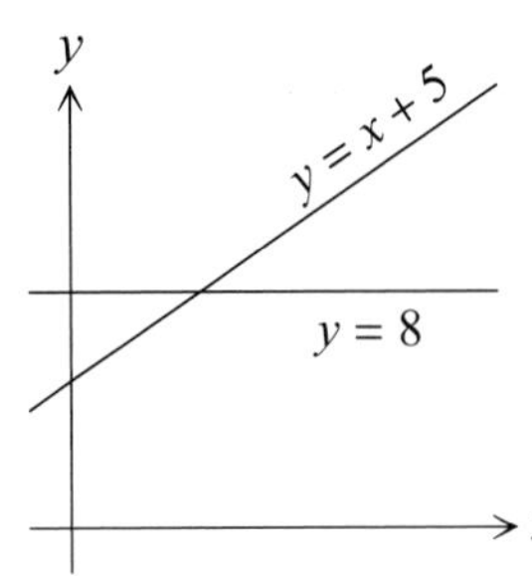

(b)

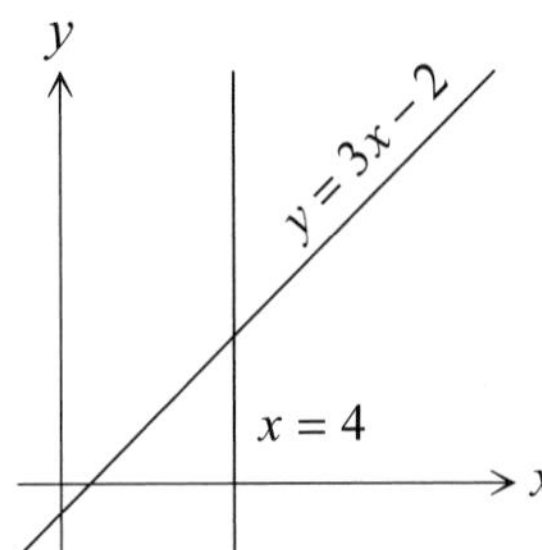

(c)

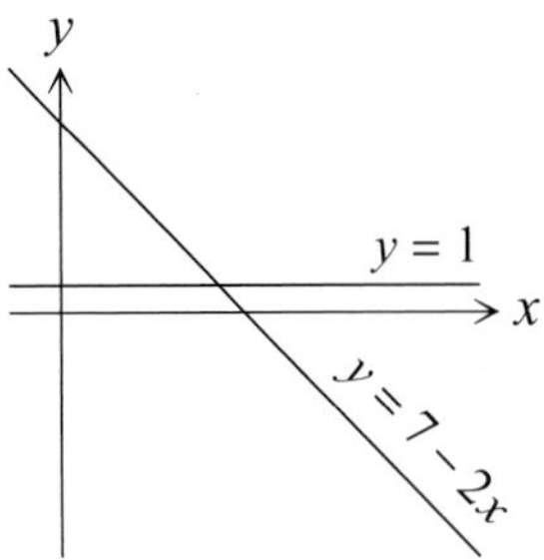

(d)

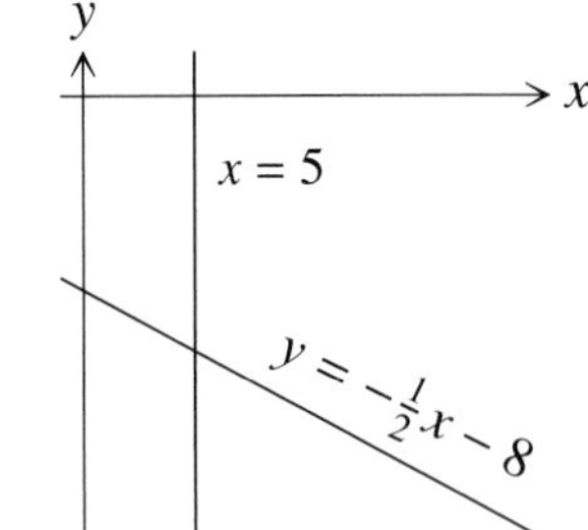

5 Find the equation of the line whose graph is:

(a)

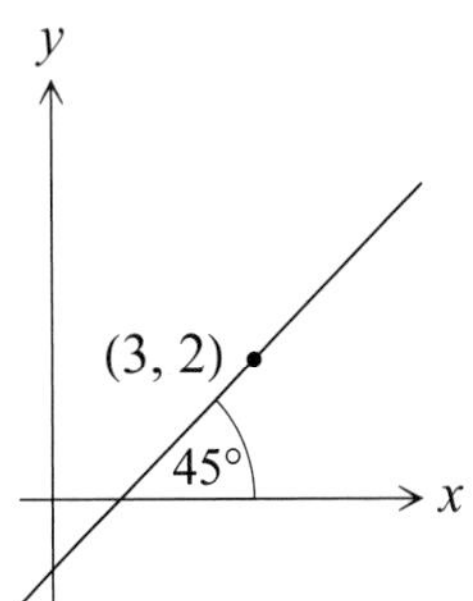

(b)

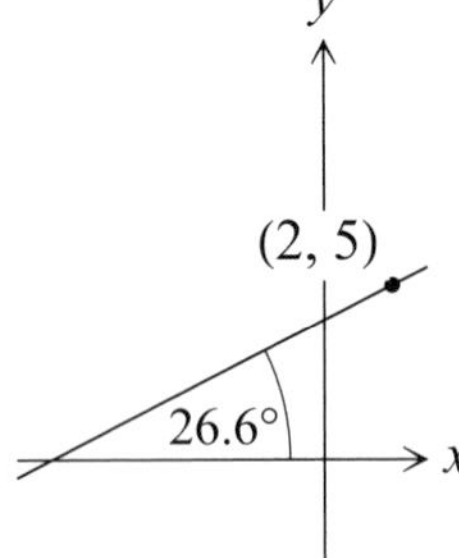

(c)

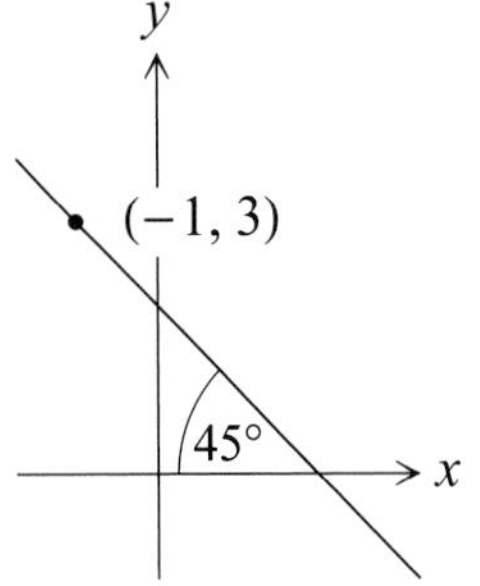

(d)

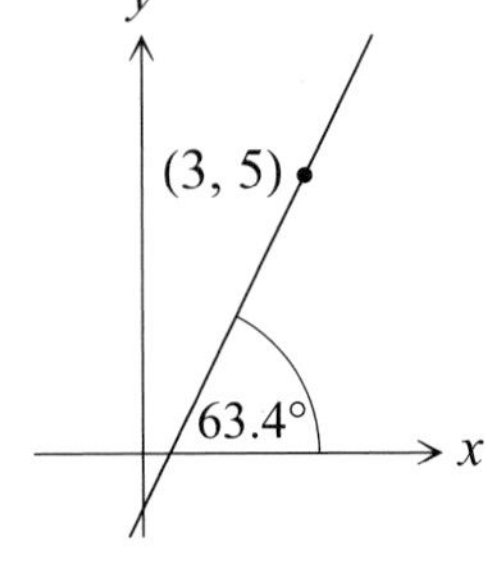

(e)

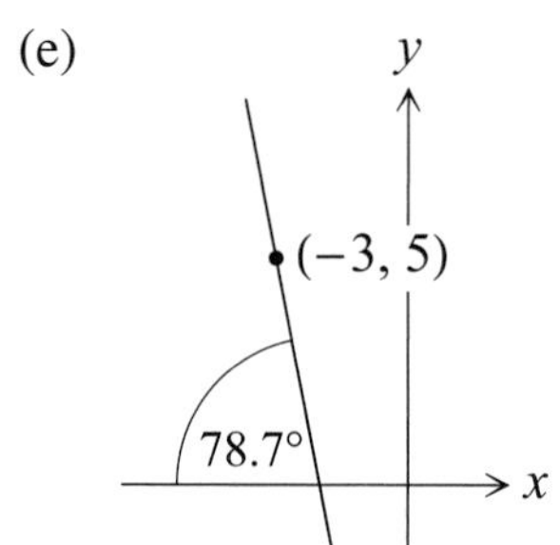

(f)

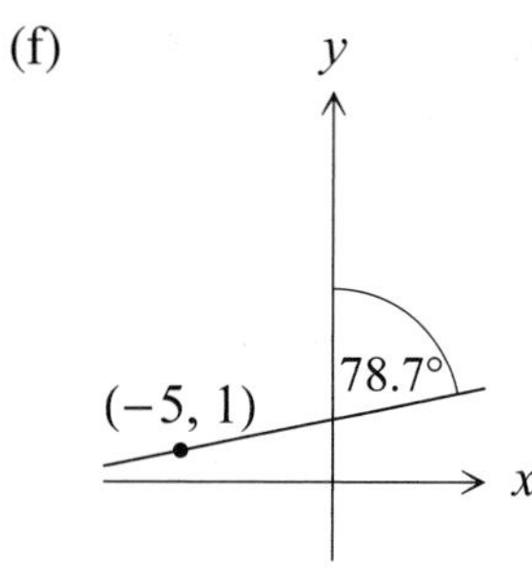

❄ 6 The diagram shows the lines $y = x + 4$ and $y = 4 - x$. By considering the angle each line makes with the x-axis, prove that the two lines are perpendicular.

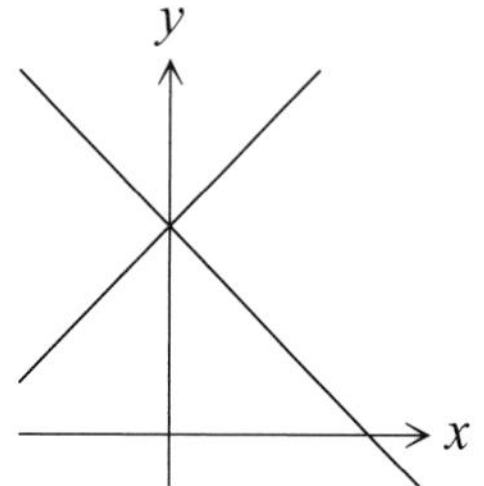

❄ 7 [This question requires knowledge of exact values—see section 1.7 on page 6.]

Find the equation of the line whose graph is shown, giving the gradient as an exact value:

(a)

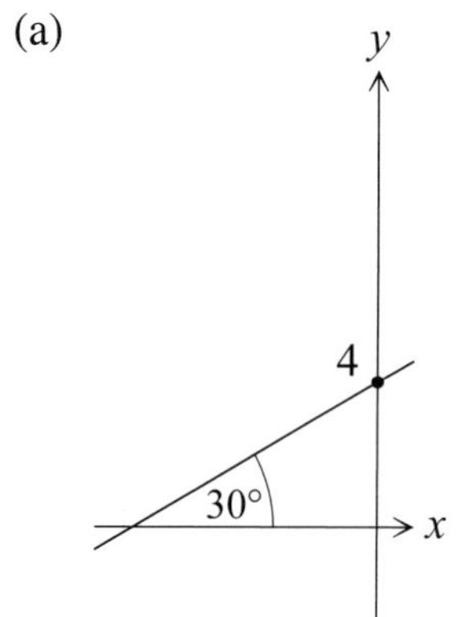

(b)

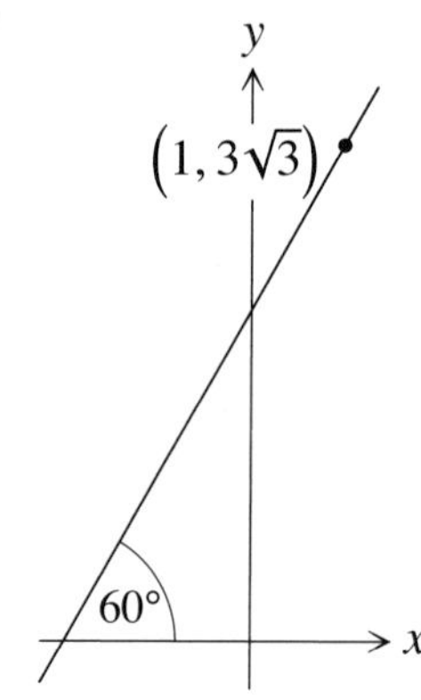

(c)

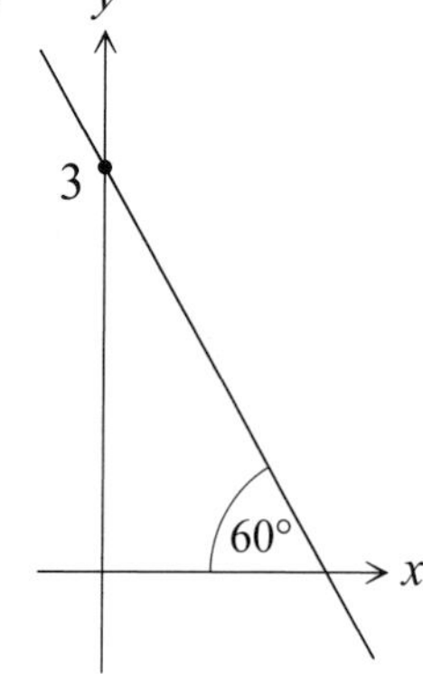

(d)

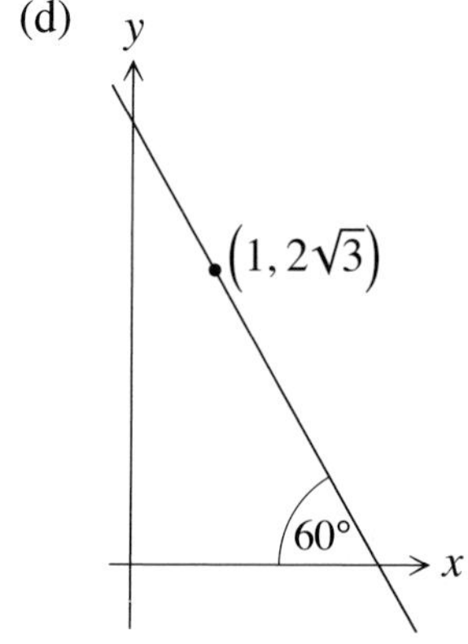

(e)

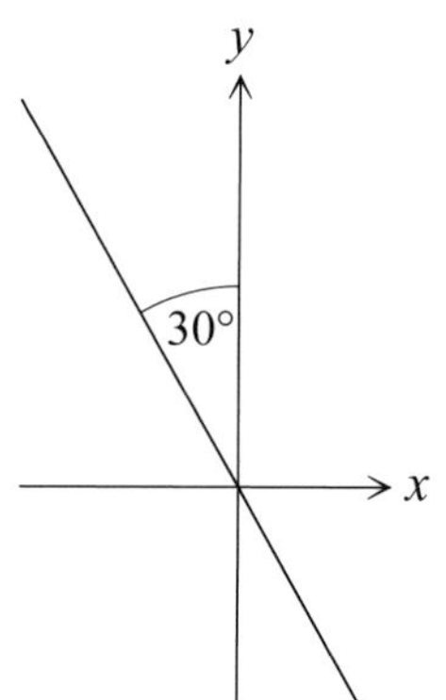

(f)

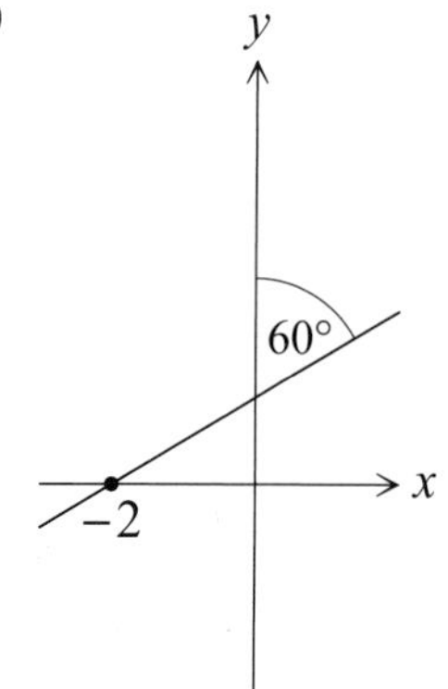

8 The diagram shows the line AB with equation $y = x + 2$, the line BC with equation $y = 2 - 3x$ and the line BD with equation $y = 2$.

(a) Find the size of the angle between lines AB and BD.

(b) Find the size of the angle between the lines BC and BD.

(c) Hence find the size of the angle between the lines AB and BC.

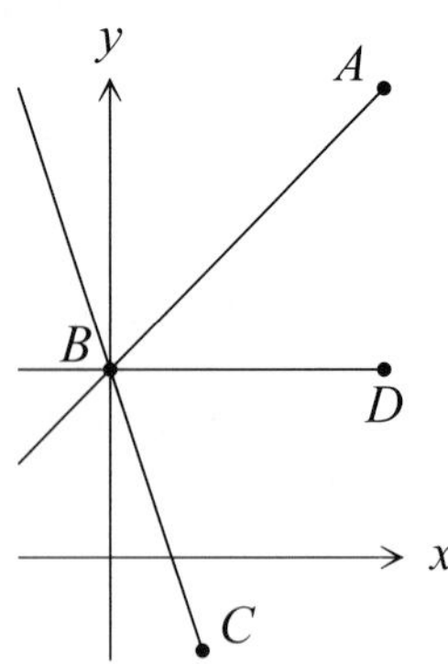

9 Find the size of the angle between the lines:

(a) $y = x + 3$ and $y = 3 - 5x$

(b) $y = x + 5$ and $y = 2x + 5$

(c) $y = 3x - 1$ and $y = -7x - 1$

(d) $y = 4 - 2x$ and $y = \frac{1}{2}x + 4$

3.7 Circles

In this exercise you will learn how to:

- ❑ use circle diagrams plotted in the coordinate plane
- ❑ use diameter and tangent properties of a circle

Finding the length of a line segment is covered in Exercise 3.4 on page 15.

1 The line joining (−4, 8) and (2, 16) is the diameter of a circle.

(a) Write down the coordinates of the centre of the circle.

(b) Calculate the length of the radius of the circle.

2 A square is formed from the lines with equations $x = 6$, $x = 2$, $y = -3$, $y = 1$.

(a) Write down the coordinates of the centre of the largest circle which can be drawn inside the square.

(b) Calculate the length of the radius of the circle which passes through all the vertices of the square.

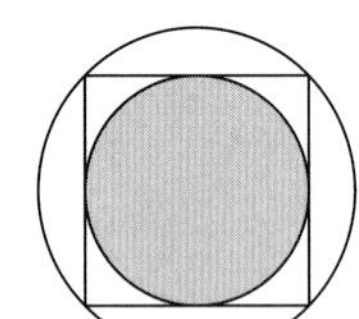

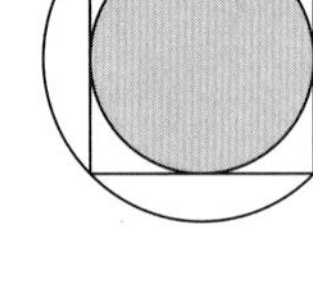

3 A circle has centre (2, 6) and one end of a diameter PQ of the circle is the point P (4, 10).

Find the coordinates of Q.

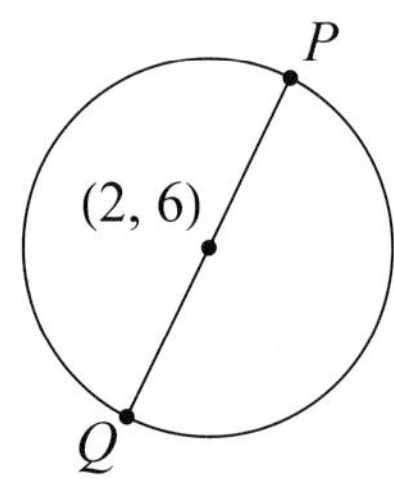

4 A circle has centre at the origin and radius 5 units. For each of the points $A\,(2,3)$, $B\,(-3,4)$, $C\,(5,5)$, $D\,(-1,7)$ and $E\,(1,-4)$, determine whether the point lies inside, outside or on the circle.

5 A circle has radius 2 units and touches both the x-axis and the y-axis. Write down the coordinates of the centre of each possible such circle.

6 A circle touches the y-axis and two diameters of the circle lie along the lines $y = 7$ and $y = x$. Write down the coordinates of the centre and the length of the radius of the circle.

❄ 7 A circle has centre $(0,4)$ and the lines $y = x$ and $y = -x$ are tangents of the circle. Calculate the length of the radius of the circle.

3.8 The distance between circles

In this exercise you will learn how to:

- ❑ calculate the distance between circles

Finding the length of a line segment is covered in Exercise 3.4 on page 15.

1 The diagram shows sixteen touching circles, each with radius 2 units, placed around the origin.

The circle labelled A has centre $(2, 2)$.

Write down the coordinates of the centres of the circles labelled B, C, D and E.

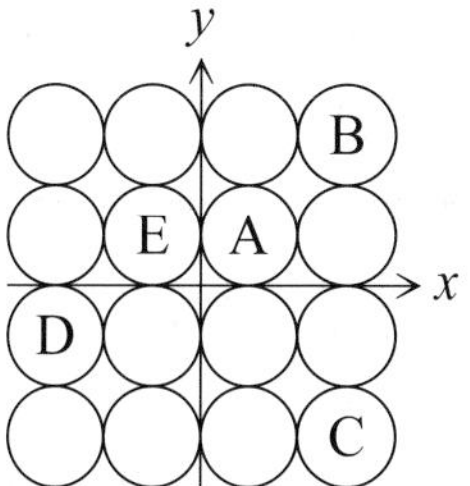

2 The diagram shows a repeating pattern of squares and rectangles. Each square has sides of length 20 units and contains one circle of radius 10 units. Each rectangle measures 10 units by 20 units and contains two circles of radius 5 units.

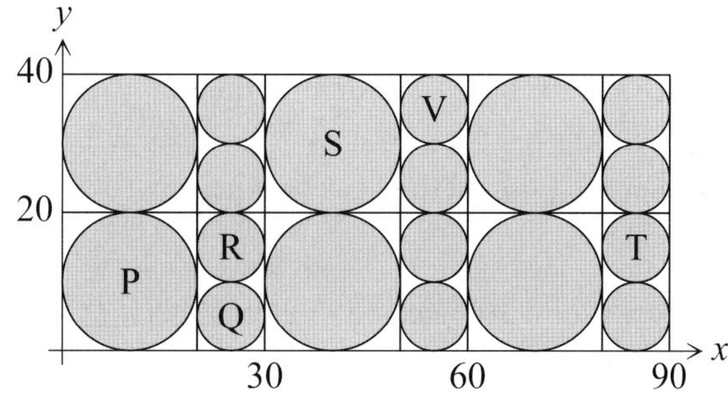

The circle labelled P has centre $(10, 10)$, circle Q has centre $(25, 5)$ and circle R has centre $(25, 15)$.

Write down the coordinates of the centres of the circles labelled S, T and V.

3 The diagram shows a rectangle whose sides have equations $y = 0$, $x = 16$, $y = 10$ and $x = 0$. Four touching circles fit exactly inside the rectangle.

The circle centre $Q\,(8, 4)$ has radius 4 units. The circles with centres P and R are congruent.

(a) Find the radii of the circles with centres P, R and S.

(b) Find the coordinates of P, R and S.

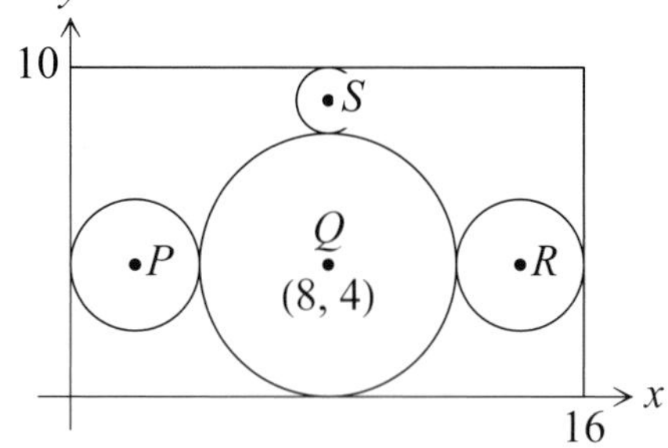

4 A circle C_1 has centre $P\,(2, 3)$ and radius 5 units. A second circle C_2 has centre $Q\,(-4, -5)$ and radius 2 units.

(a) Find the length of the line PQ.

(b) Find the shortest distance between the two circles.

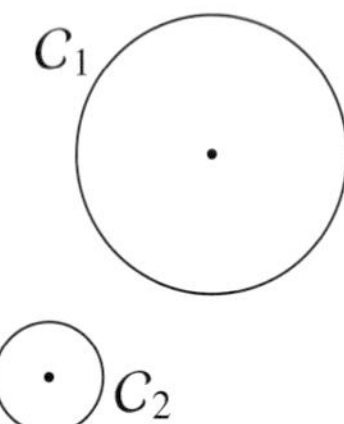

5 The circle C_3 has centre $(-1, 8)$ and radius 1 unit. The circle C_4 has centre $(2, 4)$ and radius 3 units. Calculate the shortest distance between C_3 and C_4.

6 (a) Circle C_1 has centre $(4, 2)$ and radius 4 units; circle C_2 has centre $(-1, -10)$ and radius 9 units, Show that C_1 and C_2 touch.

(b) Circle C_3 has centre $(0, 10)$ and radius 14 units; circle C_4 has centre $(7, -14)$ and radius 11 units, Show that C_3 and C_4 touch.

❄ **7** A diameter of the circle C_1 joins $(1, 5)$ to $(-7, 9)$. Another circle C_2 has centre $(5, 11)$. The point $A\,(4, 13)$ lies on the circumference of C_2.

Calculate the shortest distance between C_1 and C_2.

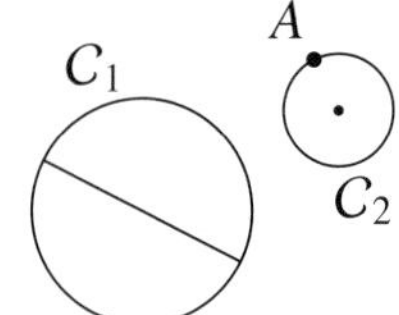

4 Graph sketching

4.1 Parabolas of the form $y = k(x - a)(x - b)$

In this exercise you will learn how to:

- ❑ sketch the graph of a parabola with equation given in the form $y = k(x - a)(x - b)$
- ❑ use the sign of k to find the shape of the curve: 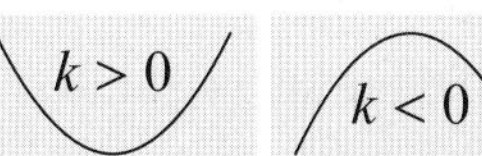

- ❑ use the y-intercept occurs where $x = 0$ to label the y-intercept (the intersection with the y-axis)
- ❑ use the zeros occur where $y = 0$ to label the zeros (the roots, or the x-intercepts)
- ❑ sketch the graph of a parabola by factorising into the form $y = k(x - a)(x - b)$

1 Sketch a graph, showing the zeros and the y-intercept, of the curve with equation:

(a) $y = (x - 1)(x + 2)$ (b) $y = (x + 3)(x + 5)$ (c) $y = (x - 2)(x - 5)$
(d) $y = (4 - x)(2 + x)$ (e) $y = (1 + 2x)(1 - x)$ (f) $y = (2x + 1)(3x - 2)$
(g) $y = x(x - 4)$ (h) $y = 3x(2 - x)$ (i) $y = 3(x - 1)(x + 1)$
(j) $y = 4(x - 1)(x + 3)$ (k) $y = 2(2 - x)(3 - x)$ (l) $y = 2(x - 2)(x - 1)$

2 Sketch a graph, showing the roots and the y-intercept, of the curve with equation:

(a) $y = (x - 2)^2$ (b) $y = -(x + 3)^2$ (c) $y = 2(x + 1)^2$
(d) $y = (1 - x)^2$ (e) $y = -2(3 - x)^2$ (f) $y = 4(2x - 1)^2$

3 Sketch a graph, showing the zeros and the intersection with the y-axis, of the curve with equation:

(a) $y = x^2 + 4x + 3$ (b) $y = x^2 - 6x + 5$ (c) $y = x^2 - 3x - 4$
(d) $y = x^2 - 16$ (e) $y = 2x^2 + x - 1$ (f) $y = x^2 + 6x$
(g) $y = 4x^2 - 9$ (h) $y = 2x^2 + 6x$ (i) $y = 4x^2 - x - 3$
(j) $y = 2x^2 - 12x + 10$ (k) $y = 4x - x^2$ (l) $y = 4 - x^2$
(m) $y = 3x^2 - 3$ (n) $y = 2 - x - x^2$ (o) $y = 3 + 2x - x^2$
(p) $y = 12 - 2x - 2x^2$

4 A curve has equation $y = (x + 2)(x - 3)$.

(a) Sketch the curve, showing the zeros and the y-intercept.

The point $(4, p)$ lies on the curve.

(b) Find the value of p.

The point $(k, 14)$ lies on the curve.

(c) Find the possible values of k.

5 A curve has equation $y = 4x^2 + 8x + 3$.

(a) Sketch the curve, showing the x-intercepts and the y-intercept.

The point $(3, q)$ lies on the curve.

(b) Find the value of q.

The point $(t, 35)$ lies on the curve.

(c) Find the possible values of t.

6 A curve has equation $y = 15 + 2x - x^2$.

(a) Sketch the curve, showing the roots and the intersection with the y-axis.

The point $(6, m)$ lies on the curve.

(b) Find the value of m.

The point $(k, 12)$ lies on the curve.

(c) Find the possible values of k.

4.2 Parabolas of the form $y = k(x - p)^2 + q$

In this exercise you will learn how to:

- ❑ sketch the graph of a parabola with equation given in the form $y = k(x - p)^2 + q$
- ❑ use the sign of k to find the shape of the curve: 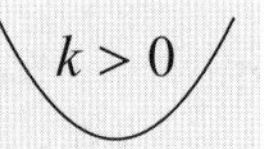 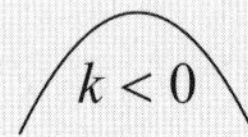
- ❑ use the turning point is at (p, q) to label the turning point
- ❑ use the y-intercept occurs where $x = 0$ to label the y-intercept (the intersection with the y-axis)
- ❑ use the zeros occur where $y = 0$ to label the zeros (the roots, or the x-intercepts)

1 Sketch a graph, showing the coordinates of the turning point and the y-intercept, of the curve with equation:

(a) $y = (x + 2)^2$ (b) $y = (x - 3)^2$ (c) $y = -(x - 1)^2$

(d) $y = -(x + 5)^2$ (e) $y = 4(x + 3)^2$ (f) $y = x^2 + 5$

(g) $y = x^2 - 4$ (h) $y = 10 - x^2$ (i) $y = -3 - x^2$

2 Sketch a graph, showing the coordinates of the turning point and the intersection with the y-axis, of the curve with equation:

(a) $y = (x - 1)^2 + 3$ (b) $y = (x + 2)^2 + 5$ (c) $y = (x + 1)^2 - 3$
(d) $y = (x + 2)^2 - 6$ (e) $y = 3 - (x + 1)^2$ (f) $y = 10 - (x - 2)^2$
(g) $y = 5 - (x - 1)^2$ (h) $y = 4(x - 1)^2 + 2$ (i) $y = 2(x + 3)^2 + 7$
(j) $y = 5 - 2(x + 3)^2$ (k) $y = 12 - 3(x + 1)^2$ (l) $y = (x - 1)^2 + 3$

Exercise 2.5 on page 10 covers the solution of equations of the form $k(x - p)^2 = q$.

3 A curve has equation $y = (x + 2)^2 - 9$.

(a) Sketch a graph of the curve showing the coordinates of the turning point and the y-intercept.

(b) Calculate the coordinates of the points where the curve crosses the x-axis.

4 Sketch the graph, showing the coordinates of the turning point and the points of intersection with both axes, of the curve whose equation is:

(a) $y = (x - 3)^2 - 16$ (b) $y = (x - 1)^2 - 4$ (c) $y = (x + 2)^2 - 25$
(d) $y = (x + 3)^2 - 9$ (e) $y = 2(x - 4)^2 - 8$ (f) $y = 5(x + 1)^2 - 45$
(g) $y = 9 - (x - 2)^2$ (h) $y = 16 - (x + 1)^2$ (i) $y = 12 - 3(x + 2)^2$

5 A curve has equation $y = (x - 4)^2 + 3$.

(a) Sketch a graph of the curve showing the coordinates of the turning point and the y-intercept.

The point $(1, k)$ lies on the curve.

(b) Find the value of k.

The point $(m, 12)$ lies on the curve.

(c) Find the possible values of m.

6 A curve has equation $y = 5 - (x + 1)^2$.

(a) Sketch a graph of the curve showing the coordinates of the turning point and the y-intercept.

The point $(-3, k)$ lies on the curve.

(b) Find the value of k.

The point $(p, -11)$ lies on the curve.

(c) Find the possible values of p.

7 A curve has equation $y = 3(x + 2)^2 - 7$.

(a) Sketch a graph of the curve showing the coordinates of the turning point and the y-intercept.

The point $(-1, t)$ lies on the curve.

(b) Find the value of t.

The point $(q, 20)$ lies on the curve.

(c) Find the possible values of q.

❄ 8 A curve has equation $y = (x + 1)^2 - 24$.

(a) Sketch a graph of the curve showing the coordinates of the turning point and the y-intercept.

(b) Leaving your answers in simplified surd form, calculate the coordinates of the points where the curve crosses the x-axis.

❄ 9 A curve has equation $y = (x - 3)^2 - 8$.

(a) Sketch a graph of the curve showing the coordinates of the turning point and the y-intercept.

(b) Leaving your answers in simplified surd form, calculate the coordinates of the points where the curve crosses the x-axis.

❄ 10 A curve has equation $y = 27 - (x + 2)^2$.

(a) Sketch a graph of the curve showing the coordinates of the turning point and the y-intercept.

(b) Leaving your answers in simplified surd form, calculate the coordinates of the x-intercepts.

❄ 11 A curve has equation $y = 20 - (x - 1)^2$.

(a) Sketch a graph of the curve showing the coordinates of the turning point and the y-intercept.

(b) Leaving your answers in simplified surd form, calculate the coordinates of the x-intercepts.

4.3 Cubic curves

In this exercise you will learn how to:

- ❑ sketch the graph of a cubic curve using the sign of k, the coefficient of x^3, to find the shape of the curve: $k > 0$ $k < 0$
- ❑ use the y-intercept occurs where $x = 0$ to label the y-intercept (the intersection with the y-axis)
- ❑ use the zeros occur where $y = 0$ to label the zeros (the roots, or the x-intercepts)

Exercise 2.6 on page 11 covers the solution of cubic equations.

❄ 1 Sketch a graph, showing the roots and the y-intercept, of the curve with equation:

(a) $y = (x - 1)(x + 2)(x + 3)$

(b) $y = (x - 5)(x - 2)(x + 1)$

(c) $y = (x - 1)(x + 1)(x + 5)$

(d) $y = x(x + 1)(x + 2)$

(e) $y = (1 - x)(1 + x)(2 + x)$

(f) $y = (1 - x)(3 - x)(4 - x)$

(g) $y = x(1 - x)(2 + x)$

❄ 2 Sketch a graph, showing the zeros and the y-intercept, of the curve with equation:

(a) $y = x^2(x + 2)$ (b) $y = x^2(1 - x)$

(c) $y = x(x + 3)^2$ (d) $y = x(x - 2)^2$

(e) $y = x(1 + x)^2$ (f) $y = x(1 - x)^2$

❄ 3 (a) Fully factorise $x^3 - x^2 - 2x$.

(b) Sketch the graph of $y = x^3 - x^2 - 2x$ showing the zeros.

❄ 4 (a) Fully factorise $3x^3 + 2x^2 - x$.

(b) Sketch the graph of $y = 3x^3 + 2x^2 - x$ showing the zeros.

❄ 5 (a) Fully factorise $4x^2 - x^3$.

(b) Sketch the graph of $y = 4x^2 - x^3$ showing the roots.

❄ 6 (a) Fully factorise $x^3 + 4x^2 + 4x$.

(b) Sketch the graph of $y = x^3 + 4x^2 + 4x$ showing the roots.

5 Equations of curves

5.1 The parabola equation $y = kx^2 + q$

In this exercise you will learn how to:

- find an equation of a parabola in the form $y = kx^2 + q$ from a graph
- find q using the y-intercept occurs where $x = 0$, or by moving the curve $y = kx^2$ in a direction parallel to the y-axis
- find k by substituting the coordinates of a point on the curve into the equation
- check the sign of k from the shape of the curve: 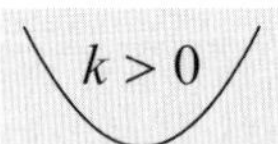

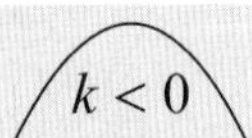

1 Find an equation of the form $y = kx^2$ for the curve:

(a)

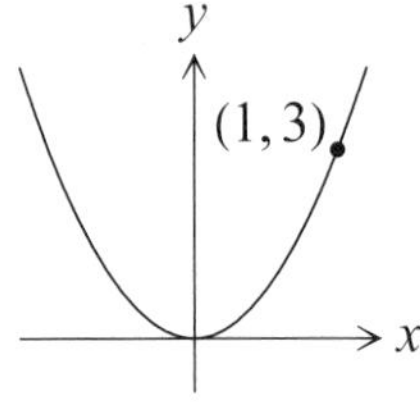

(b)

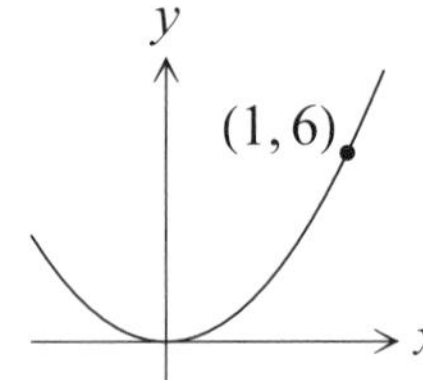

(c)

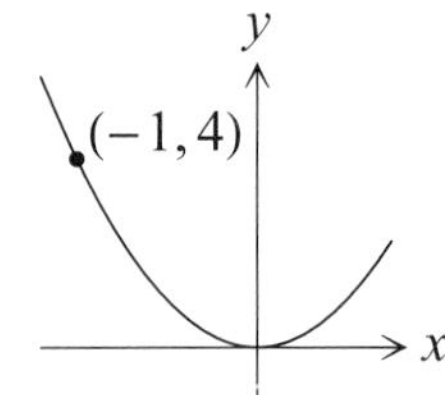

(d)

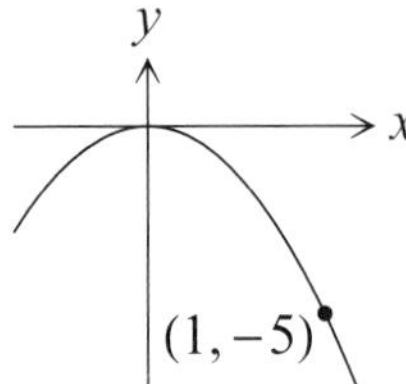

(e)

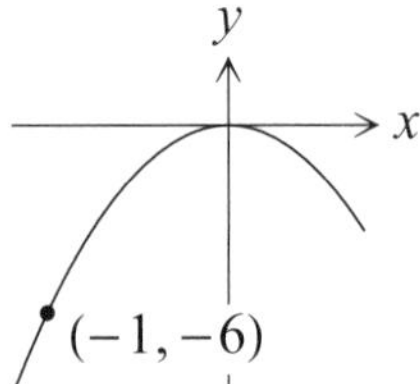

(f)

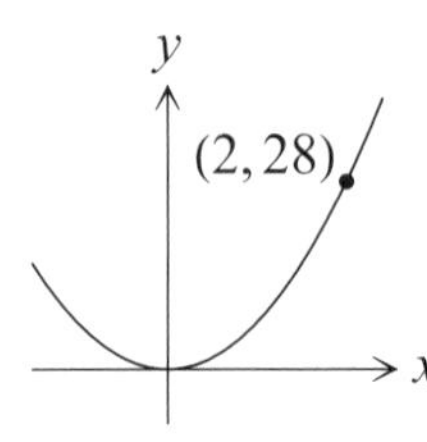

(g)

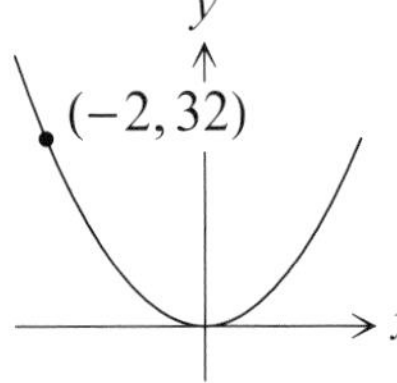

(h)

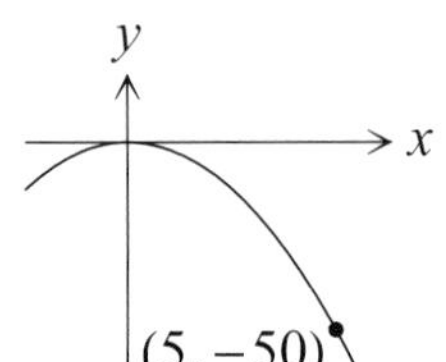

(i)

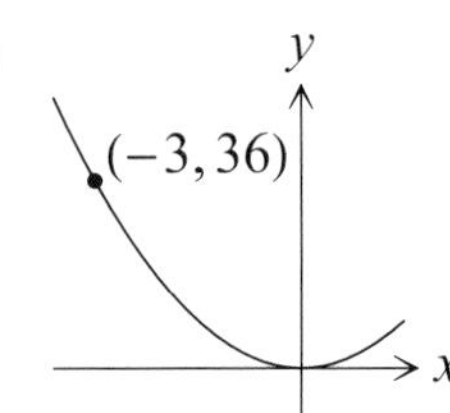

(j)

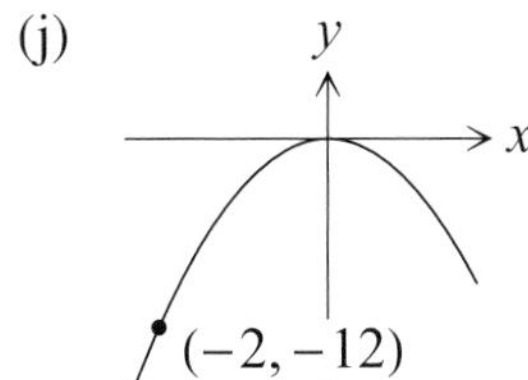

(k)

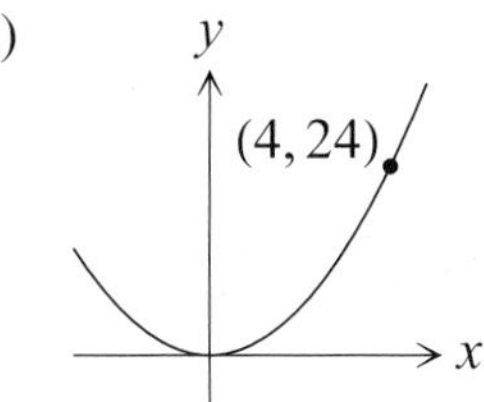

(l)

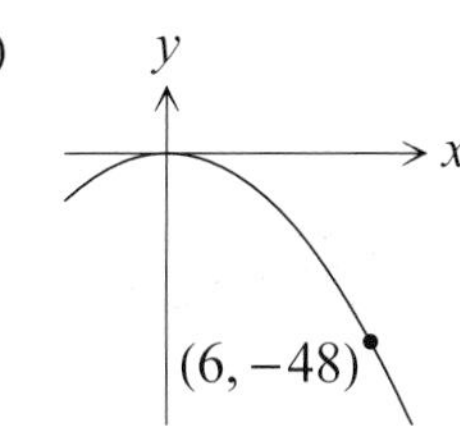

2 Find an equation of the form $y = kx^2 + q$ for the curve:

(a)

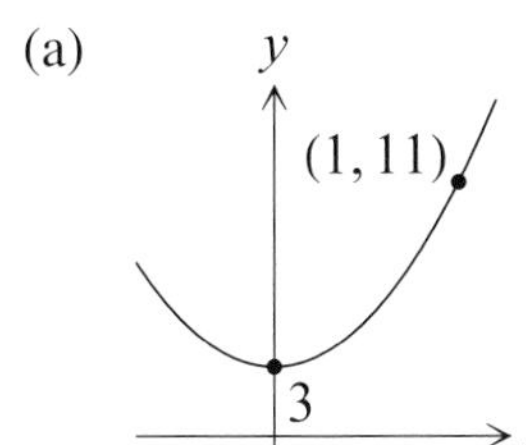

(b)

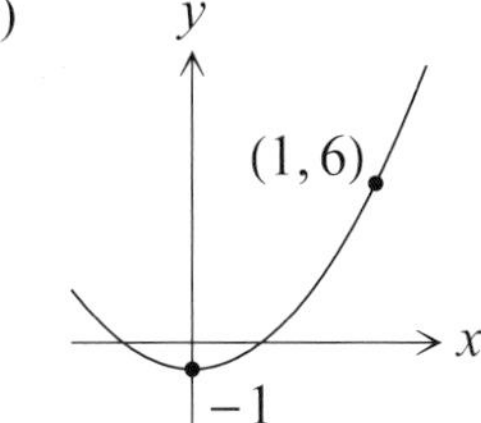

(c)

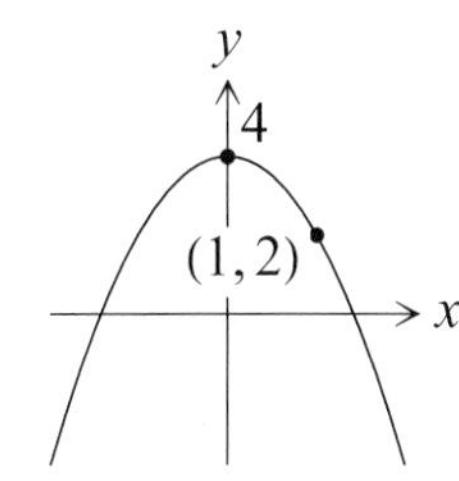

(d)

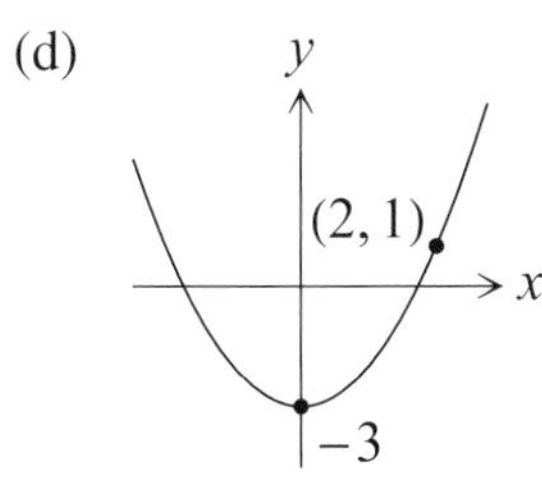

(e)

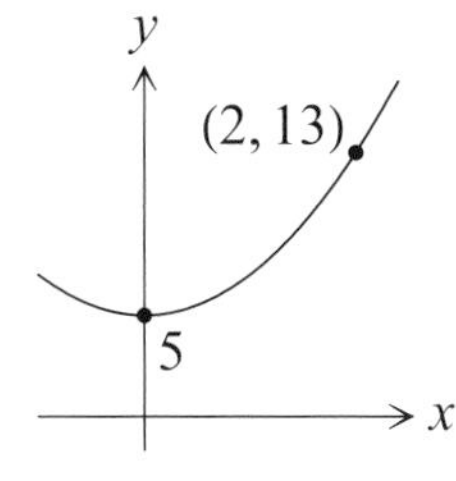

(f)

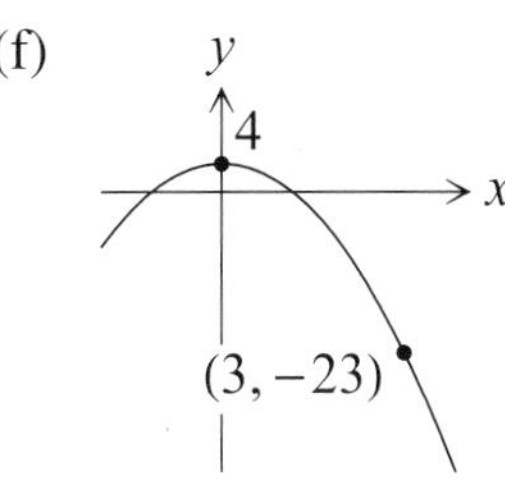

(g)

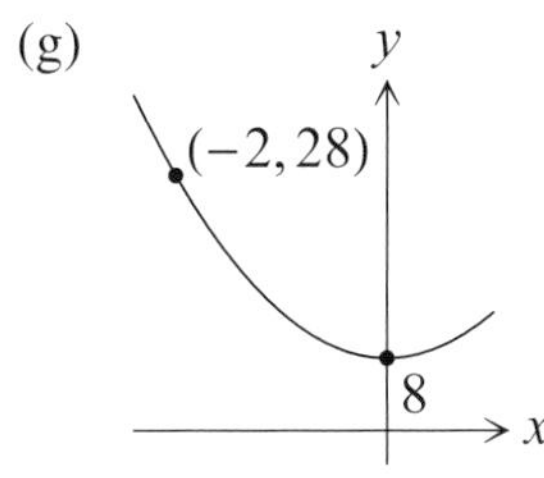

(h)

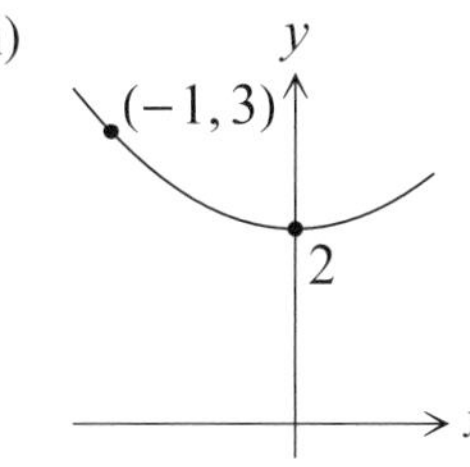

(i)

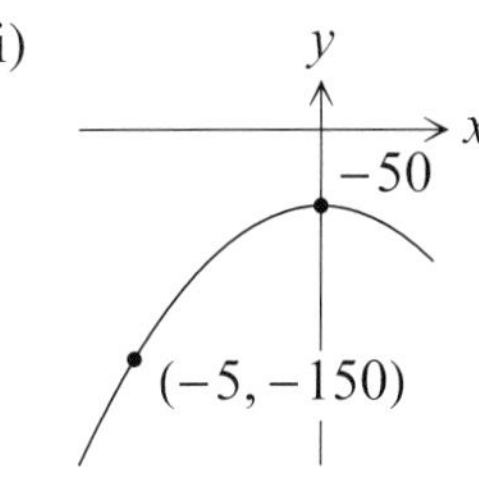

(j)

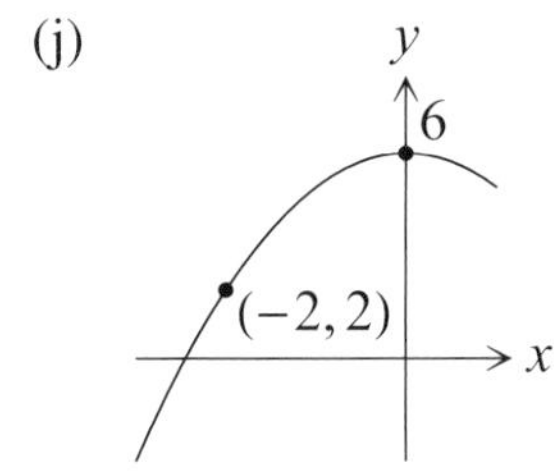

(k)

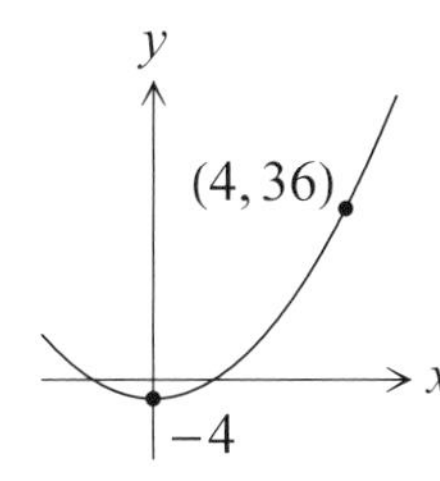

(l)

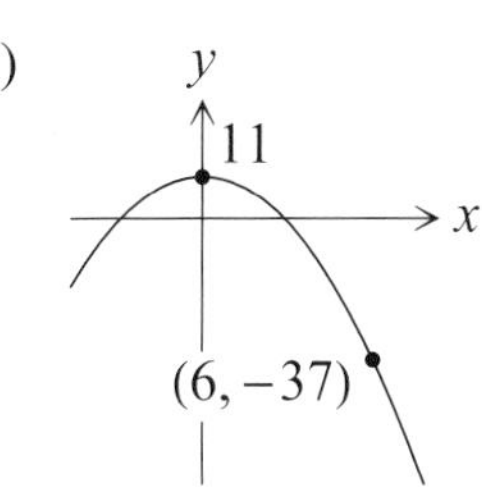

❄ 3 The parabola with equation $y = kx^2 + q$ passes through the points $(1, 2)$ and $(-2, 11)$. Find the values of k and q.

❄ 4 The parabola with equation $y = cx^2 + d$ passes through the points $(-3, -1)$ and $(-2, 9)$. Find the values of c and d.

5.2 The parabola equation $y = k(x - a)(x - b)$

In this exercise you will learn how to:

- ❑ find an equation of a parabola in the form $y = k(x - a)(x - b)$ from a graph
- ❑ find a and b from the zeros, using the zeros occur where $y = 0$
- ❑ find k using the y-intercept occurs where $x = 0$, or by substituting the coordinates of a point on the curve into the equation
- ❑ check the sign of k from the shape of the curve: 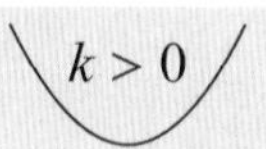

$k < 0$

1 Find an equation of the form $y = k(x - a)(x - b)$ for the curve:

(a)
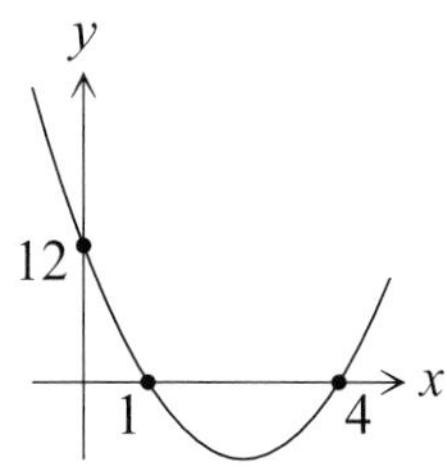

(b)
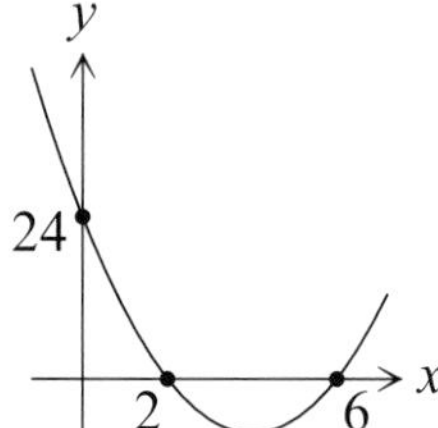

(c)
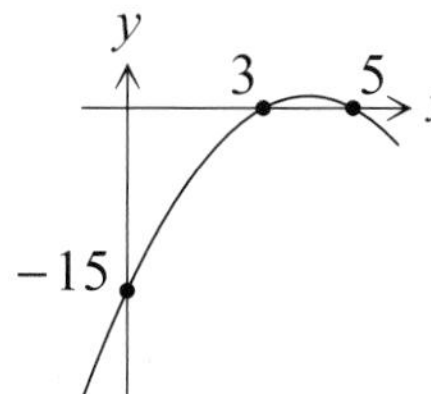

(d)
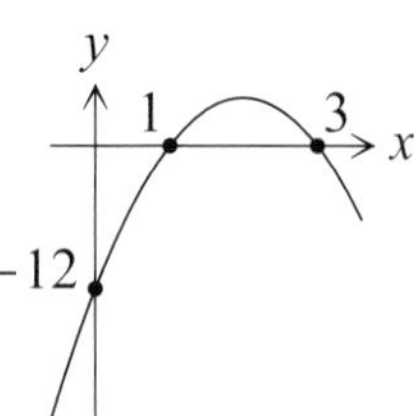

(e)
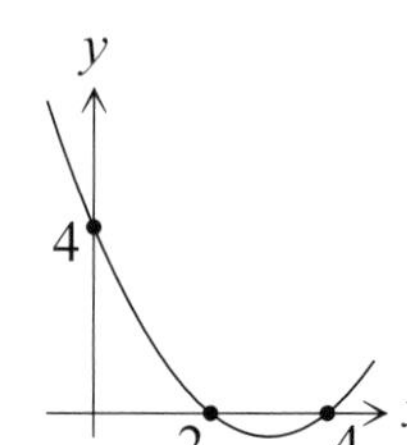

(f)
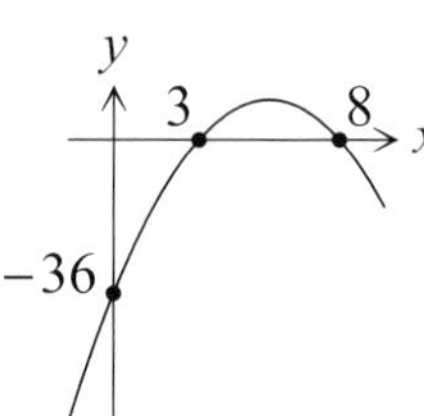

(g)
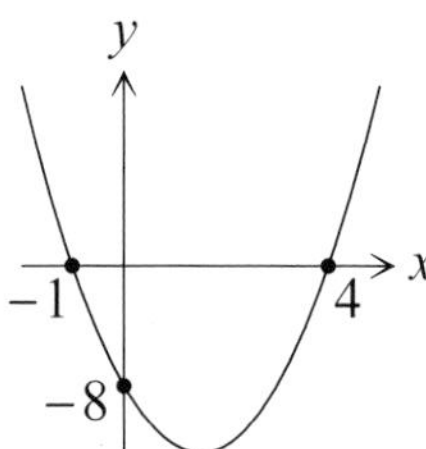

(h)
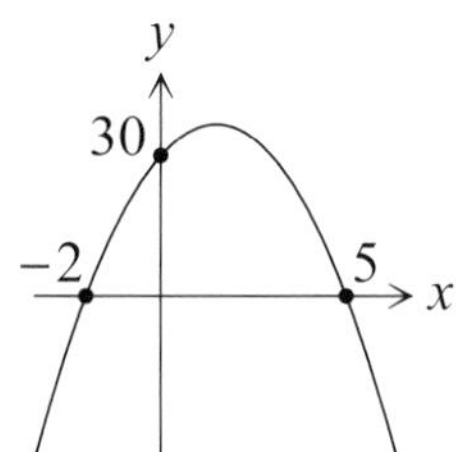

(i)
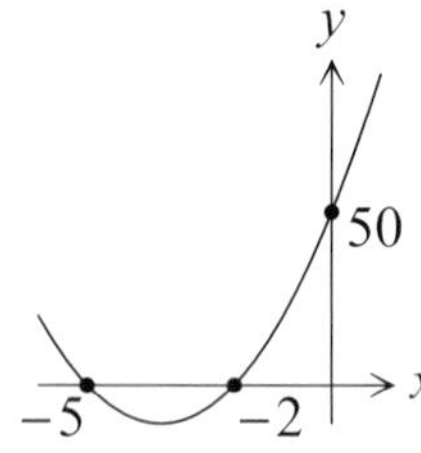

(j)
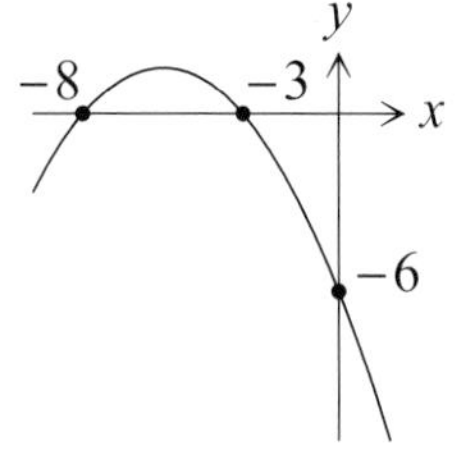

(k)
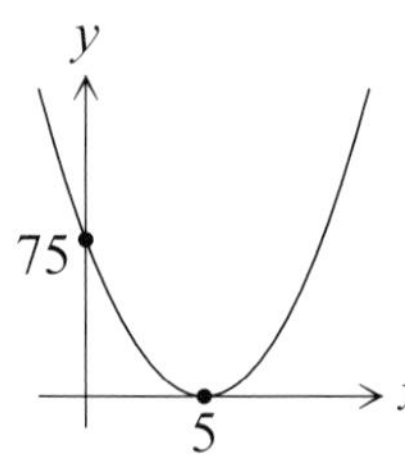

(l)
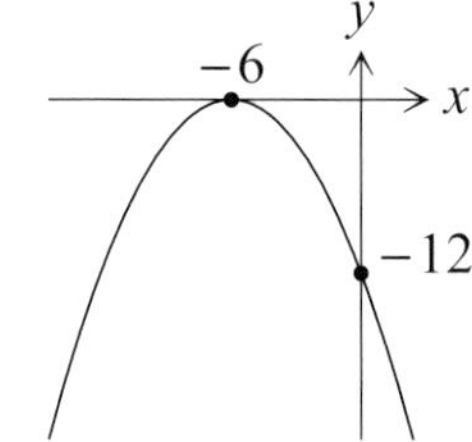

2 Find an equation of the form $y = k(x - a)(x - b)$ for the curve:

(a)

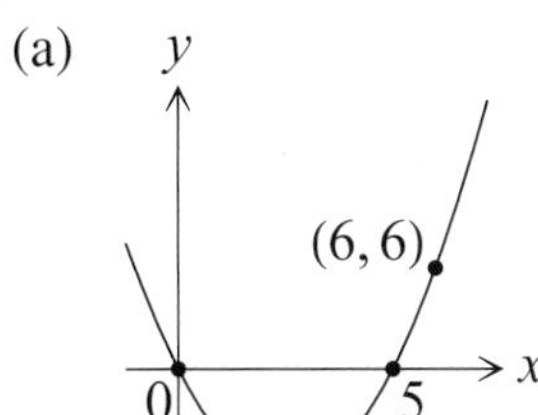

(b)

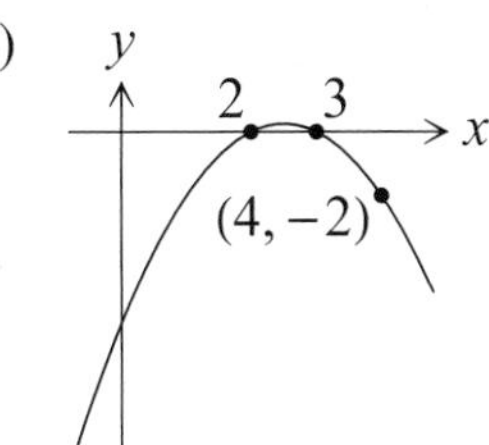

(c)

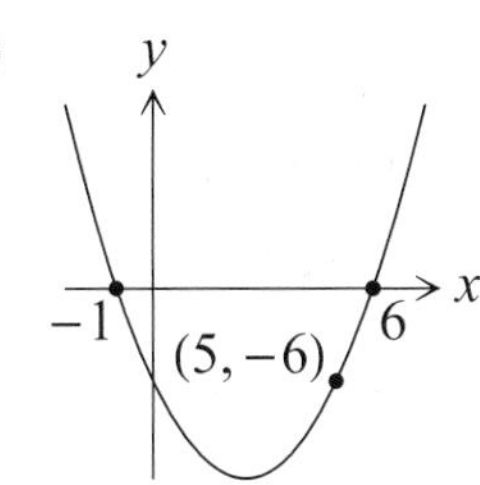

(d)

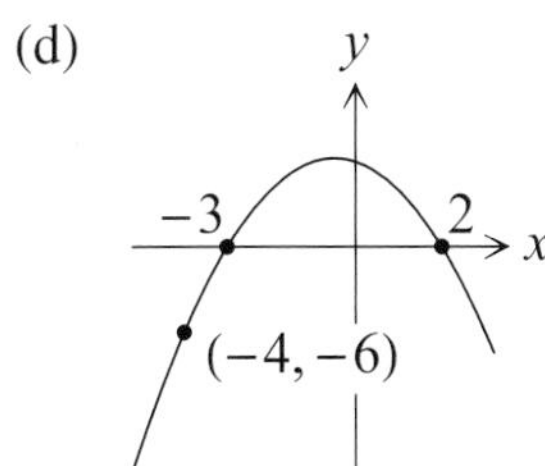

(e)

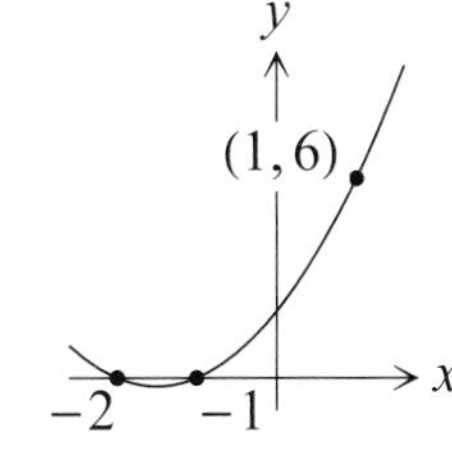

(f)

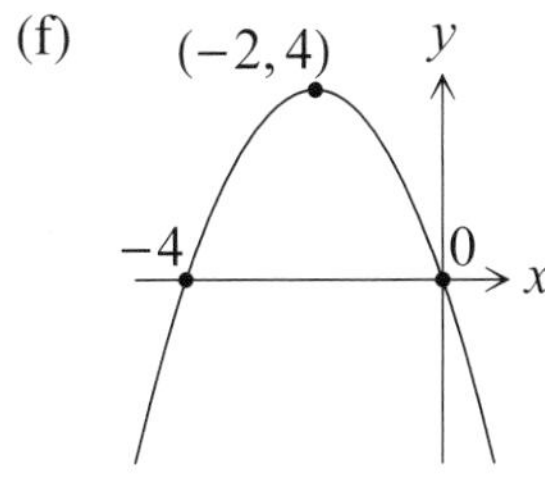

(g)

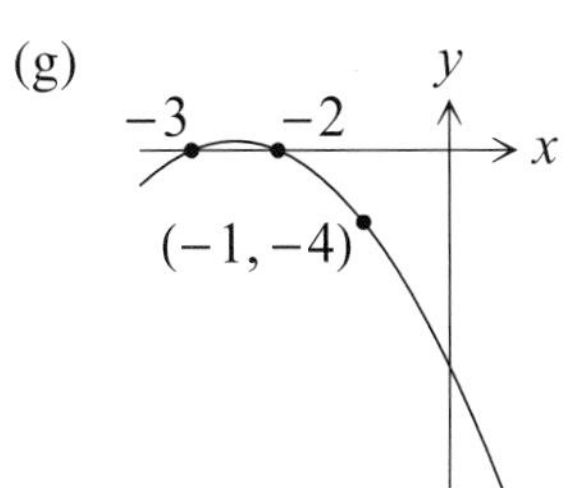

(h)

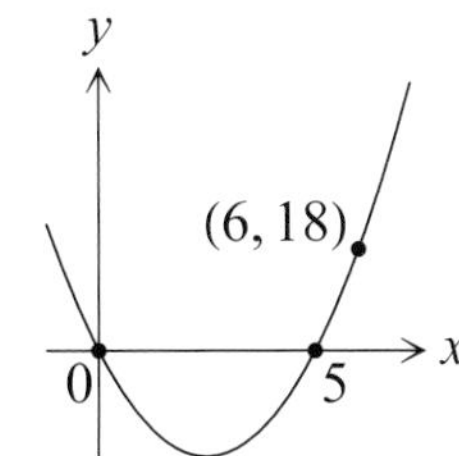

(i)

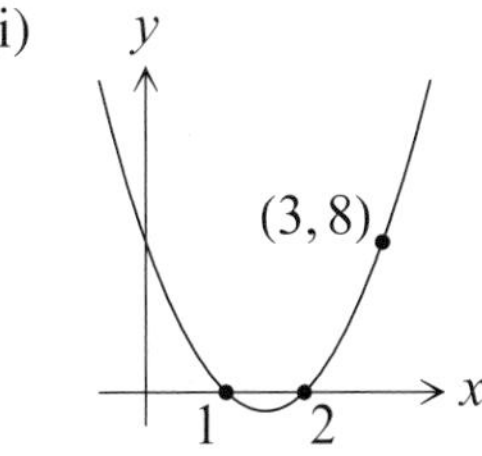

(j)

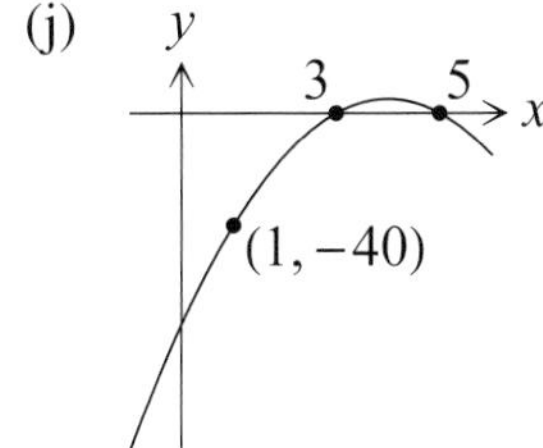

(k)

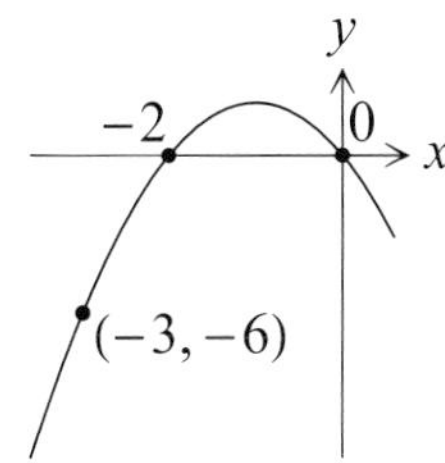

(l)

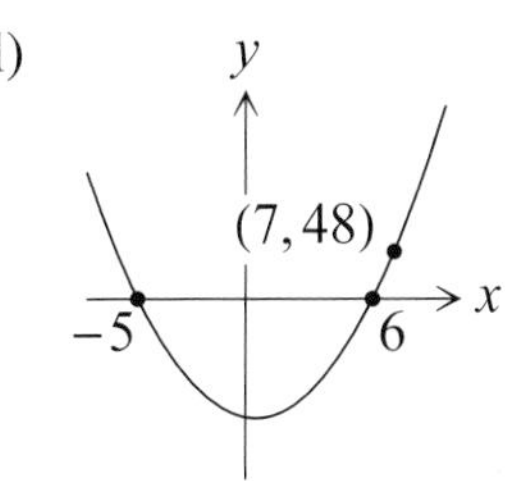

❄ 3 The parabola with equation $y = (x - a)(x - b)$ passes through the points $(2, 4)$ and $(-1, -2)$. Find the value of ab.

❄ 4 The parabola with equation $y = 3(x - c)(x - d)$ passes through the points $(1, 6)$ and $(5, 18)$. Find the value of cd.

5.3 The turning point of the parabola $y = k(x - p)^2 + q$

In this exercise you will learn how to:

- write down the coordinates of the turning point of a parabola given in the form $y = k(x-p)^2 + q$ using the turning point is (p, q)
- use the sign of k to determine the nature of the turning point:

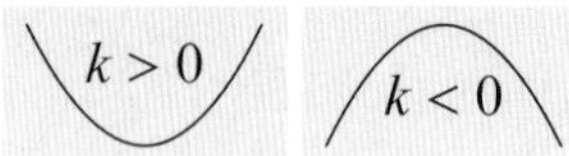

1 Write down the coordinates of the turning point, stating whether it is a minimum or a maximum point, for the parabola with equation:

(a) $y = (x-4)^2 + 2$ (b) $y = (x-2)^2 - 5$ (c) $y = -(x-3)^2 - 8$
(d) $y = 7 - (x-5)^2$ (e) $y = (x+2)^2 + 9$ (f) $y = (x+6)^2 - 4$
(g) $y = 6 - (x+11)^2$ (h) $y = -(x+7)^2 - 1$

2 Write down the coordinates of the turning point, stating whether it is a minimum or a maximum point, for the parabola with equation:

(a) $y = 2(x-3)^2 + 9$ (b) $y = 5(x-4)^2 - 6$ (c) $y = 11 - \frac{1}{2}(x-7)^2$
(d) $y = -8(x-1)^2 - 3$ (e) $y = \frac{3}{4}(x+1)^2 + 8$ (f) $y = \frac{1}{4}(x+5)^2 - 7$
(g) $y = 6 - 2(x+8)^2$ (h) $y = -9(x+3)^2 - 13$

5.4 The parabola equation $y = k(x - p)^2 + q$

In this exercise you will learn how to:

- find an equation of a parabola in the form $y = k(x-p)^2 + q$ from a graph
- find p and q using (p, q) is the turning point
- find k using the y-intercept occurs where $x = 0$, or by substituting the coordinates of a point on the curve into the equation
- check the sign of k from the shape of the curve: 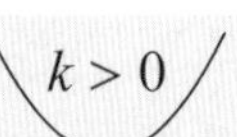 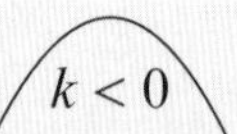

1 Find an equation of the form $y = (x-p)^2 + q$ or $y = -(x-p)^2 + q$ for the curve:

(a)

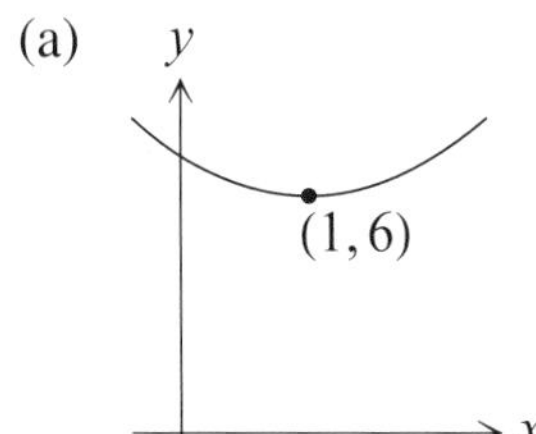

(b)

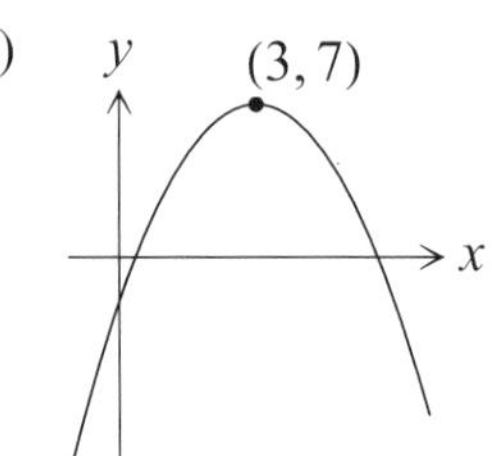

(c)

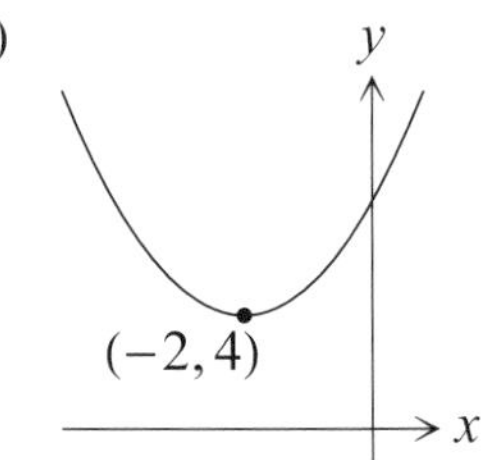

(d)

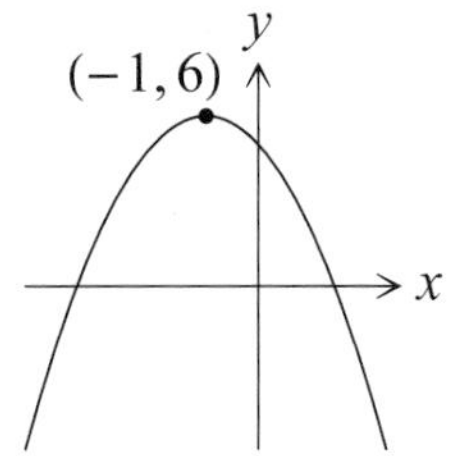

(e)

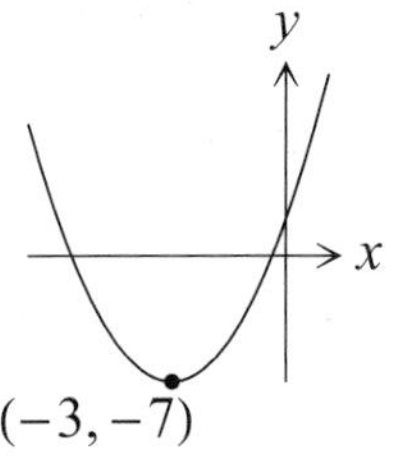

(f)

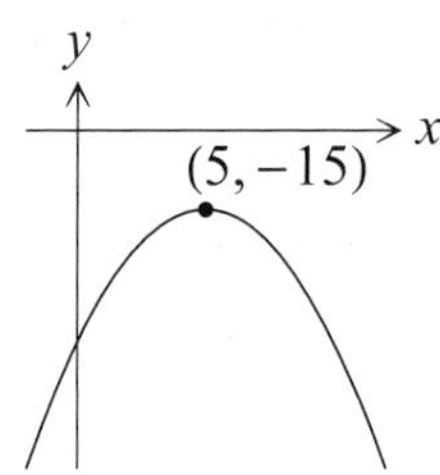

(g)

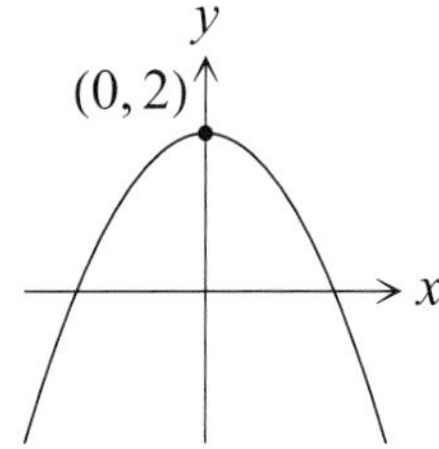

(h)

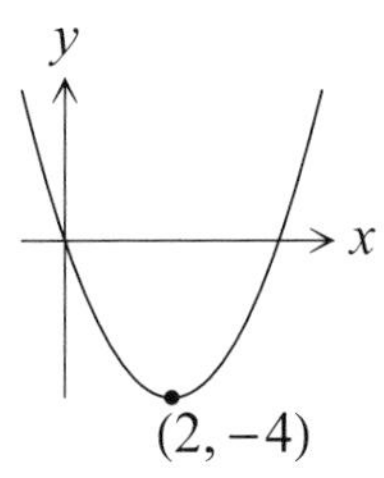

(i)

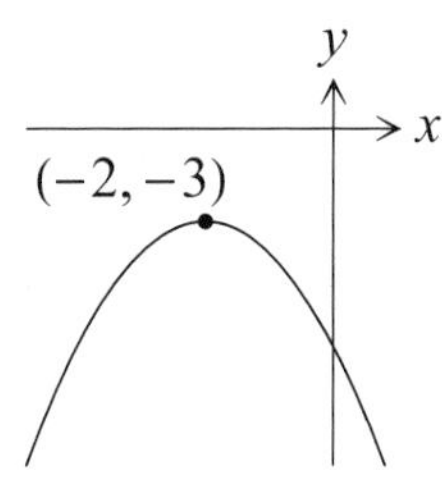

2 The diagram shows the curve with equation $y = k(x - 5)^2 + 6$.

(a) State the coordinates of the turning point.

(b) Find the value of k.

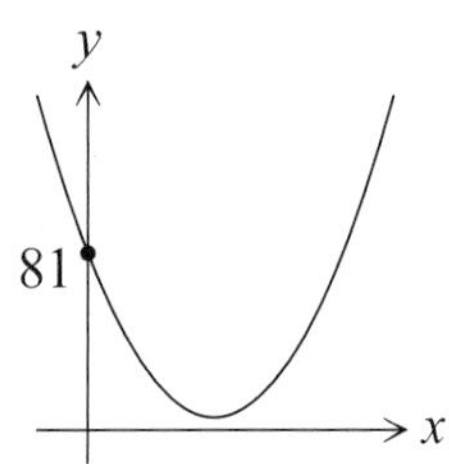

3 Find an equation of the form $y = k(x - p)^2 + q$ for the curve:

(a)

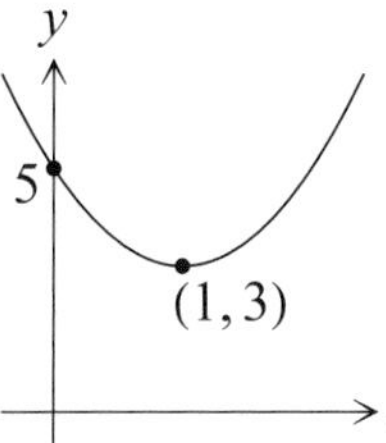

(b)

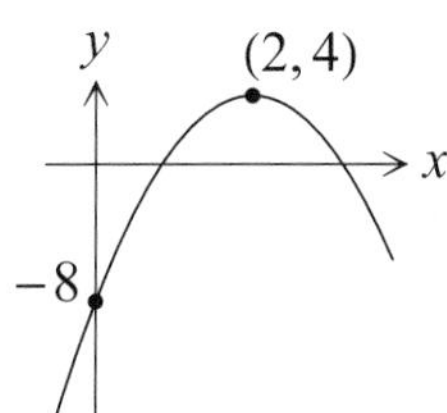

(c)

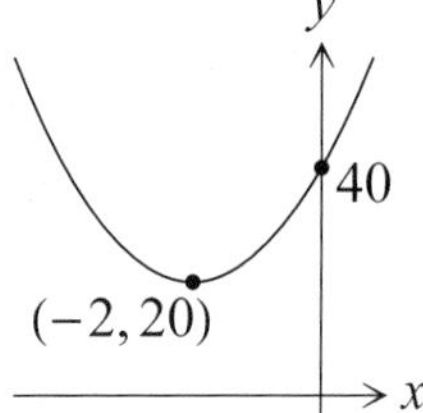

(d)

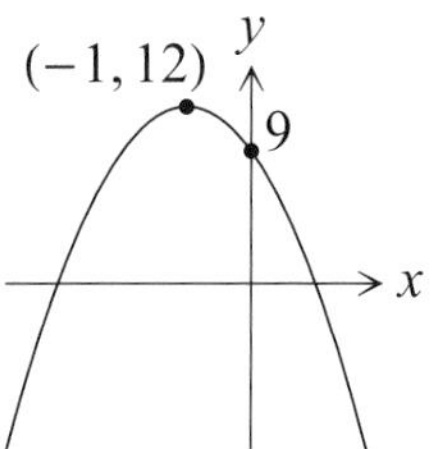

(e)

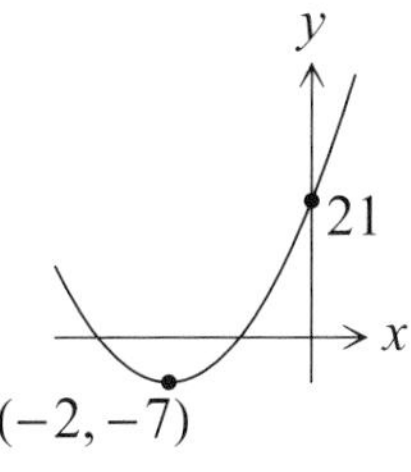

(f)

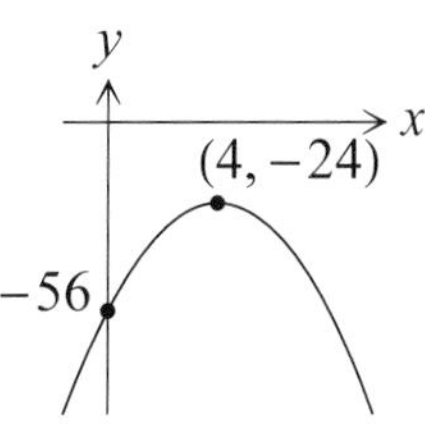

(g)

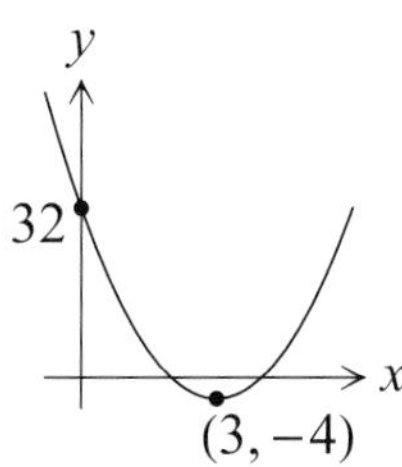

(h)

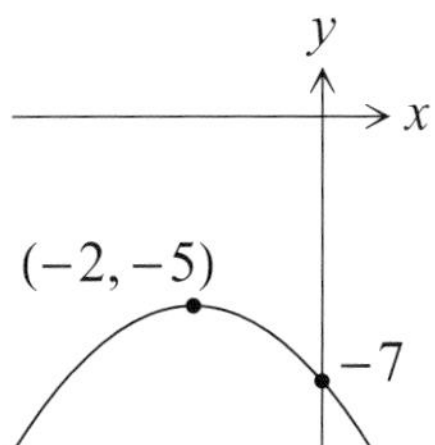

(i)

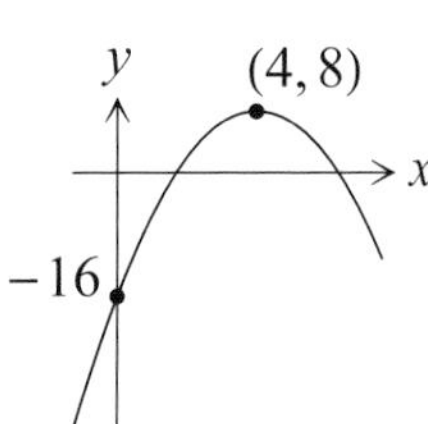

5.5 The equation of a parabola

In this exercise you will learn how to:

- ❑ find an equation of a parabola from the information given in a graph
- ❑ use the form $y = k(x - a)(x - b)$ when the zeros are given
- ❑ use the form $y = k(x - p)^2 + q$ when the turning point is given
- ❑ find an equation of the form $y = ax^2 + bx + c$ by expanding brackets and collecting like terms

1 Find an equation for the curve:

(a)
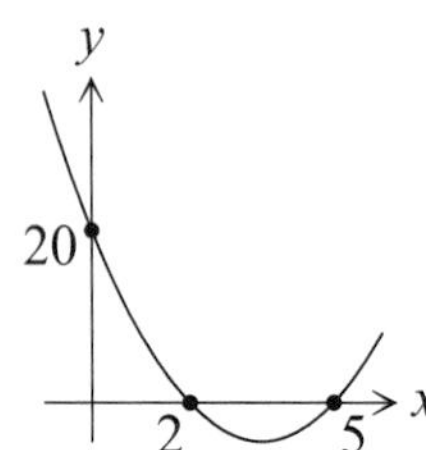

(b)
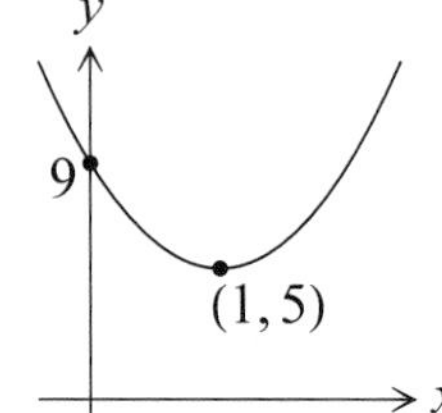

(c)
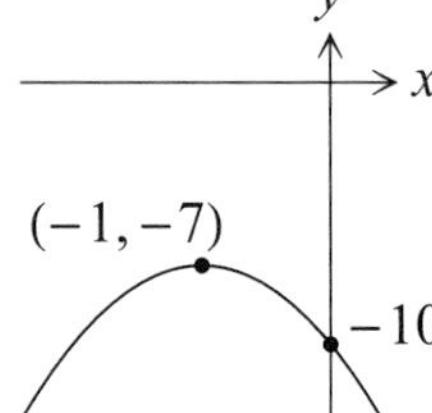

(d)
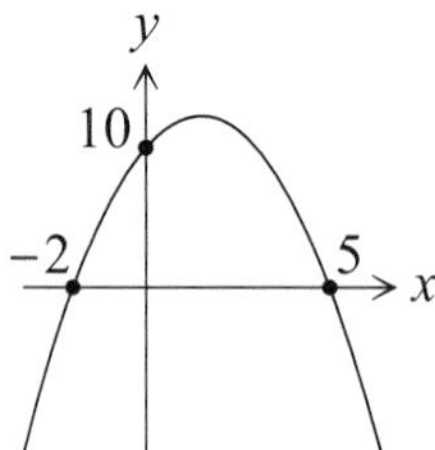

(e)
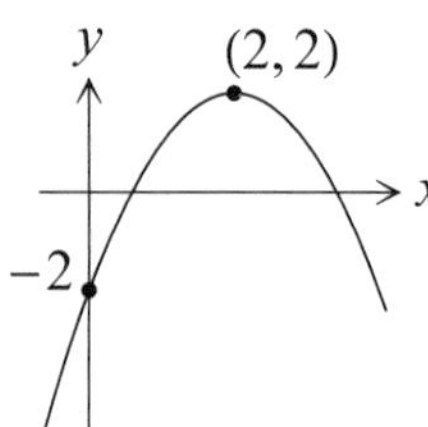

(f)
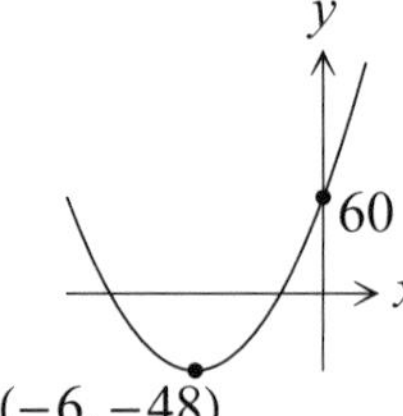

(g)
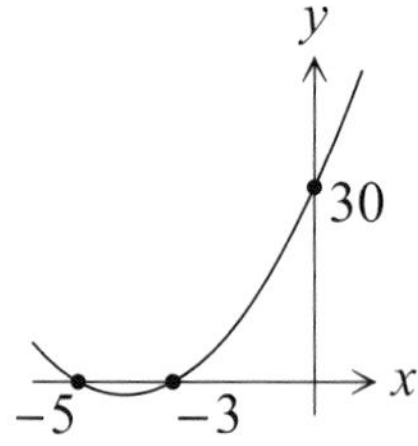

(h)
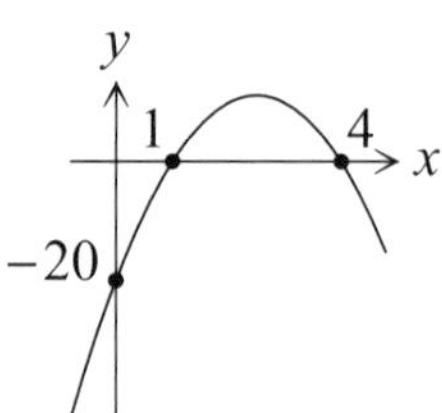

(i)
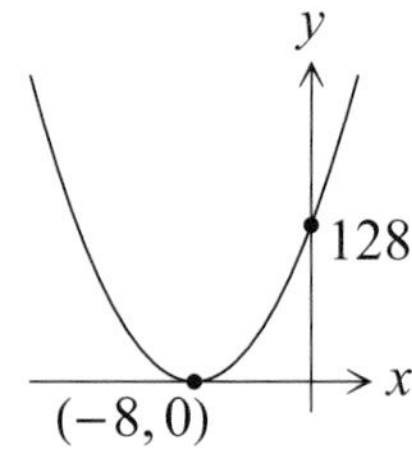

(j)
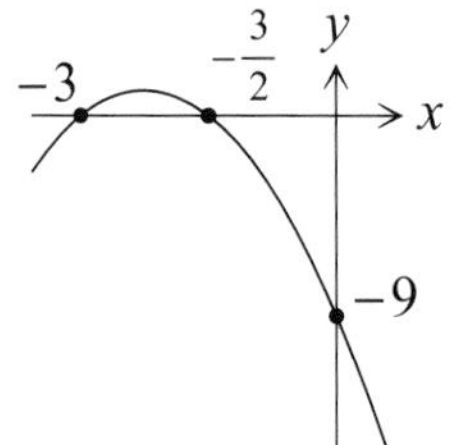

(k)
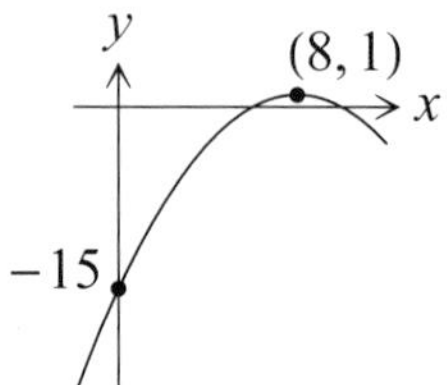

(l)
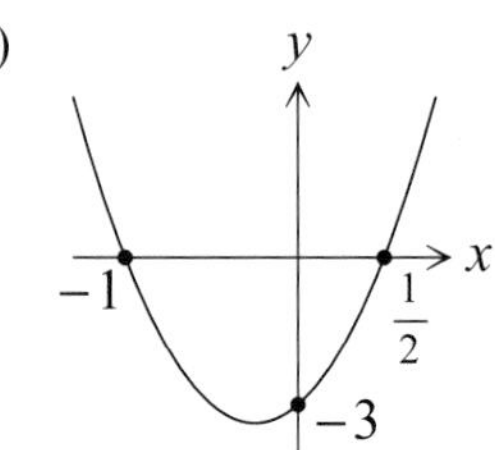

❄ **2** Find an equation of the form $y = ax^2 + bx + c$ for the curve:

(a)

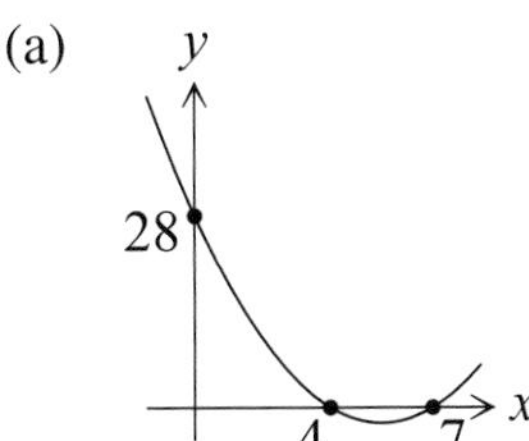

(b)

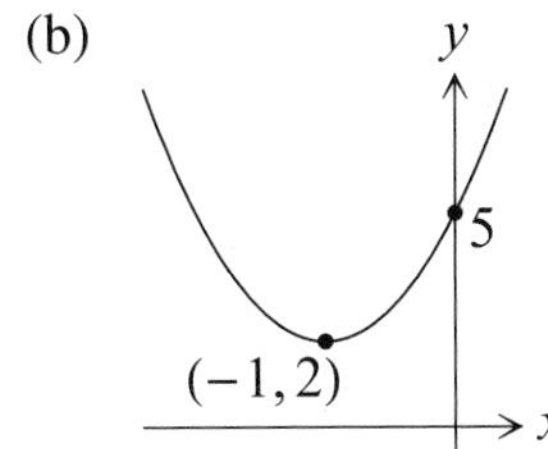

(c)

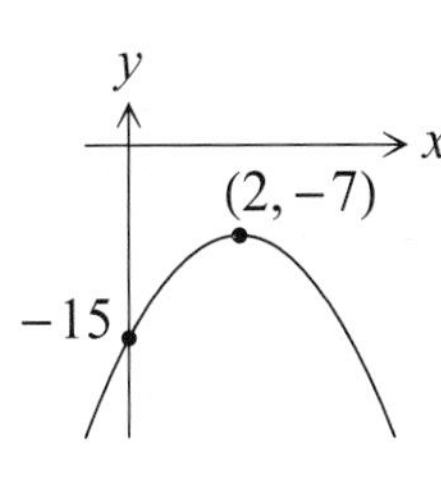

(d)

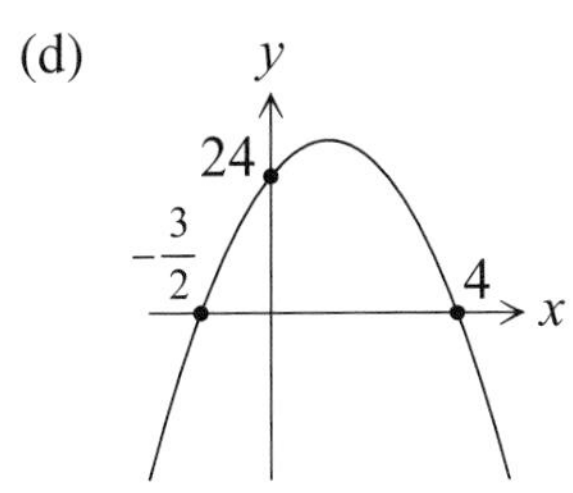

(e)

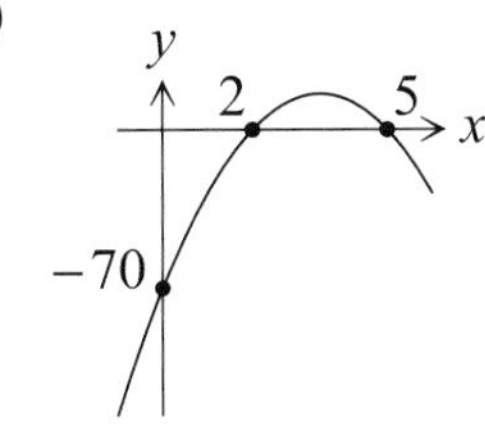

(f)

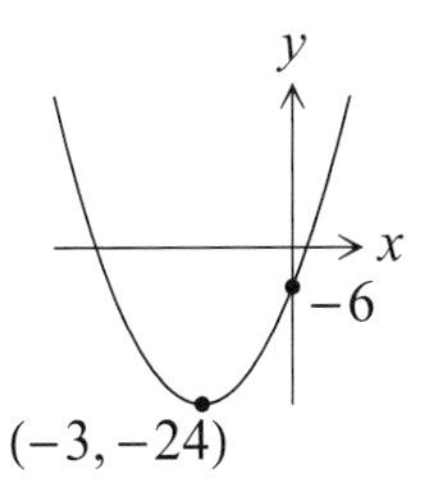

5.6 Changing the form of a parabola equation

In this exercise you will learn how to:

- ❑ change the equation of a parabola from the form $y = k(x - a)(x - b)$ to the form $y = k(x - p)^2 + q$
- ❑ use the axis of symmetry of a parabola bisects the zeros
- ❑ find p and q using the turning point of a parabola lies on the axis of symmetry

❄ **1** The diagram shows the parabola with equation $y = (x - a)(x - b)$.

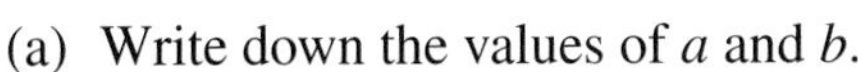

(a) Write down the values of a and b.

(b) State the equation of the axis of symmetry of the curve.

The point $(3, n)$ lies on the curve.

(c) Find the value of n.

(d) Find an equation of the parabola in the form $y = (x - p)^2 - q$.

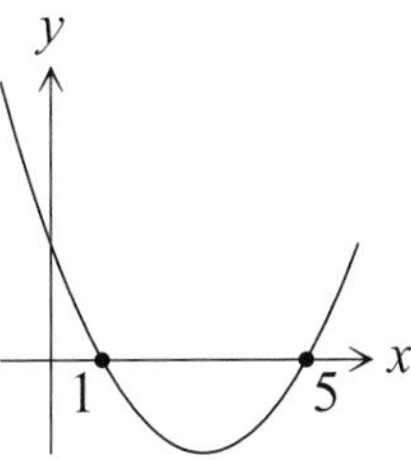

❄ **2** The diagram shows the parabola with equation $y = -(x - a)(x - b)$.

(a) Write down the values of a and b.

(b) State the equation of the axis of symmetry of the curve.

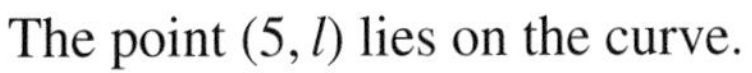

The point $(5, l)$ lies on the curve.

(c) Find the value of l.

(d) Find an equation of the parabola in the form $y = -(x - p)^2 + q$.

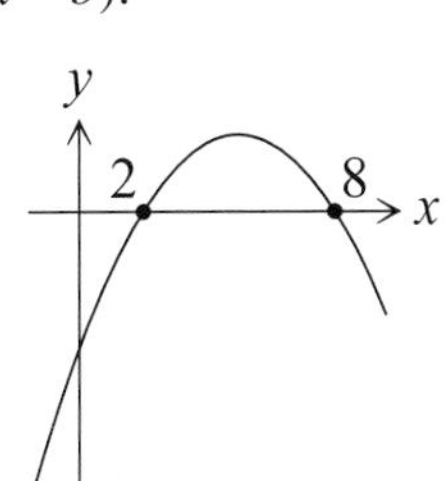

3 The diagram shows the parabola with equation $y = k(x - a)(x - b)$.

(a) Find the values of a, b and k.

(b) State the equation of the axis of symmetry of the curve.

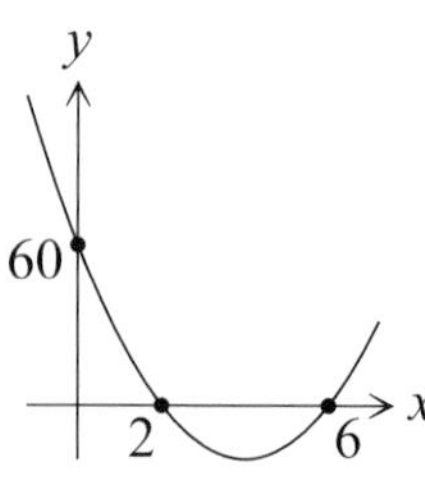

The point $(4, m)$ lies on the curve.

(c) Find the value of m.

(d) Find an equation of the parabola in the form $y = k(x - p)^2 - q$.

4 The diagram shows the parabola with equation $y = k(x - a)(x - b)$.

(a) Find the values of a, b and k.

(b) State the equation of the axis of symmetry of the curve.

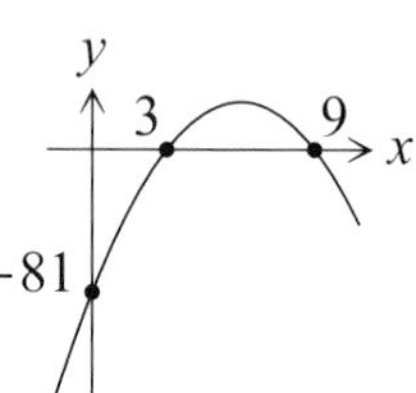

The point $(6, c)$ lies on the curve.

(c) Find the value of c.

(d) Find an equation of the parabola in the form $y = k(x - p)^2 + q$.

5 The diagram shows the parabola with equation $y = (x - a)(x - b)$.

(a) Write down the values of a and b.

(b) State the equation of the axis of symmetry of the curve.

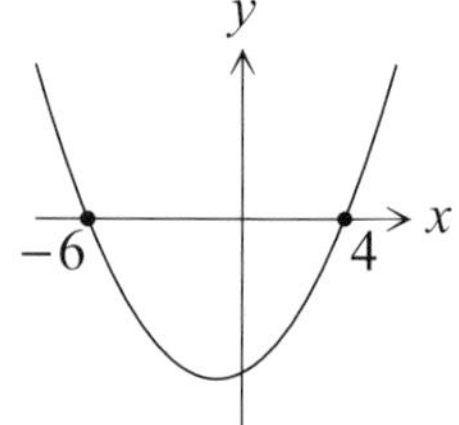

(c) Find the coordinates of the turning point.

(d) Find an equation of the parabola in the form $y = (x + p)^2 - q$.

6 The diagram shows the parabola with equation $y = -(x - a)(x - b)$.

(a) Write down the values of a and b.

(b) State the equation of the axis of symmetry of the curve.

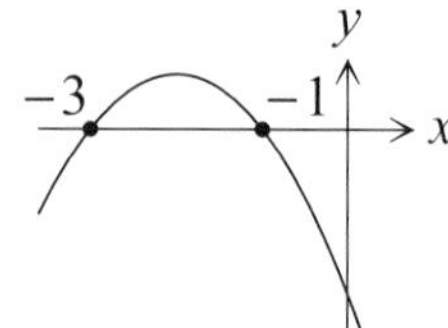

(c) Find the coordinates of the turning point.

(d) Find an equation of the parabola in the form $y = -(x + p)^2 + q$.

7 The diagram shows the parabola with equation $y = k(x - a)(x - b)$.

(a) Find the values of a, b and k.

(b) State the equation of the axis of symmetry of the curve.

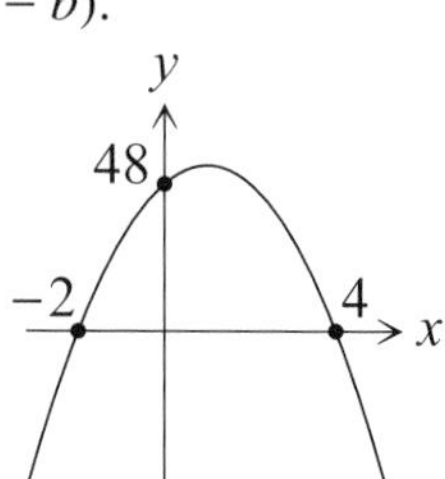

(c) Find the coordinates of the turning point.

(d) Find an equation of the parabola in the form $y = k(x - p)^2 + q$.

8 The diagram shows the parabola with equation $y = k(x - a)(x - b)$.

(a) Find the values of a, b and k.

(b) State the equation of the axis of symmetry of the curve.

(c) Find the coordinates of the turning point.

(d) Find an equation of the parabola in the form $y = k(x + p)^2 - q$.

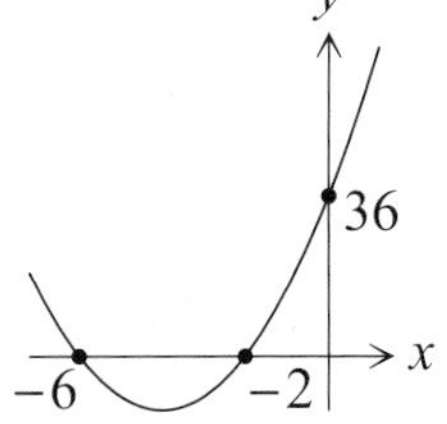

9 The diagram shows a parabola.

(a) Find an equation of the parabola in the form $y = k(x - a)(x - b)$.

(b) Find an equation of the parabola in the form $y = k(x + p)^2 + q$.

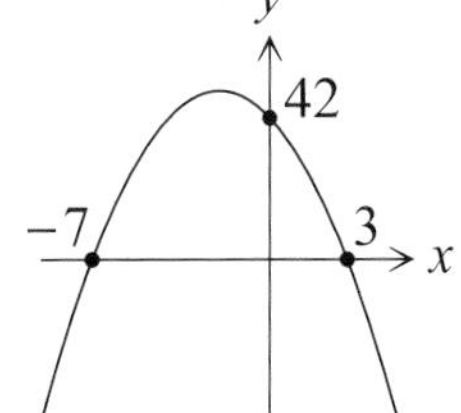

10 The diagram shows the parabola.

(a) Find an equation of the parabola in the form $y = k(x - a)(x - b)$.

(b) Find an equation of the parabola in the form $y = k(x - p)^2 - q$.

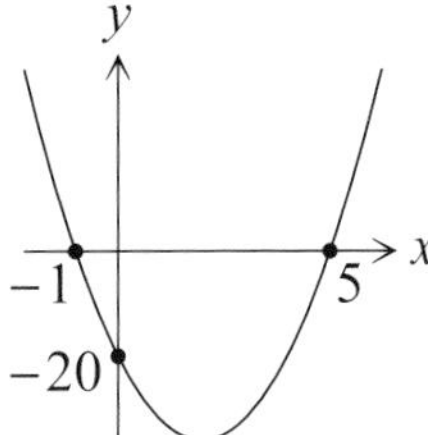

11 A parabola has equation $y = x^2 - 8x + 15$.

(a) Find an equation of the parabola in the form $y = (x - a)(x - b)$.

(b) State the equation of the axis of symmetry of the curve.

(c) Find the coordinates of the turning point of the parabola.

(d) Find an equation of the parabola in the form $y = (x - p)^2 - q$.

12 A parabola has equation $y = x^2 + 12x + 20$.

(a) Find an equation of the parabola in the form $y = (x - a)(x - b)$.

(b) State the equation of the axis of symmetry of the curve.

(c) Find the coordinates of the turning point of the parabola.

(d) Find an equation of the parabola in the form $y = (x + p)^2 - q$.

5.7 The cubic curve equation $y = k(x - a)(x - b)(x - c)$

In this exercise you will learn how to:

- ❑ find an equation of a cubic curve in the form $y = k(x - a)(x - b)(x - c)$ from a given graph
- ❑ find a, b and c using the zeros occur where $y = 0$
- ❑ find k by using the y-intercept occurs where $x = 0$, or by substituting the coordinates of a point on the curve into the equation
- ❑ check the sign of k from the shape of the curve: $k > 0$ $k < 0$

❄ **1** Find an equation of the form $y = (x - a)(x - b)(x - c)$ or $y = -(x - a)(x - b)(x - c)$ for the curve:

(a)
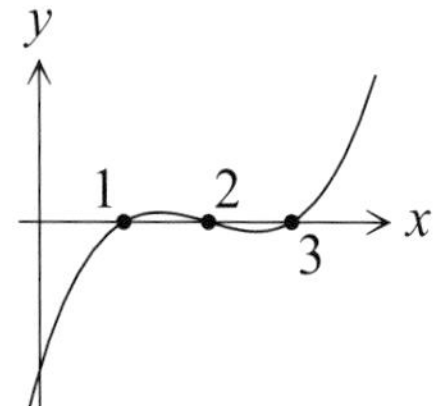

(b)
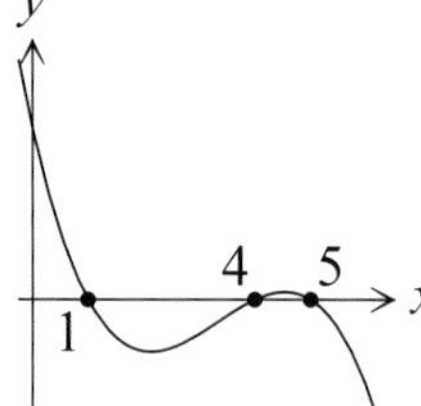

(c)
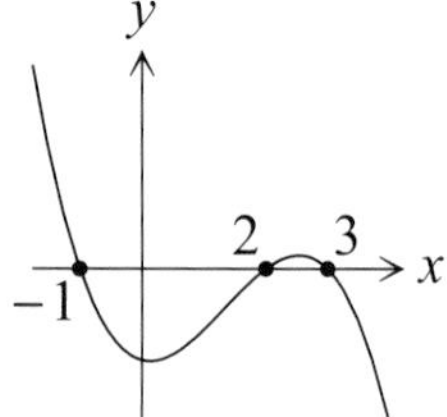

(d)
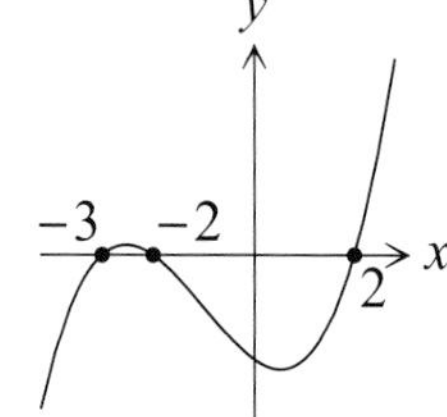

(e)
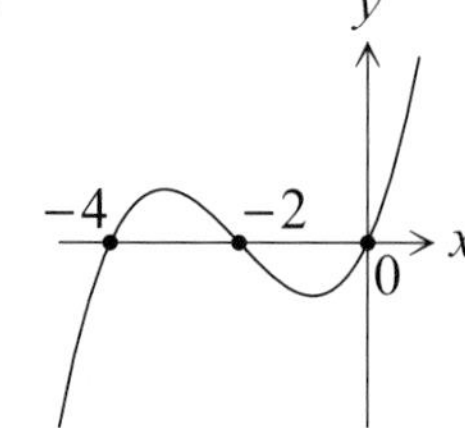

(f)
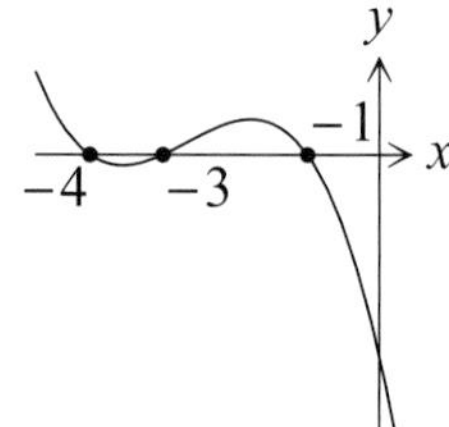

(g)
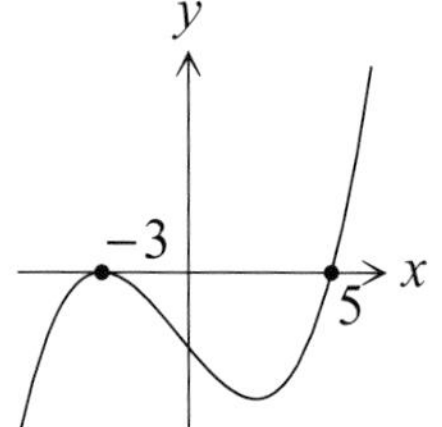

(h)
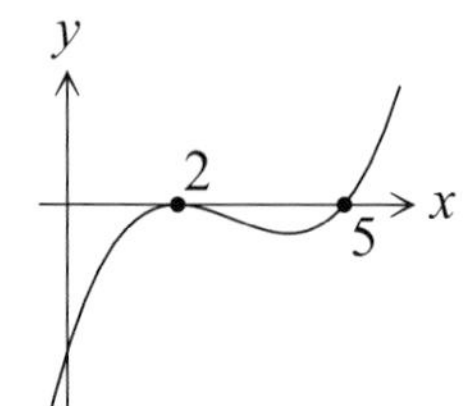

(i)
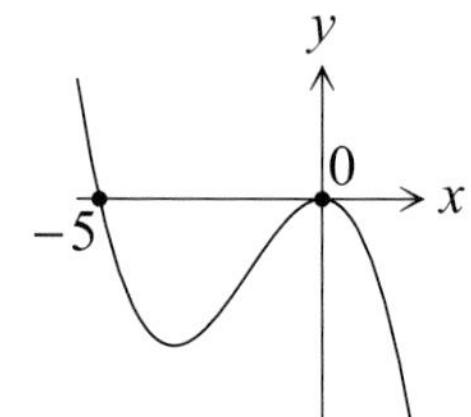

❄ **2** Find an equation of the form $y = k(x-a)(x-b)(x-c)$ for the curve:

(a)

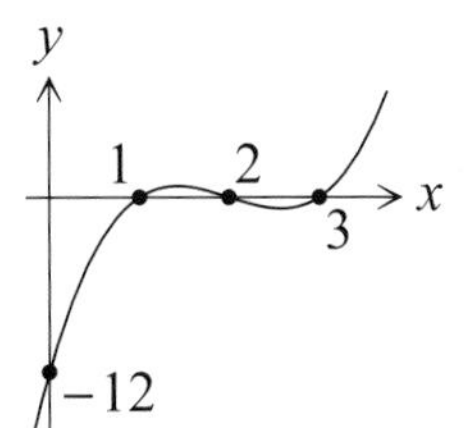

(b)

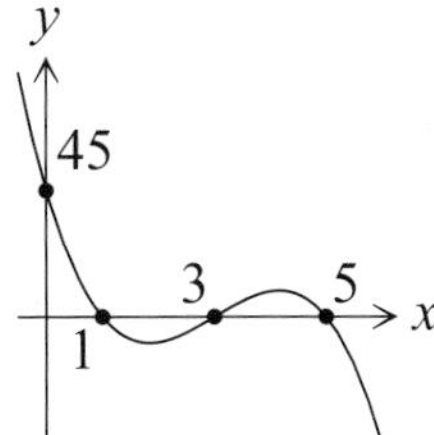

(c)

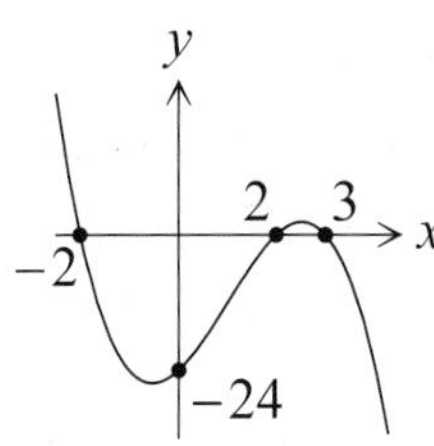

(d)

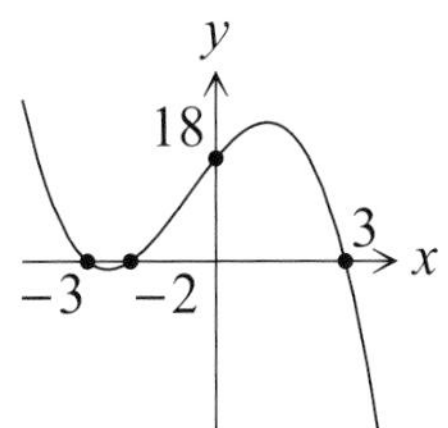

(e)

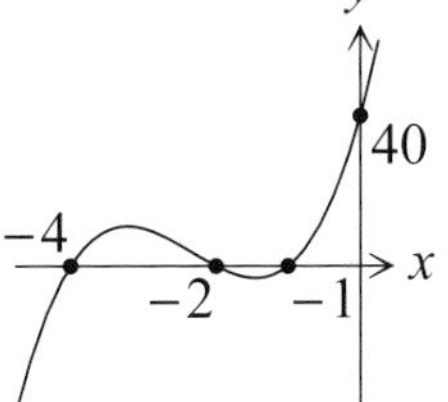

(f)

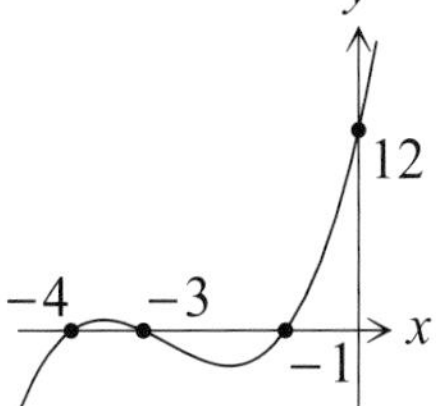

(g)

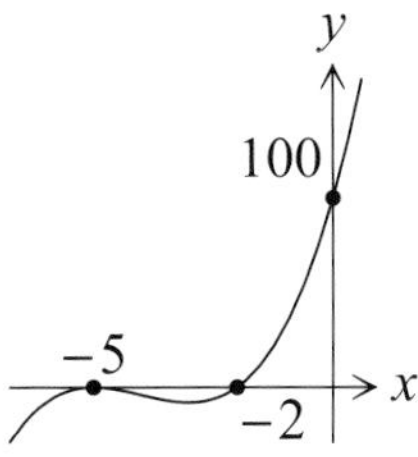

(h)

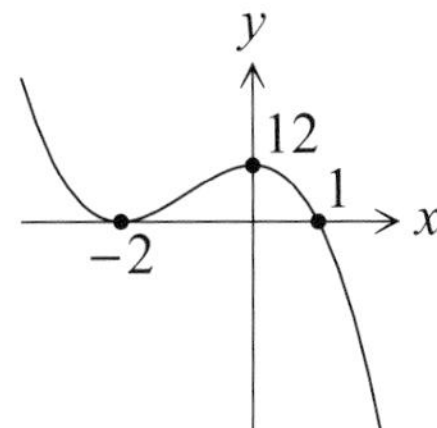

(i)

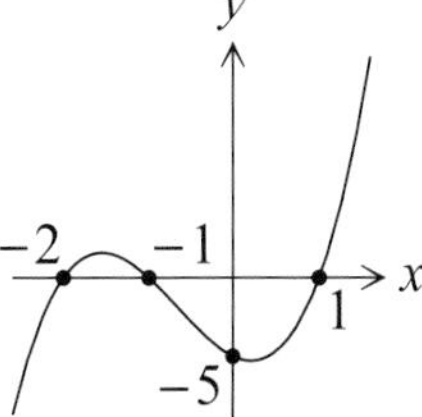

❄ **3** Find an equation of the form $y = k(x-a)(x-b)(x-c)$ for the curve:

(a)

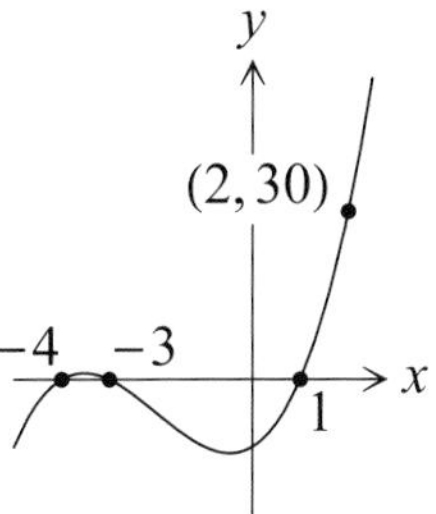

(b)

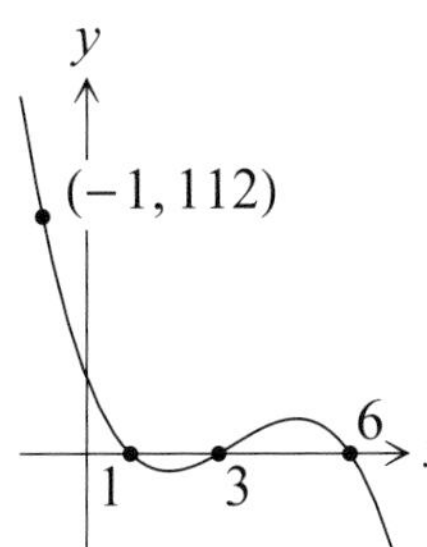

(c)

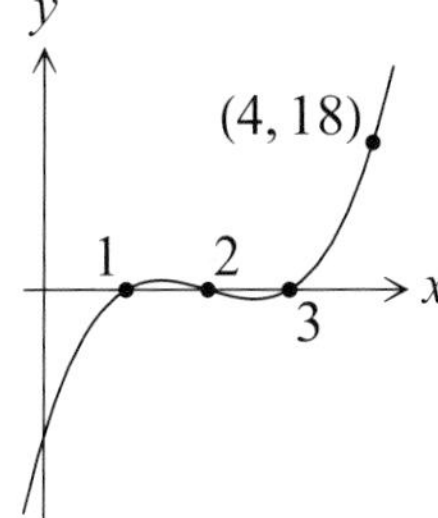

(d)

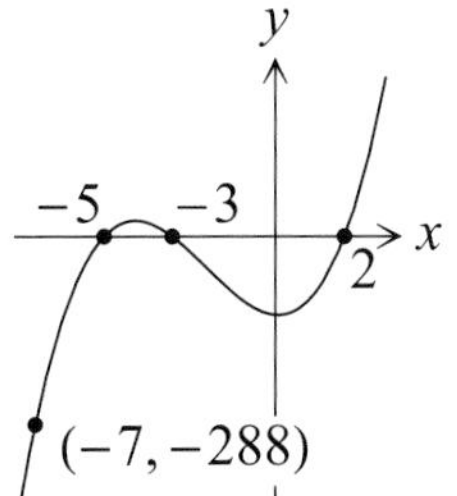

(e)

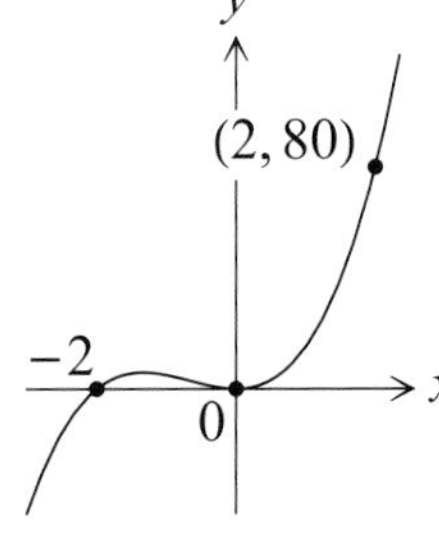

(f)

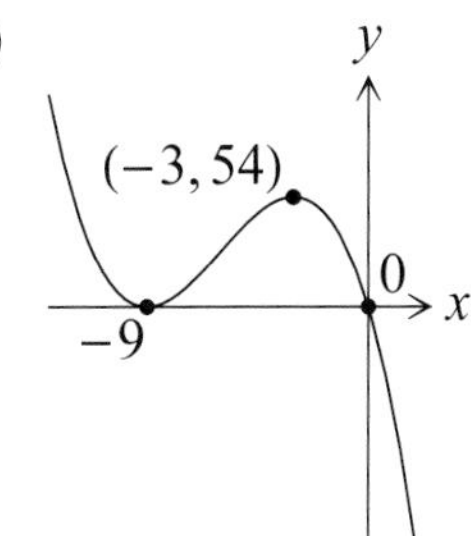

6 Intersecting lines and curves

6.1 The intersection of two straight lines

In this exercise you will learn how to:

- ❑ find the point of intersection of two straight lines

1 The diagram shows the straight lines with equations $x = 5$ and $y = 2x + 1$.

The lines intersect at the point B.

Calculate the coordinates of B.

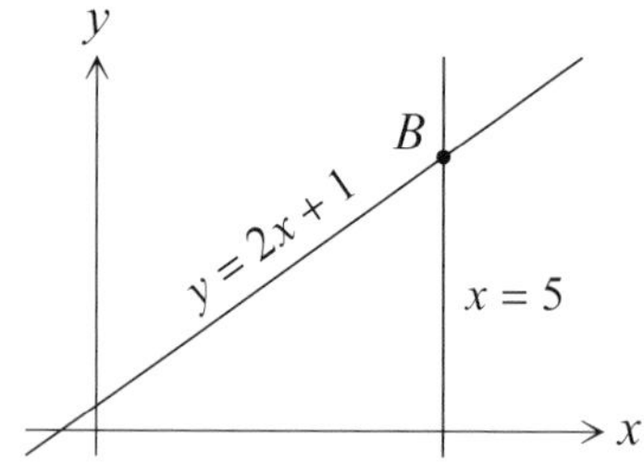

2 The diagram shows the straight lines with equations $y = 3$ and $y = 5x - 2$.

The lines intersect at the point A.

Calculate the coordinates of A.

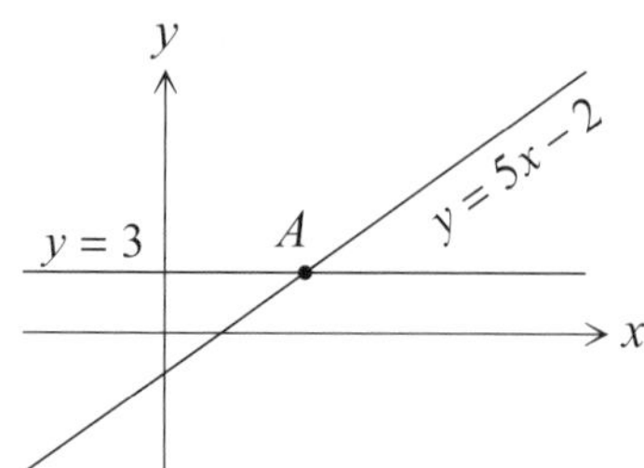

3 The diagram shows the straight lines with equations $x = -2$ and $x + y = 7$.

The lines intersect at the point C.

Calculate the coordinates of C.

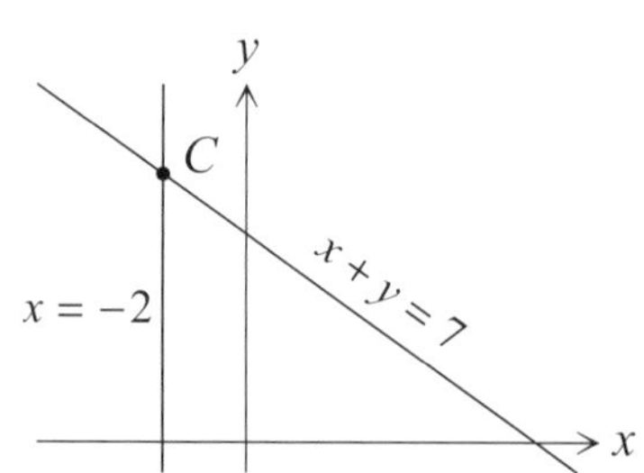

4 The diagram shows the straight lines with equations $y = -2$ and $3x + y = 10$.

The lines intersect at the point R.

Calculate the coordinates of R.

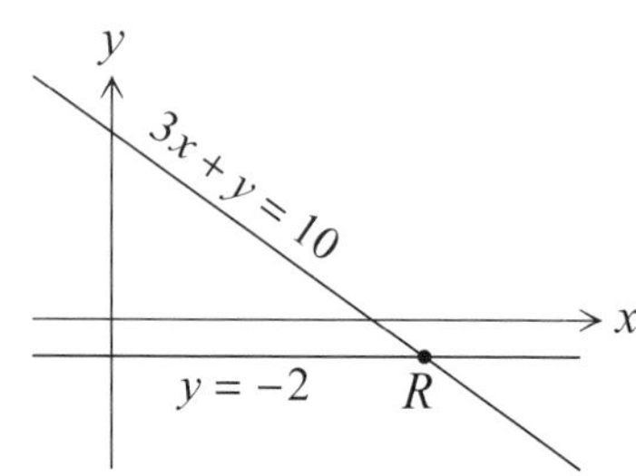

5 The diagram shows the straight lines with equations $y = 2x - 7$ and $y = x - 2$.
The lines intersect at the point P.
Calculate the coordinates of P.

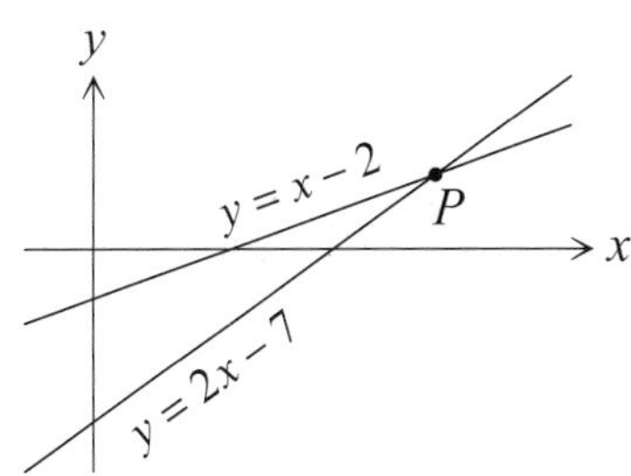

6 The diagram shows the straight lines with equations $y = x + 3$ and $y = 3x - 5$.
The lines intersect at the point Q.
Calculate the coordinates of Q.

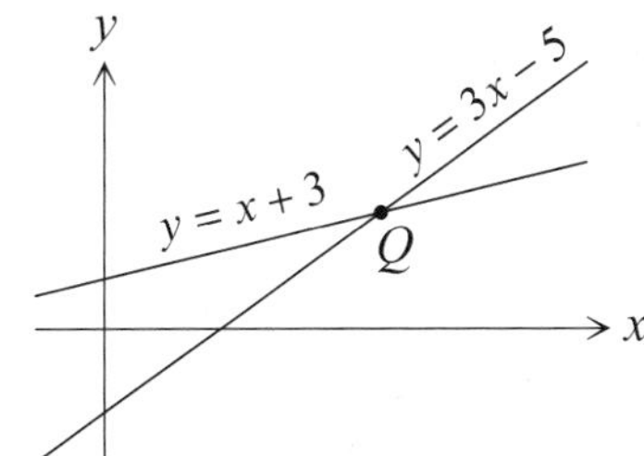

7 The diagram shows the straight lines with equations $y = 2x - 5$ and $y = 7 - x$.
The lines intersect at the point R.
Calculate the coordinates of R.

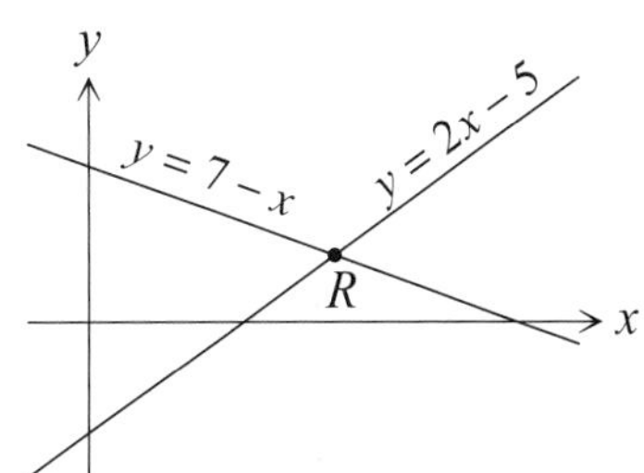

8 The diagram shows the straight lines with equations $y = 2x$ and $y = 3x + 2$.
The lines intersect at the point T.
Calculate the coordinates of T.

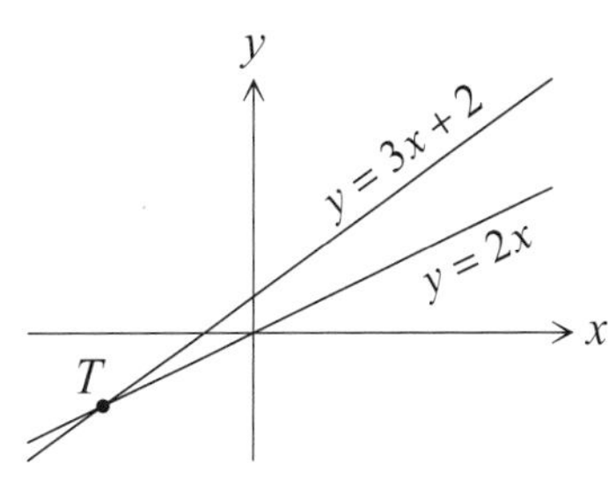

9 The diagram shows the straight lines with equations $y = 2x + 9$ and $x + y + 6 = 0$.
The lines intersect at the point A.
Calculate the coordinates of A.

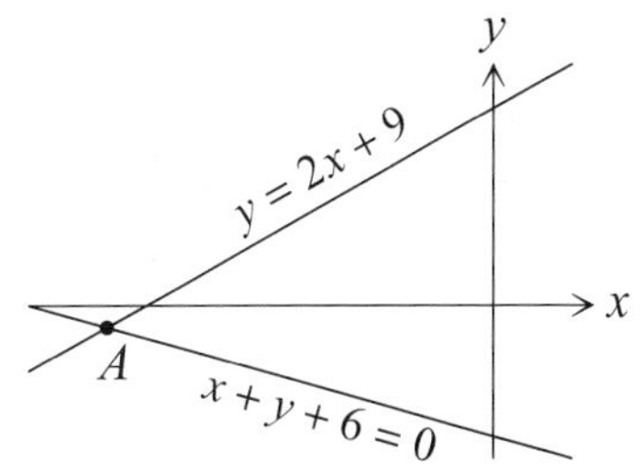

10 The diagram shows the straight lines with equations $2x + y = 12$ and $y = x - 9$.

The lines intersect at the point B.

Calculate the coordinates of B.

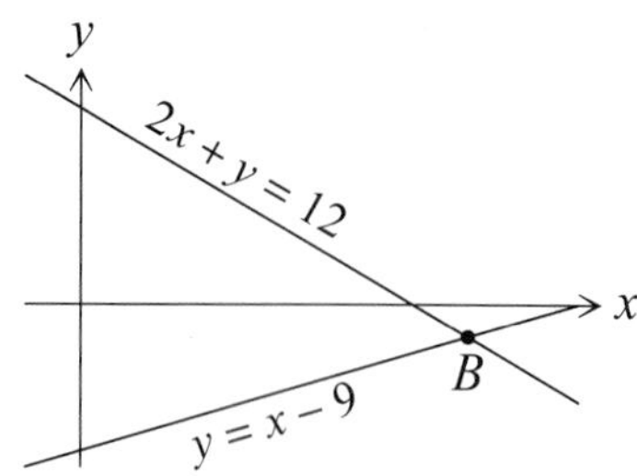

11 The diagram shows the straight lines with equations $y = 2x + 10$ and $2x + 3y + 2 = 0$.

The lines intersect at the point C.

Calculate the coordinates of C.

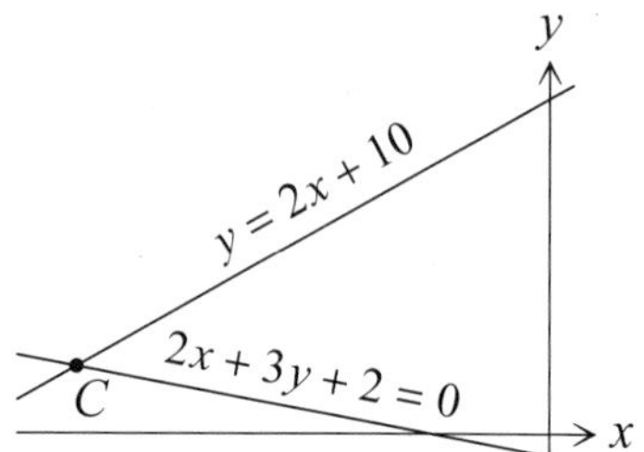

12 The diagram shows the straight lines with equations $x + y = 4$ and $2x - y = 8$.

The lines intersect at the point D.

Calculate the coordinates of D.

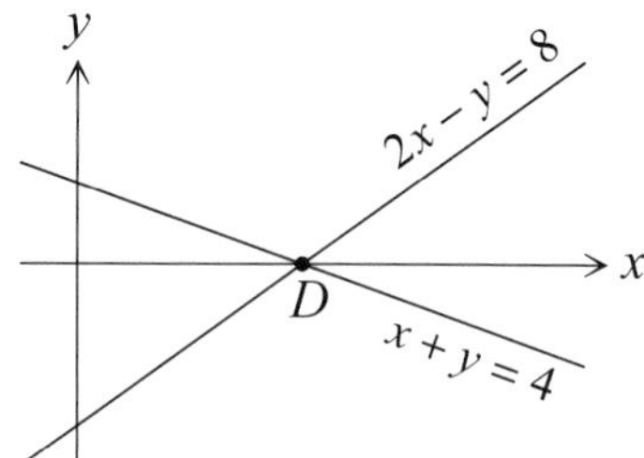

13 The diagram shows triangle ABC.

The side AB is parallel to the y-axis.

(a) Write down the equation of AB.

The side BC is parallel to the x-axis.

(b) Write down the equation of BC.

The line AC has equation $y = 2x + 1$.

(c) Calculate the coordinates of A and C.

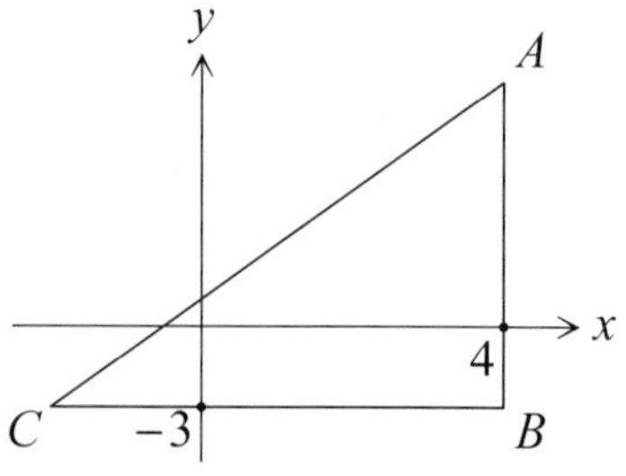

14 The diagram shows two straight lines AB and CD.

The line AB passes through $(0, 5)$ and has gradient 2.

(a) Write down the equation of AB.

The line CD passes through $(0, 15)$ and has gradient -3.

(b) Write down the equation of CD.

The lines AB and CD intersect at the point E.

(c) Calculate the coordinates of E.

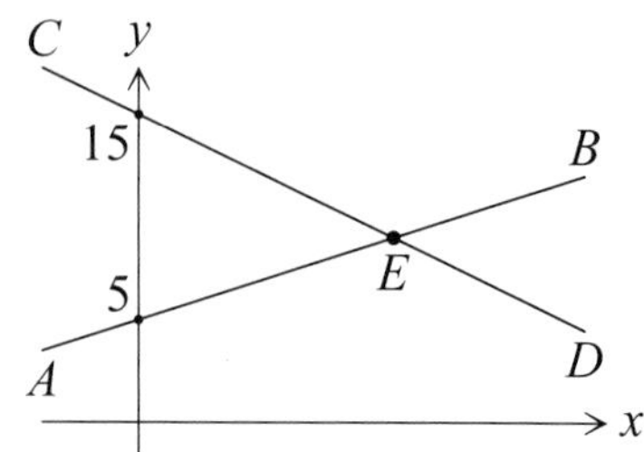

15 The diagram shows triangle PQR.
Calculate the coordinates of the vertices P, Q and R.

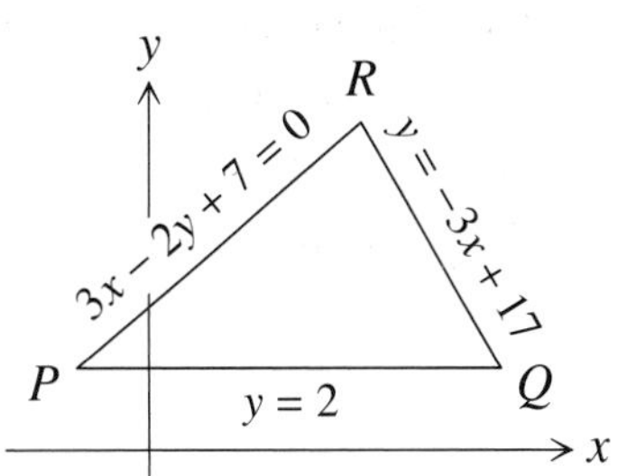

16 The diagram shows parallelogram $PQRS$. The equation of PQ is $y = 2x - 1$, the equation of RQ is $y = -4x + 35$ and S is the point $(0, 5)$.

(a) Calculate the coordinates of Q.
(b) Write down the equation of SP.
(c) Calculate the coordinates of P.
(d) Write down the equation of SR.
(e) Calculate the coordinates of R.

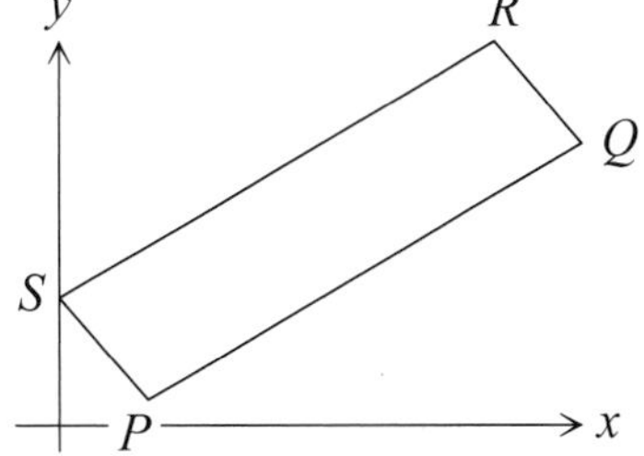

6.2 The intersection of a straight line and a parabola

In this exercise you will learn how to:

- find the points of intersection of a straight line and a parabola

1 The diagram shows the straight line with equation $y = 8$ and the parabola with equation $y = x^2 - 8$.
The line and the parabola intersect at the points A and B.
Calculate the coordinates of A and B.

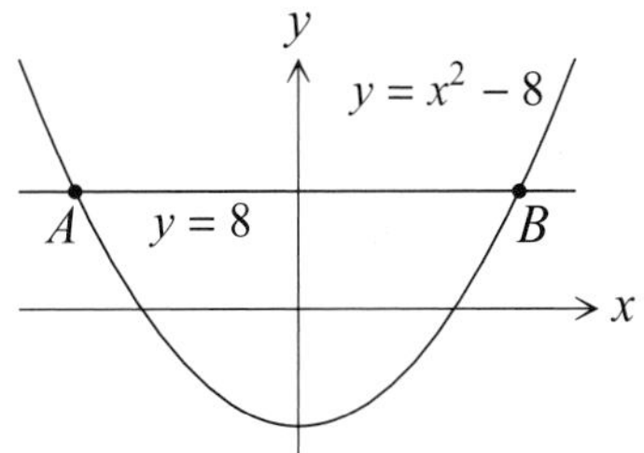

2 The diagram shows the straight line with equation $y = 4$ and the parabola with equation $y = 13 - x^2$.
The line and the parabola intersect at the points P and Q.
Calculate the coordinates of P and Q.

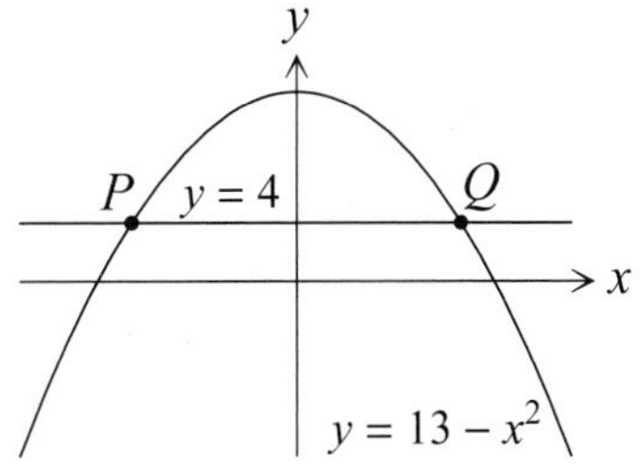

3 The diagram shows the parabola with equation $y = x^2 - 4x + 3$.

The line KL is parallel to the x-axis.

(a) Write down the equation of KL.

The line and parabola intersect at K and L.

(b) Calculate the coordinates of K and L.

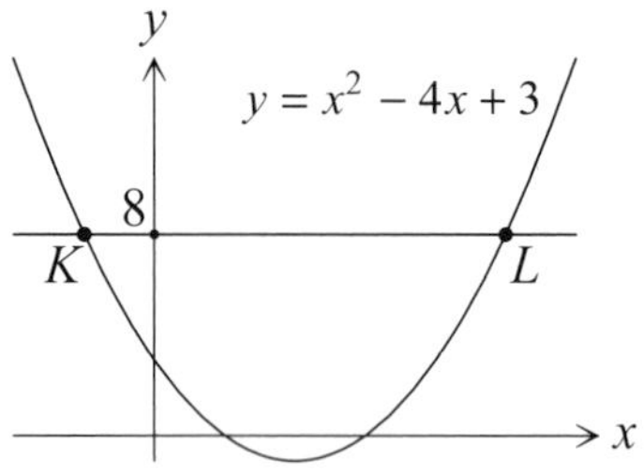

4 The diagram shows the parabola with equation $y = 3 + 2x - x^2$.

The line AB is parallel to the x-axis.

(a) Write down the equation of AB.

The line and parabola intersect at A and B.

(b) Calculate the coordinates of A and B.

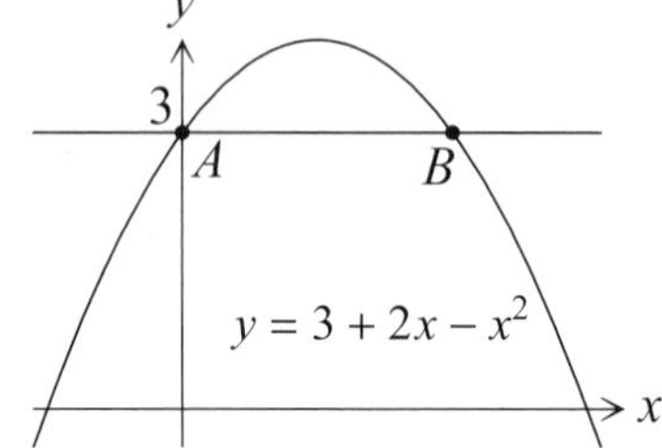

5 The diagram shows the parabola with equation $y = (x + 3)^2 - 4$.

The line through T is parallel to the x-axis.

(a) Write down the equation of the line through T.

The line and parabola intersect at T.

(b) Calculate the coordinates of T.

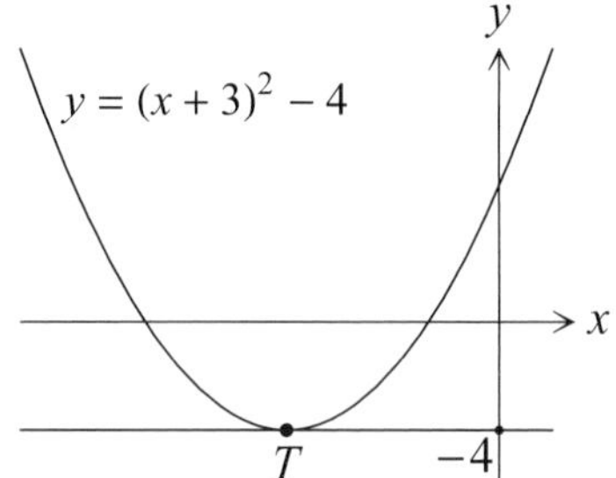

6 The diagram shows the straight line with equation $y = 11 - x$ and the parabola with equation $y = x^2 - 3x - 4$.

The line and the parabola intersect at the points P and Q.

Calculate the coordinates of P and Q.

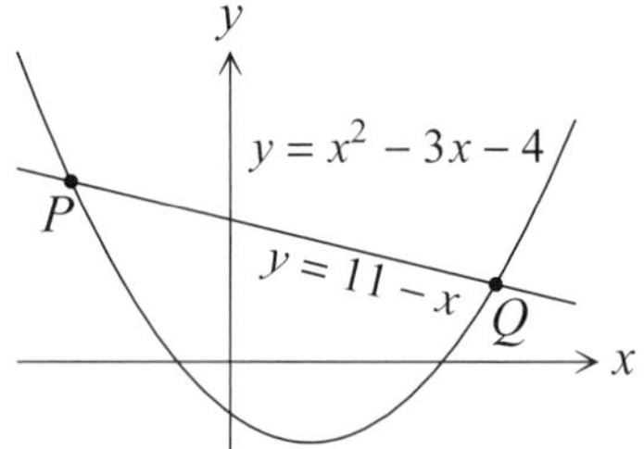

7 The diagram shows the straight line with equation $y = x - 5$ and the parabola with equation $y = 5 + 4x - x^2$.

The line and the parabola intersect at the points A and B.

Calculate the coordinates of A and B.

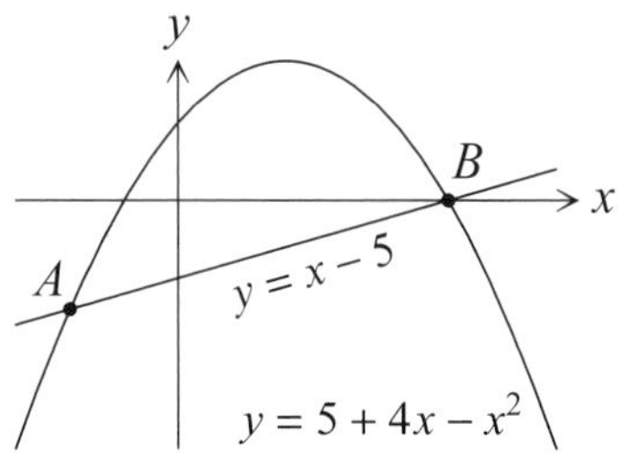

8 The diagram shows the straight line with equation $y = x + 1$ and the parabola with equation $y = 2x^2$.

The line and the parabola intersect at the points P and Q.

Calculate the coordinates of P and Q.

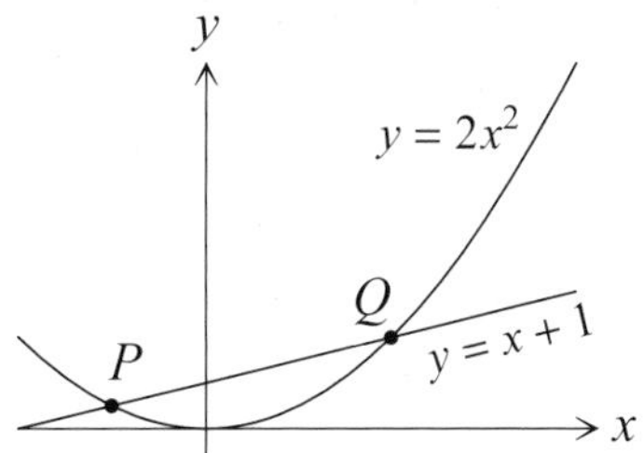

9 The diagram shows the straight line with equation $y = 4 - 7x$ and the parabola with equation $y = 3 - 5x - x^2$.

The line and parabola intersect at T.

Calculate the coordinates of T.

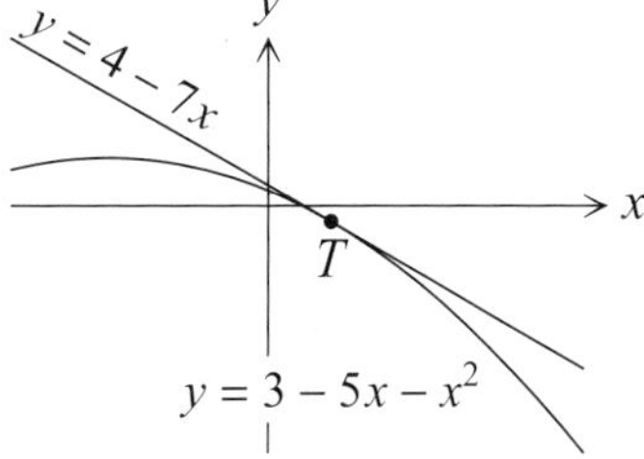

10 The diagram shows the straight line with equation $y = 4x$ and the parabola with equation $y = (x - 2)^2 + 11$.

The line and the parabola intersect at the points A and B.

Calculate the coordinates of A and B.

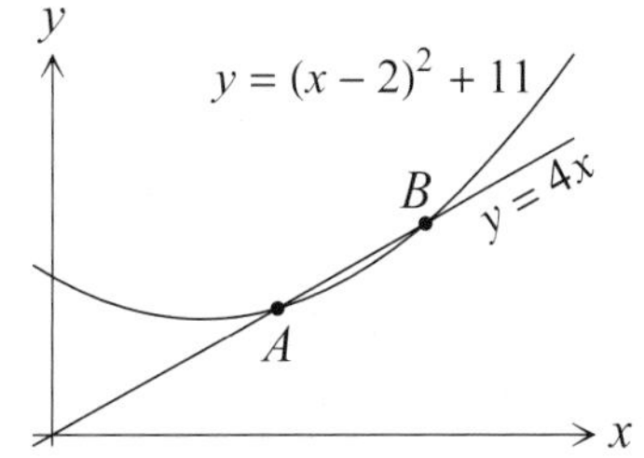

11 The diagram shows the straight line with equation $y = 3x + 1$ and the parabola with equation $y = (x - 2)^2 - 11$.

The line and the parabola intersect at the points R and S.

Calculate the coordinates of R and S.

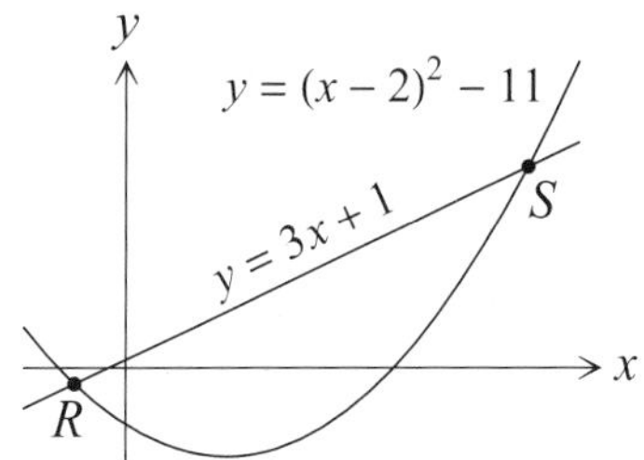

12 The diagram shows the straight line with equation $y = x + 1$ and the parabola with equation $y = 2(x + 1)^2 - 10$.

The line and the parabola intersect at the points A and B.

Calculate the coordinates of A and B.

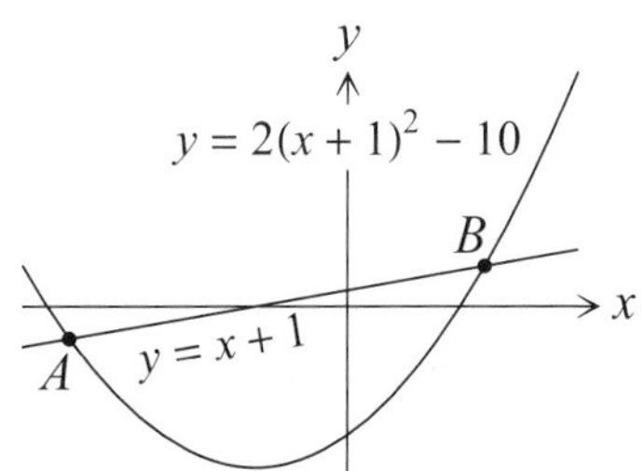

13 The diagram shows a parabola and a straight line. The parabola has an equation of the form $y = (x - a)(x - b)$.

(a) Write down an equation of the parabola.

The line has gradient -2 and passes through the point $(0, 10)$.

(b) Write down the equation of the line.

The line and parabola intersect at the points P and Q.

(c) Calculate the coordinates of P and Q.

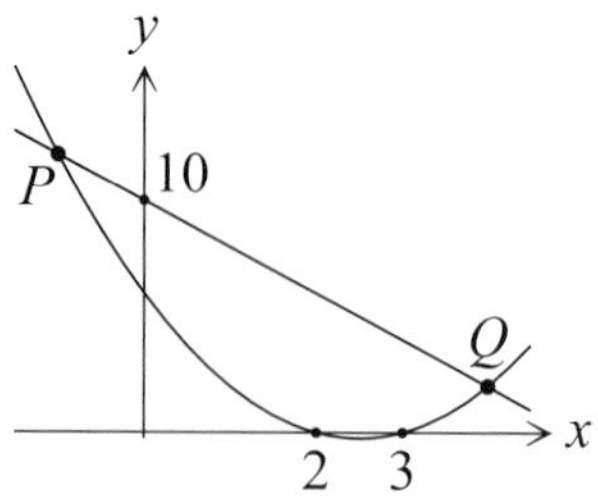

14 The diagram shows a parabola and a straight line. The parabola has an equation of the form $y = (x - a)^2 + b$.

(a) Write down an equation of the parabola.

The line has gradient 1 and passes through the origin.

(b) Write down the equation of the line.

The line and parabola intersect at the points A and B.

(c) Calculate the coordinates of A and B.

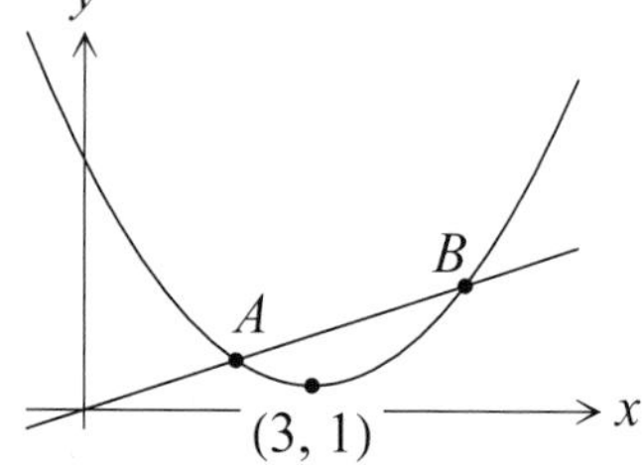

6.3 The intersection of two parabolas

In this exercise you will learn how to:

- ❑ find the points of intersection of two parabolas

1 The diagram shows the curves with equations $y = x^2$ and $y = 8 - x^2$.

The curves intersect at the points P and Q.

Calculate the coordinates of P and Q.

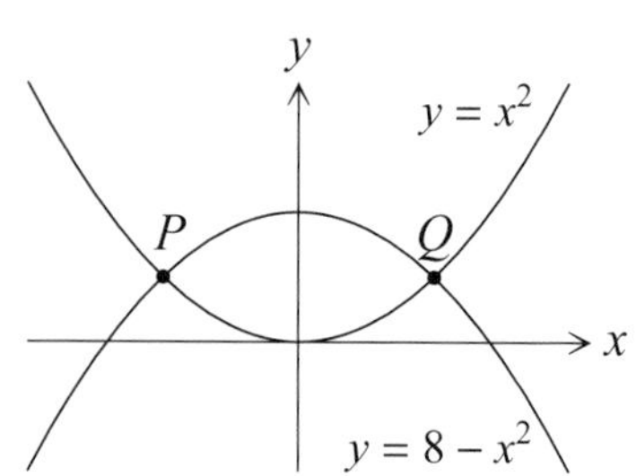

2 The diagram shows the curves with equations $y = 3x^2$ and $y = 36 - x^2$.

The curves intersect at the points A and B.

Calculate the coordinates of A and B.

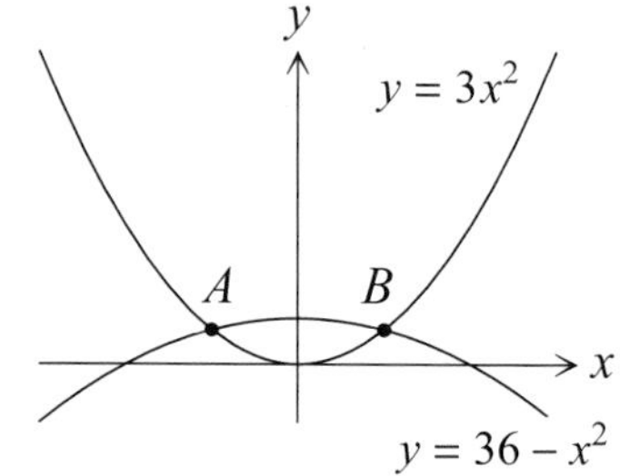

3 The diagram shows the curves with equations $y = x^2 - 50$ and $y = -x^2$.

The curves intersect at the points P and Q.

Calculate the coordinates of P and Q.

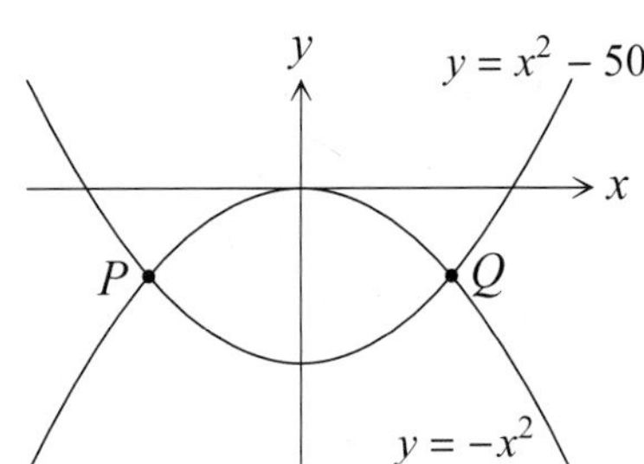

4 The diagram shows the curves with equations $y = x^2$ and $y = 4x - x^2$.

The curves intersect at the points A and B.

Calculate the coordinates of A and B.

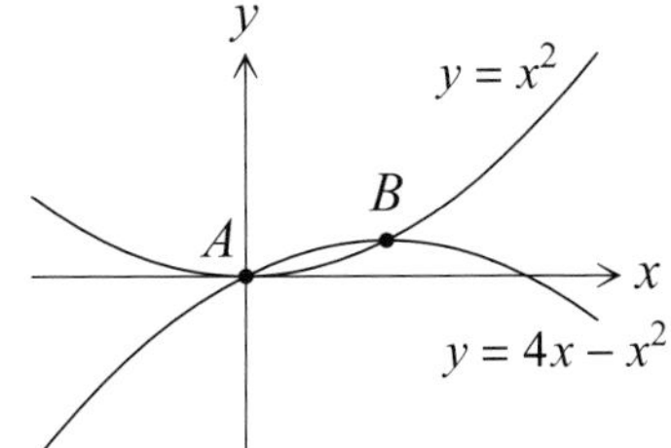

5 The diagram shows the curves with equations $y = 2x^2$ and $y = x^2 + 4$.

The curves intersect at the points K and L.

Calculate the coordinates of K and L.

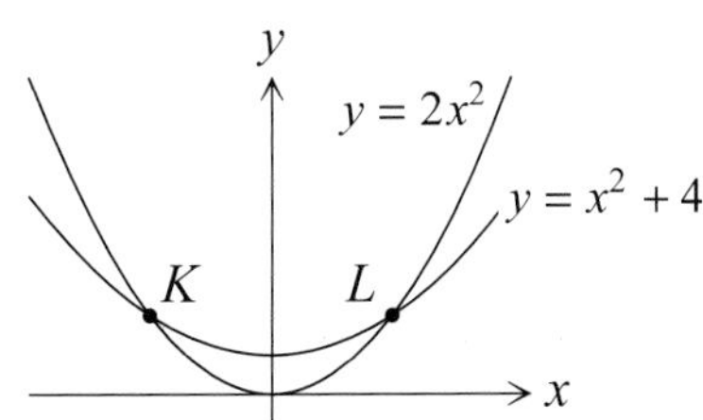

6 The diagram shows the curves with equations $y = x^2 - 8x$ and $y = -x^2$.

The curves intersect at the points P and Q.

Calculate the coordinates of P and Q.

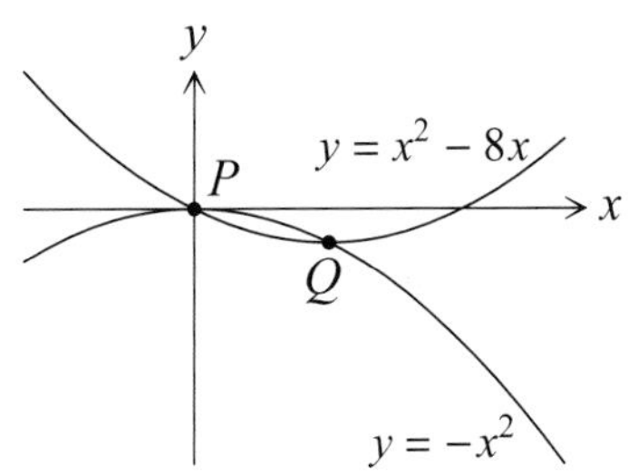

❄ **7** The diagram shows the curves with equations $y = 8 + 2x - x^2$ and $y = (x - 1)^2 + 1$.

The curves intersect at the points P and Q.

Calculate the coordinates of P and Q.

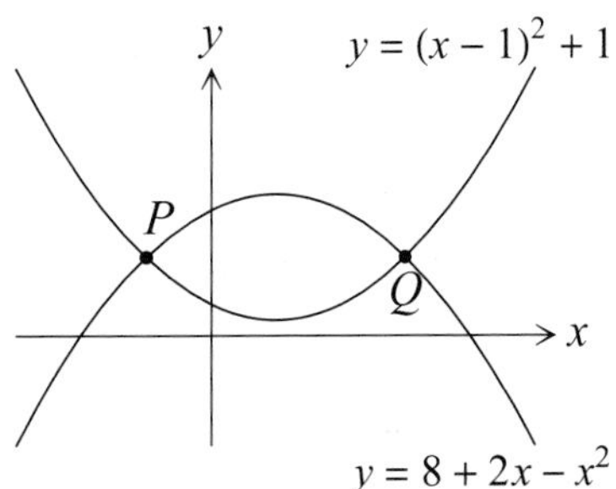

❄ **8** The diagram shows the curves with equations $y = (x - 4)^2 + 2$ and $y = 4 - (x - 4)^2$.

The curves intersect at the points R and S.

Calculate the coordinates of R and S.

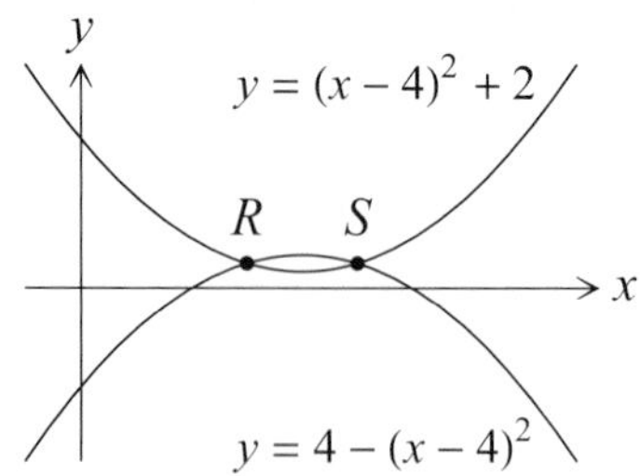

❄ **9** The diagram shows the curves with equations $y = 8 + 2x - x^2$ and $y = x^2 + 4$.

The curves intersect at the points A and B.

Calculate the coordinates of A and B.

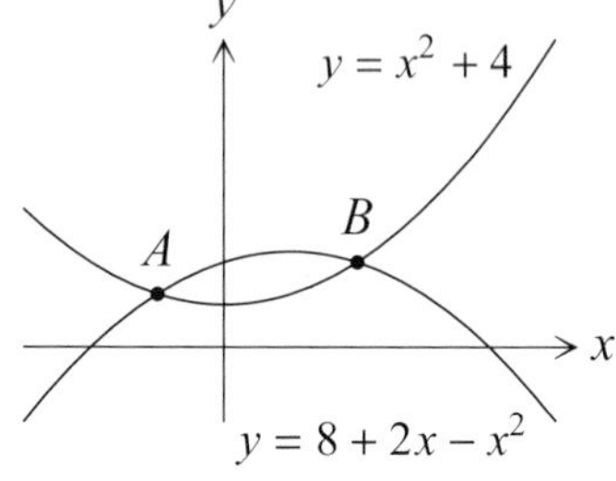

❄ **10** The diagram shows the curves with equations $y = 4 - (x - 3)^2$ and $y = (x - 2)^2 - 1$.

The curves intersect at the points P and Q.

Calculate the coordinates of P and Q.

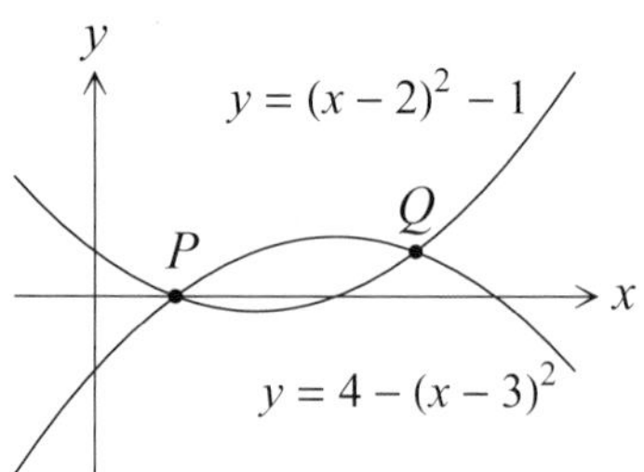

❄ **11** The diagram shows the curves with equations $y = (x - 3)^2 - 6$ and $y = 3 + 4x - x^2$.

The curves intersect at the points P and Q.

Calculate the coordinates of P and Q.

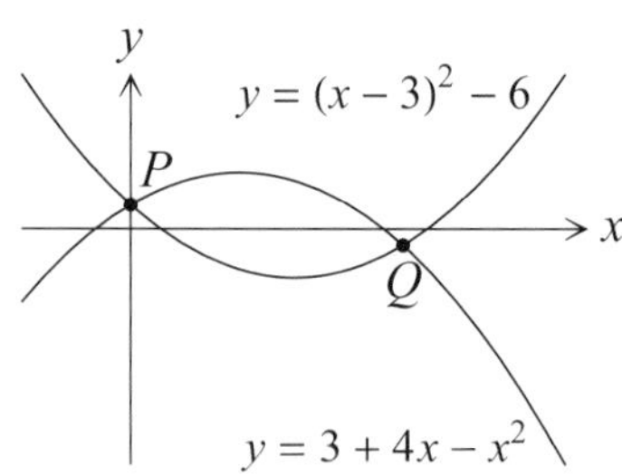

❄ **12** The diagram shows the curves with equations $y = 8 + 2x - x^2$ and $y = x^2 - 8x + 16$.

The curves intersect at the points K and L.

Calculate the coordinates of K and L.

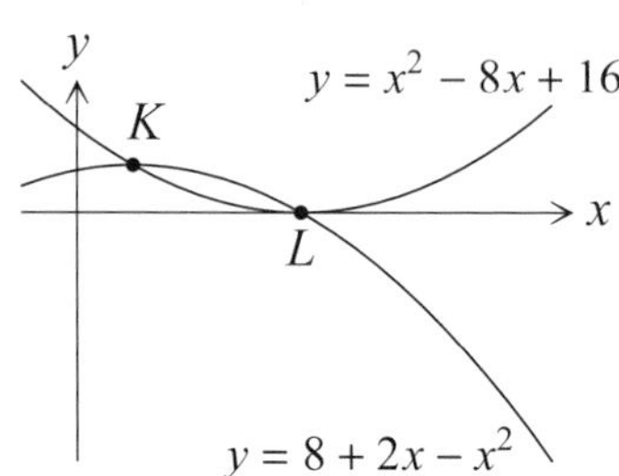

6.4 The intersection of a straight line and a cubic curve

In this exercise you will learn how to:

- ❑ find the points of intersection of a straight line and a cubic curve

1 The diagram shows the curve with equation $y = x^3$ and the straight line with equation $y = x$.

The line intersects the curve at the points P, Q and R.

Calculate the coordinates of P, Q and R.

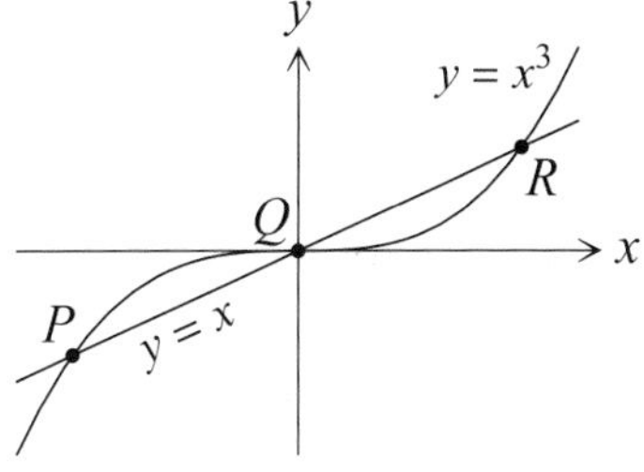

2 The diagram shows the curve with equation $y = 4x^3$ and the straight line with equation $y = x$.

The line intersects the curve at the points A, B and C.

Calculate the coordinates of A, B and C.

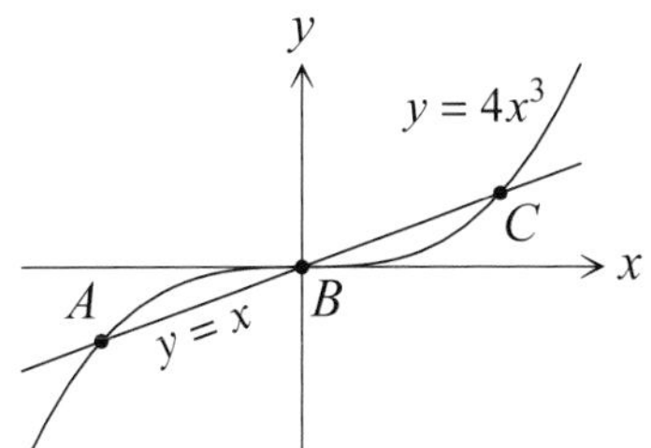

3 The diagram shows the curve with equation $y = x^3 - 6x^2 + 8x$ and the straight line with equation $y = 3x$.

The line intersects the curve at the points A, B and C.

Calculate the coordinates of A, B and C.

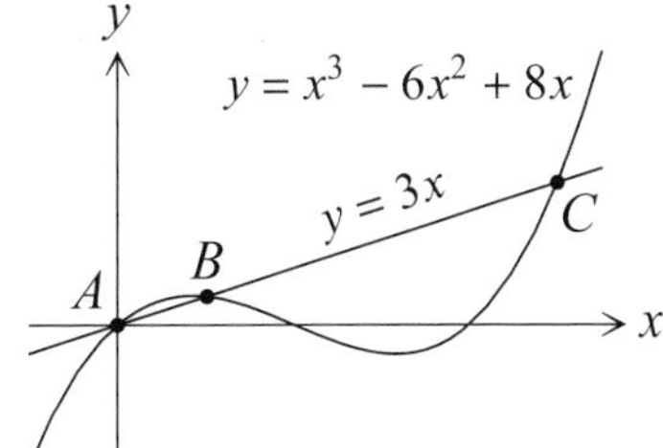

4 The diagram shows the curve with equation $y = 5x^2 - x^3$ and the straight line with equation $y = 4x$.

The line intersects the curve at the points A, B and C.

Calculate the coordinates of A, B and C.

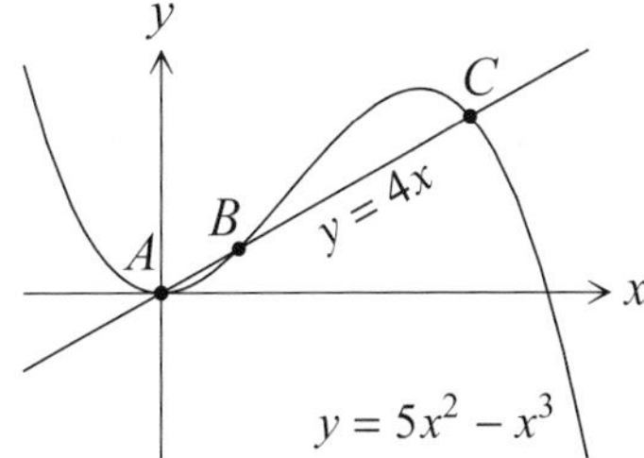

5 The diagram shows the curve with equation $y = -x^3 + 3x + 3$ and the straight line with equation $y = 3 - x$.

The line intersects the curve at the points P, Q and R.

Calculate the coordinates of P, Q and R.

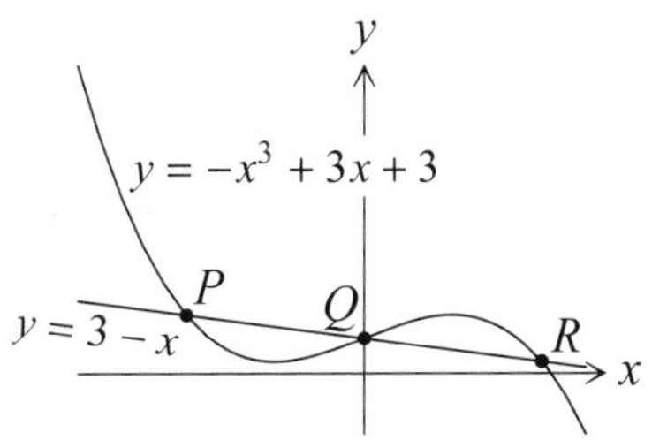

❄ **6** The diagram shows the curve with equation $y = x^3 + 5x^2 + x - 2$ and the straight line with equation $y = x - 2$.

The line intersects the curve at the points P and Q.

Calculate the coordinates of P and Q.

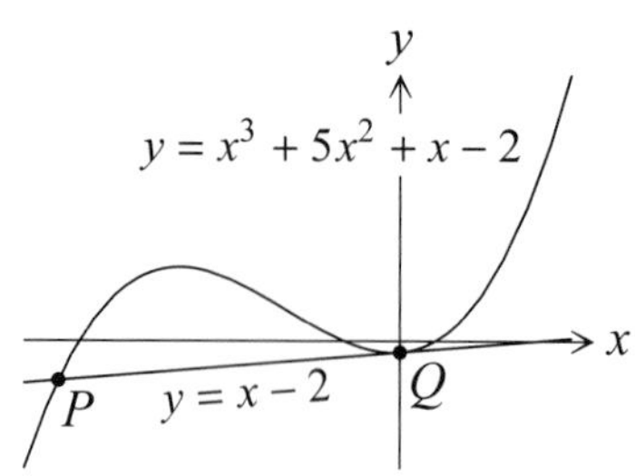

❄ **7** The diagram shows the curve with equation $y = x^3 + x^2 - 7x + 2$ and the straight line with equation $y = 2 - x$.

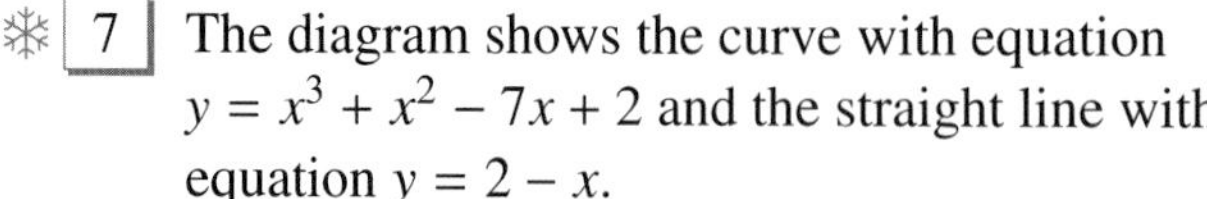

The line intersects the curve at the points A, B and C.

Calculate the coordinates of A, B and C.

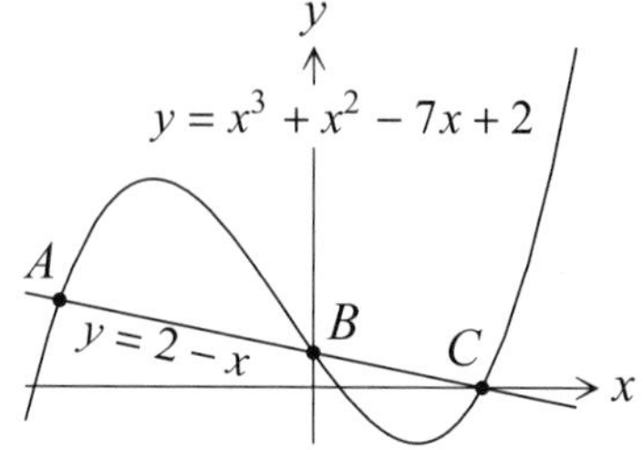

❄ **8** The diagram shows the curve with equation $y = -2x^3 + 3x^2 + x + 4$ and the straight line with equation $y = 4 - x$.

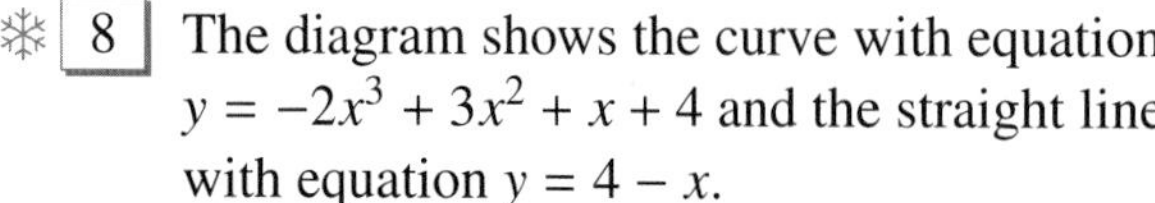

The line intersects the curve at the points A, B and C.

Calculate the coordinates of A, B and C.

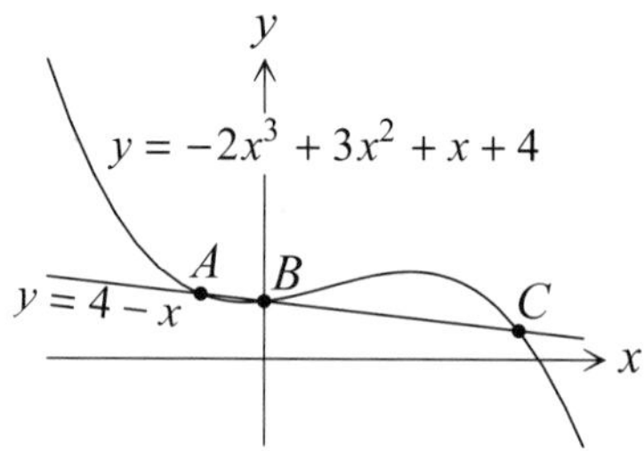

❄ **9** The diagram shows the curve with equation $y = 2x^3 + x^2 - 2x - 1$ and the straight line with equation $y = x - 1$.

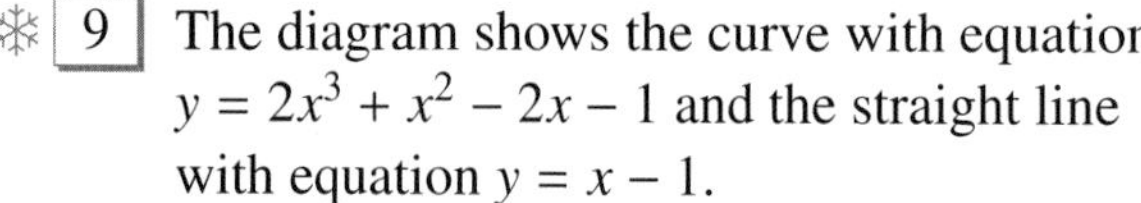

The line intersects the curve at the points K, L and M.

Calculate the coordinates of K, L and M.

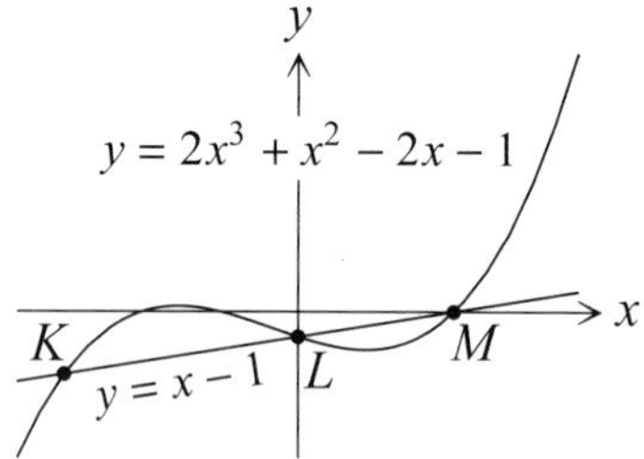

7 Trigonometric graphs

7.1 Basic trigonometric graphs

In this exercise you will learn how to:

- ❏ sketch the graphs $y = \sin x$, $y = \cos x$ and $y = \tan x$
- ❏ use a sketch graph to solve simple trigonometric equations

This is a non-calculator exercise.

1 Sketch the graph of $y = \sin x°$ for $0 \leq x \leq 360$. Use the graph to:

(a) write down the coordinates of the maximum turning point

(b) write down the coordinates of the minimum turning point

(c) solve $\sin x° = 1$ for $0 \leq x \leq 360$

(d) solve $\sin x° = -1$ for $0 \leq x \leq 360$

(e) solve $\sin x° = 0$ for $0 \leq x \leq 360$

2 Sketch the graph of $y = \cos x°$ for $0 \leq x \leq 360$. Use the graph to:

(a) write down the coordinates of the maximum turning points

(b) write down the coordinates of the minimum turning point

(c) solve $\cos x° = 1$ for $0 \leq x \leq 360$

(d) solve $\cos x° = -1$ for $0 \leq x \leq 360$

(e) solve $\cos x° = 0$ for $0 \leq x \leq 360$

3 Sketch the graph of $y = \sin t°$ for $0 \leq t \leq 720$.
Use the graph to solve, for $0 \leq t \leq 720$:

(a) $\sin t° = 1$ (b) $\sin t° = -1$ (c) $\sin t° = 0$

4 Sketch the graph of $x = \cos t°$ for $-180 \leq t \leq 180$.
Use the graph to solve, for $-180 \leq t \leq 180$:

(a) $\cos t° = 1$ (b) $\cos t° = -1$ (c) $\cos t° = 0$

5 *Draw an appropriate graph for each part of this question.*
Use a sketch graph to solve:

(a) $\sin x° = 1$ for $-360 \leq x \leq 360$ (b) $\cos x° = -1$ for $0 \leq x \leq 720$

(c) $\sin t° = 0$ for $0 \leq t \leq 1080$ (d) $\cos x° = 0$ for $-360 \leq x \leq 360$

(e) $\sin t° + 1 = 0$ for $-180 \leq t \leq 180$ (f) $\cos t° - 1 = 0$ for $0 \leq t \leq 1080$

(g) $\tan x° = 0$ for $0 \leq x \leq 360$

7.2 Graphs of the form $y = p \sin qx°$ or $y = p \cos qx°$

In this exercise you will learn how to:

- ❏ use graphs of the form $y = p \sin qx°$ or $y = p \cos qx°$
- ❏ find the equation from the graph
- ❏ find the points of intersection with the x-axis
- ❏ find the maximum and minimum values and corresponding values of x

1 The diagram shows the curve with equation $y = p \sin qx°$.
Write down the values of p and q.

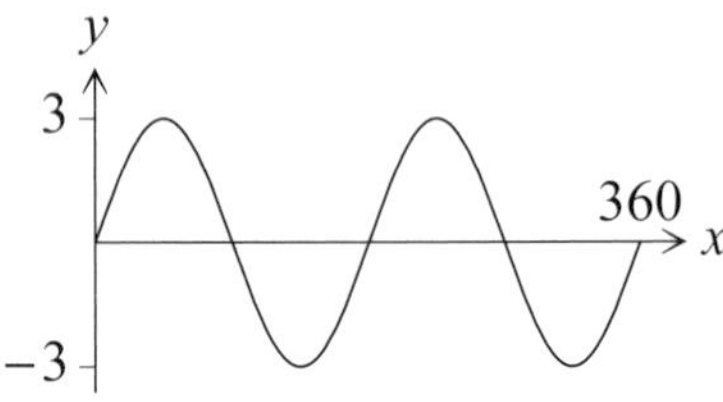

2 The diagram shows the curve with equation $y = a \sin fx°$.
Write down the values of a and f.

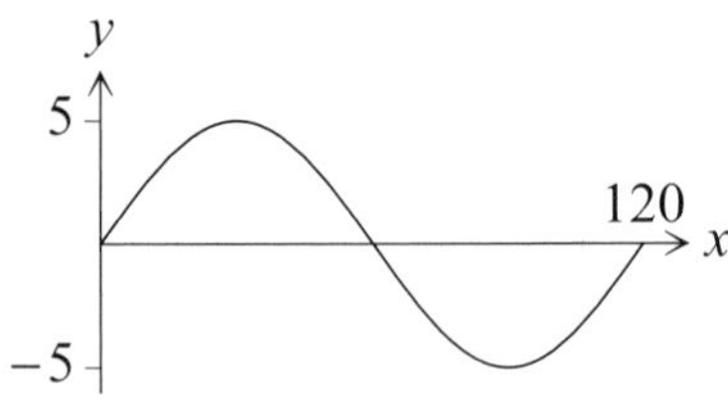

3 The diagram shows the curve with equation $y = p \cos qx°$.
Write down the values of p and q.

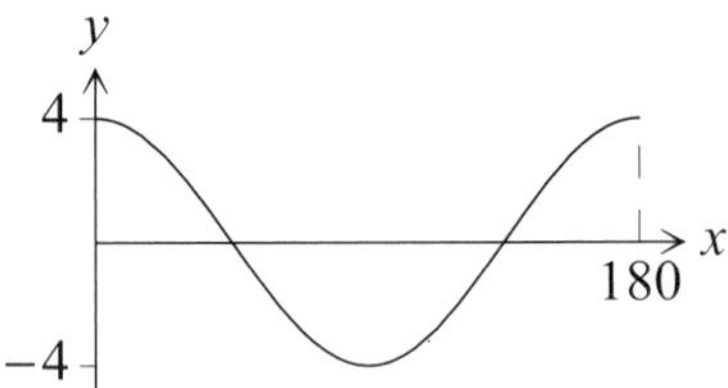

4 The diagram shows the curve with equation $y = a \cos fx°$.
Write down the values of a and f.

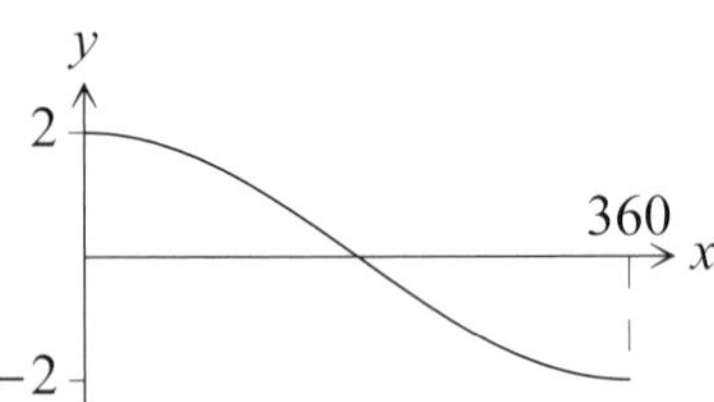

5 The diagram shows the curve with equation $y = 4 \sin 2x°$. The curve crosses the x-axis at A and B.

(a) Write down the coordinates of A and B.

The point P is a maximum turning point and the point Q is a minimum turning point.

(b) Write down the coordinates of P and Q.

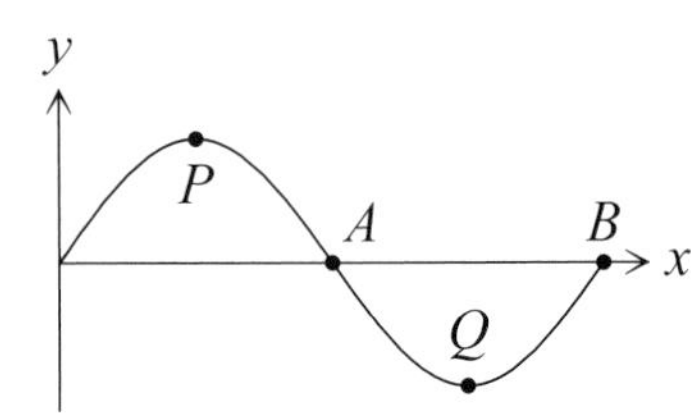

6 The diagram shows the curve with equation $y = 3\cos 2t°$. The curve crosses the t-axis at A and B.

(a) Write down the coordinates of A and B.

The point Q is a minimum turning point.

(b) Write down the coordinates of Q.

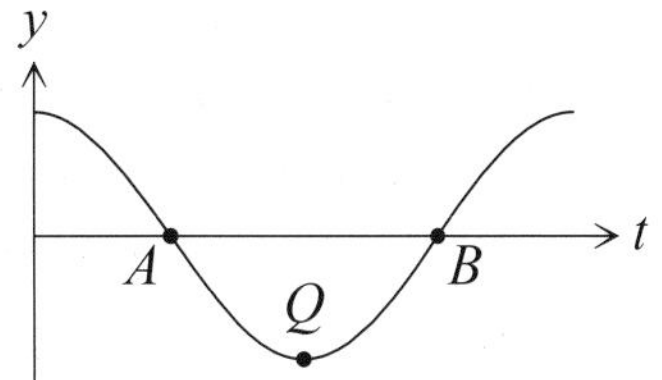

7 The diagram shows the curve with equation $x = f(t)$, where $f(t) \equiv 5\sin 3t°$. The curve crosses the t-axis at A and B.

(a) Write down the coordinates of A and B.

(b) State the maximum value of $f(t)$ and a corresponding value of t.

(c) State the minimum value of $f(t)$ and a corresponding value of t.

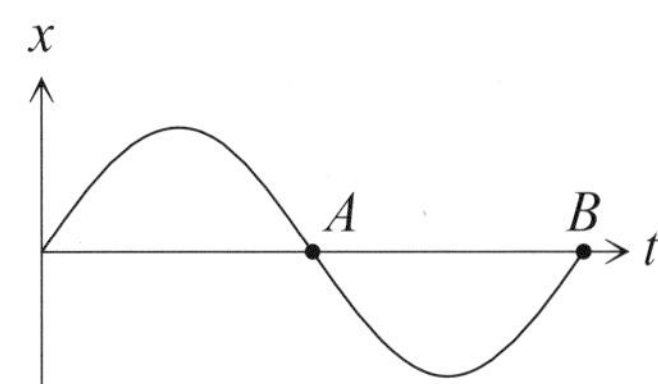

8 The diagram shows the curve with equation $y = f(x)$, where $f(x) \equiv 10\cos 3x°$. The curve crosses the x-axis at A and B.

(a) Write down the coordinates of A and B.

(b) State the maximum value of $f(x)$ and a corresponding positive value of x.

(c) State the minimum value of $f(x)$ and a corresponding value of x.

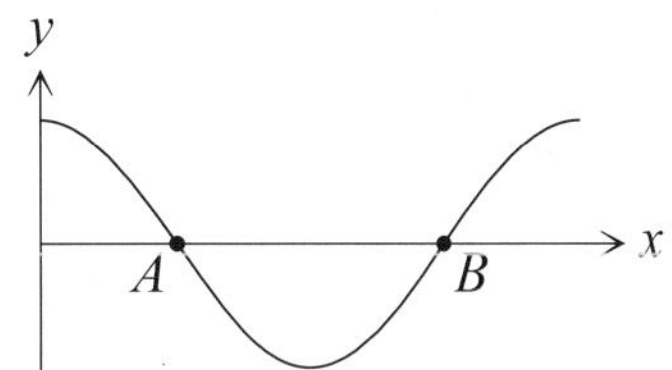

9 By considering the graph of each curve, complete a copy of the following table.

Curve equation	Maximum value	Least positive corresponding value of x	Minimum value	Least positive corresponding value of x
$y = 7\sin 3x°$				
$y = 8\cos 2x°$				
$y = 2\sin 4x°$				
$y = 6\cos 3x°$				
$y = 7\sin 2x°$				
$y = 7\cos 4x°$				

7.3 Graphs of the form $y = p\sin x° + s$ or $y = p\cos x° + s$

In this exercise you will learn how to:

- ❑ use graphs of the form $y = p\sin x° + s$ or $y = p\cos x° + s$
- ❑ find the equation from the graph
- ❑ find the y-intercept (the point of intersection with the y-axis)
- ❑ find the maximum and minimum values and corresponding values of x

1 The diagram shows the curve with equation $y = p\sin x° + s$.
Write down the values of p and s.

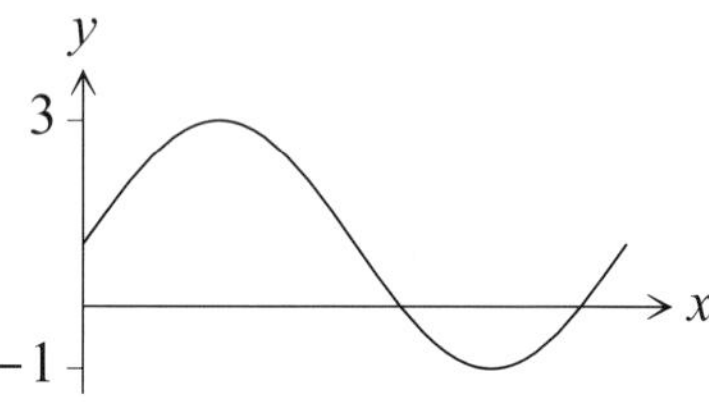

2 The diagram shows the curve with equation $y = a\cos x° + c$.
Write down the values of a and c.

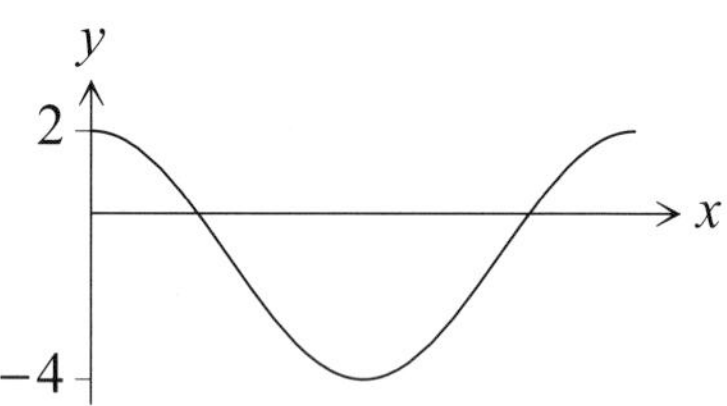

3 The diagram shows the curve with equation $y = p\cos x° + s$.
Write down the values of p and s.

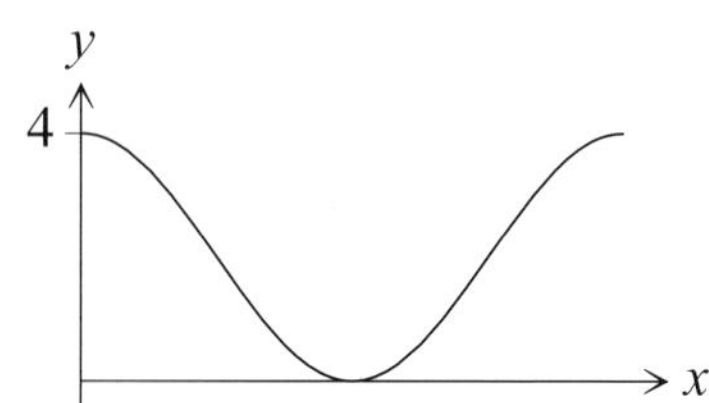

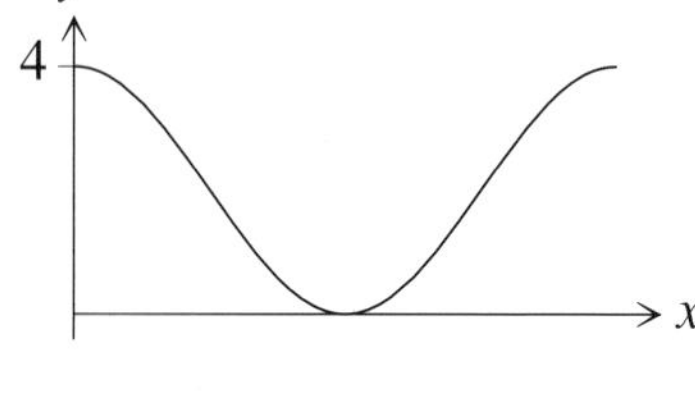

4 The diagram shows the curve with equation $y = a\sin t° + c$.
Write down the values of a and c.

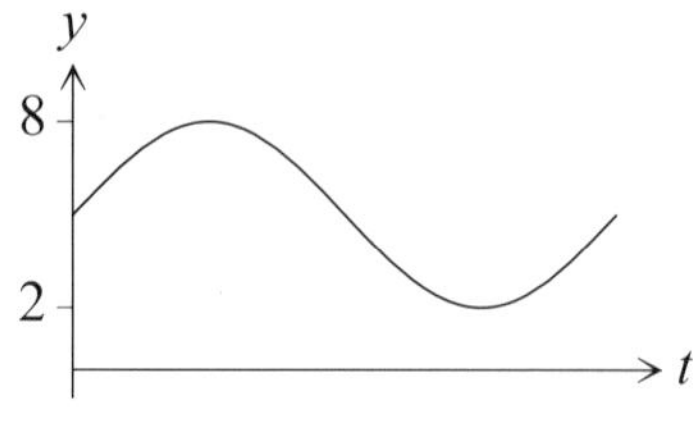

5 The diagram shows the curve with equation $x = p\sin t° + s$.
Write down the values of p and s.

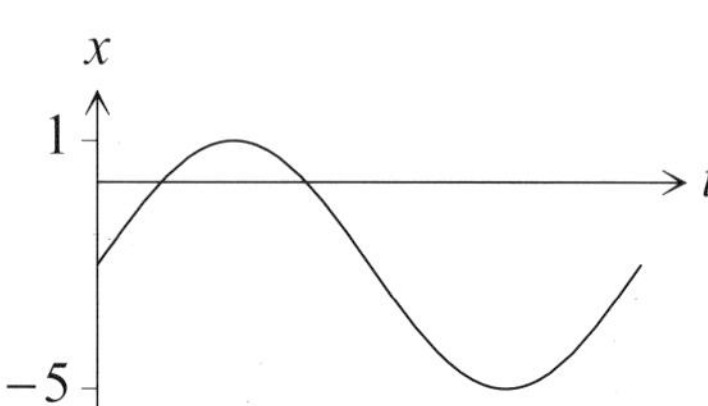

6 The diagram shows the curve with equation $y = 2\sin x° - 1$. The curve crosses the y-axis at A.

(a) Write down the coordinates of A.

The points P and Q are maximum and minimum turning points.

(b) Write down the coordinates of P and Q.

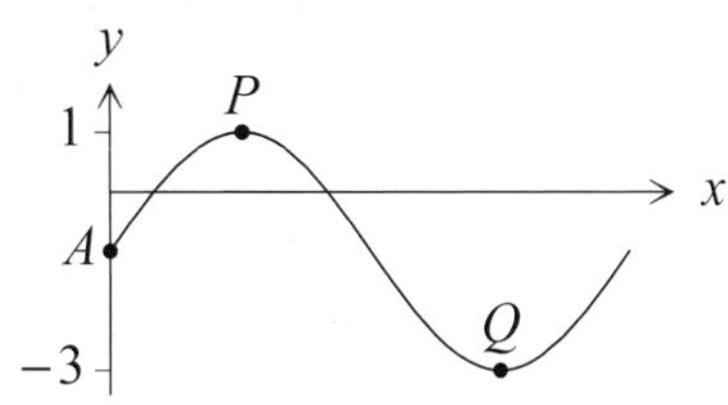

7 The diagram shows the curve with equation $y = 3\sin t° + 1$. The curve crosses the y-axis at A.

(a) Write down the coordinates of A.

The points P and Q are maximum and minimum turning points.

(b) Write down the coordinates of P and Q.

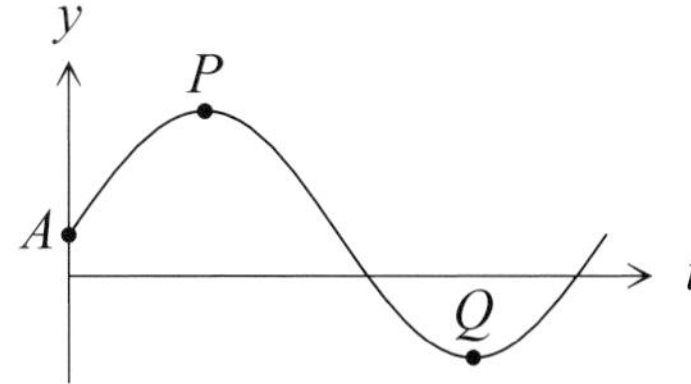

8 The diagram shows the curve with equation $x = 2\cos t° + 3$. The curve crosses the x-axis at A.

(a) Write down the coordinates of A.

The point Q is a minimum turning point.

(b) Write down the coordinates of Q.

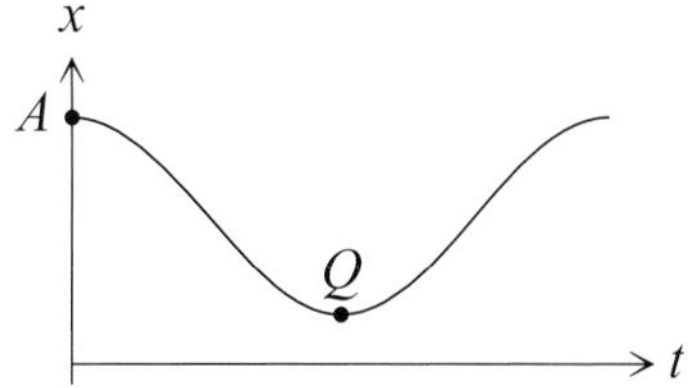

9 The diagram shows the curve with equation $y = 5\cos x° + 1$. The curve crosses the y-axis at A.

(a) Write down the coordinates of A.

The point R is a minimum turning point.

(b) Write down the coordinates of R.

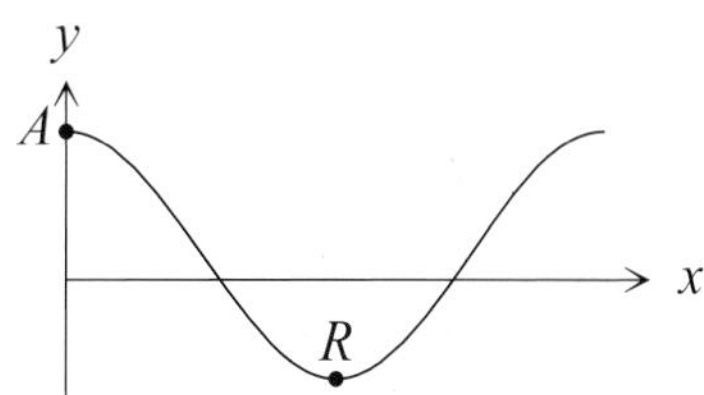

10 The diagram shows the curve with equation $y = f(x)$, where $f(x) \equiv \sin x° + 3$. The curve crosses the y-axis at P.

(a) Write down the coordinates of P.

(b) State the maximum value of $f(x)$ and a corresponding value of x.

(c) State the minimum value of $f(x)$ and a corresponding value of x.

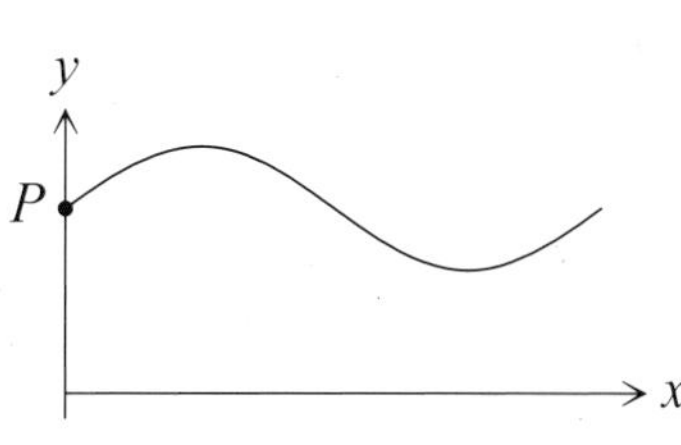

11 The diagram shows the curve with equation $x = f(t)$, where $f(t) \equiv 5\cos t° - 3$. The curve crosses the x-axis at T.

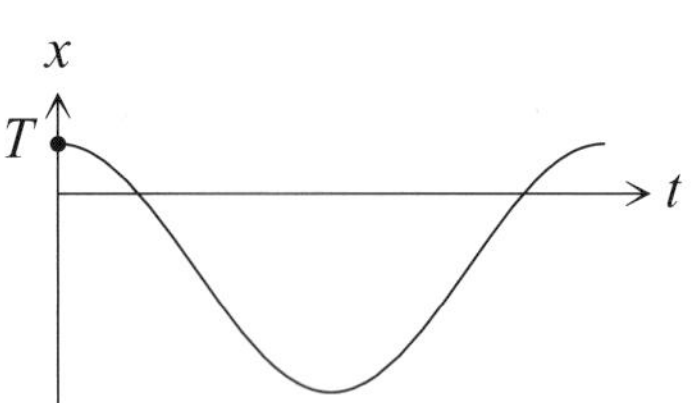

(a) Write down the coordinates of T.

(b) Find the maximum value of $f(t)$ and a corresponding positive value of t.

(c) State the minimum value of $f(t)$ and a corresponding value of t.

12 By considering the graph of each curve, complete a copy of the following table.

Curve equation	Maximum value	Least positive corresponding value of x	Minimum value	Least positive corresponding value of x
$y = 3\sin x° + 2$				
$y = 5\cos x° - 4$				
$y = 4\sin x° + 2$				
$y = \cos x° + 2$				
$y = \sin x° - 2$				
$y = 3\cos x° - 3$				

7.4 Graphs of the form $y = p\sin(x + r)°$ or $y = p\cos(x + r)°$

In this exercise you will learn how to:

- use graphs of the form $y = p\sin(x + r)°$ or $y = p\cos(x + r)°$
- find the equation from the graph
- find the points of intersection with the x-axis
- find the maximum and minimum values and corresponding values of x

1 The diagram shows the curve with equation $y = p\sin(x - r)°$.

Write down the values of p and r.

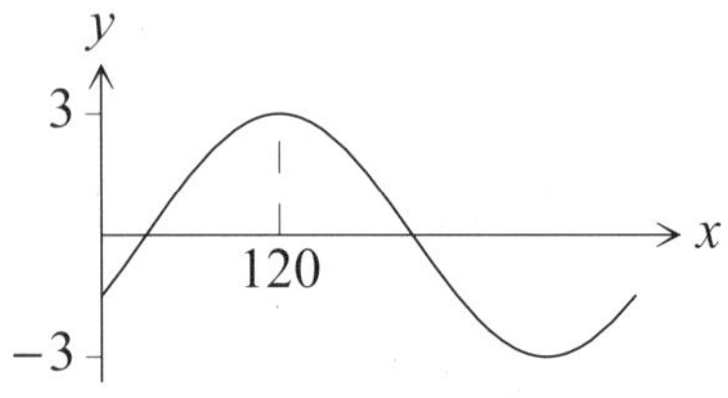

2 The diagram shows the curve with equation $y = a\sin(t + b)°$.

Write down the values of a and b.

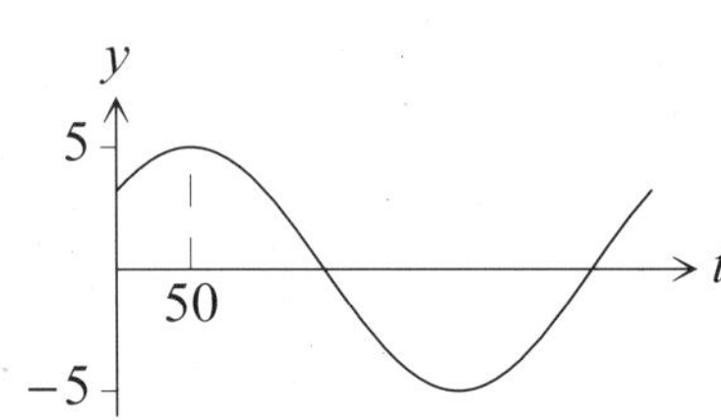

3 The diagram shows the curve with equation $y = a\cos(x - b)°$.

Write down the values of a and b.

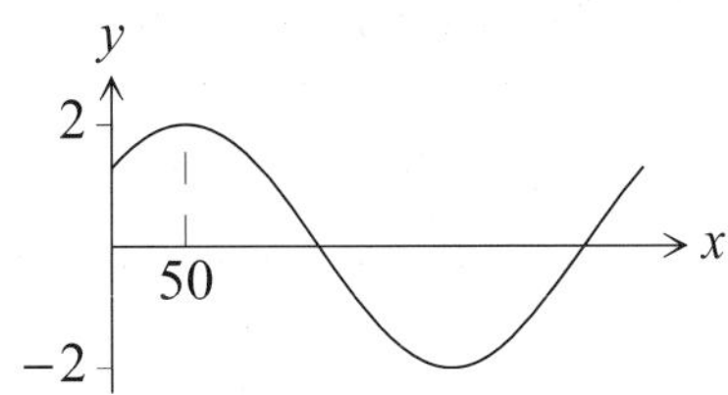

4 The diagram shows the curve with equation $x = p\cos(t + r)°$.

Write down the values of p and r.

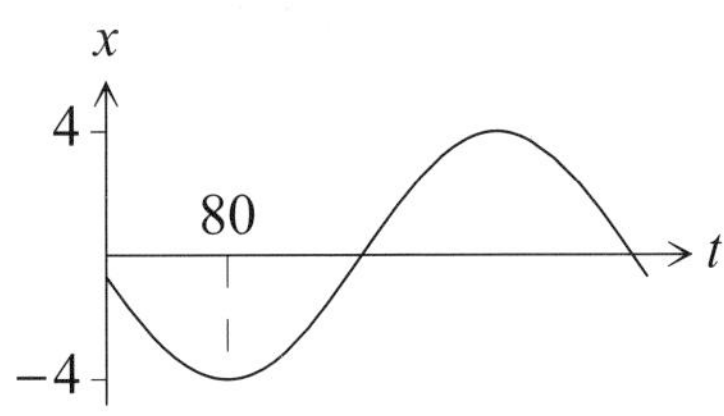

5 The diagram shows the curve with equation $y = 4\sin(x - 20)°$. The curve crosses the x-axis at A and B.

(a) Write down the coordinates of A and B.

The points P and Q are maximum and minimum turning points.

(b) Write down the coordinates of P and Q.

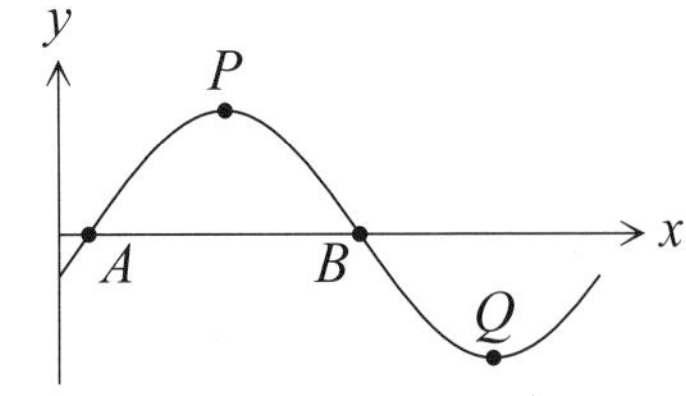

6 The diagram shows the curve with equation $y = 3\cos(t + 70)°$. The curve crosses the t-axis at A and B.

(a) Write down the coordinates of A and B.

The point Q is a minimum turning point.

(b) Write down the coordinates of Q.

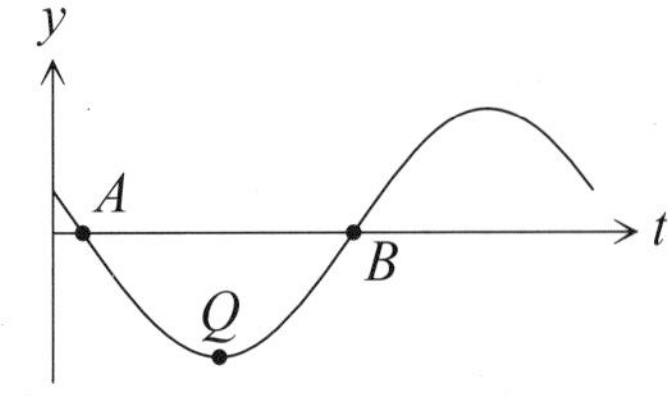

7 The diagram shows the curve with equation $v = f(t)$, where $f(t) \equiv 5\sin(t - 60)°$. The curve crosses the t-axis at A and B.

(a) Write down the coordinates of A and B.

(b) State the maximum value of $f(t)$ and a corresponding value of t.

(c) State the minimum value of $f(t)$ and a corresponding value of t.

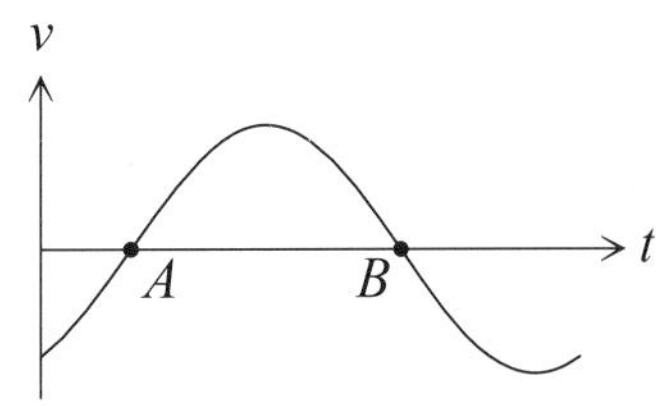

8 The diagram shows the curve with equation $y = f(x)$, where $f(x) \equiv 10\cos(x + 120)°$. The curve crosses the x-axis at A and B.

(a) Write down the coordinates of A and B.

(b) State the maximum value of $f(x)$ and a corresponding positive value of x.

(c) State the minimum value of $f(x)$ and a corresponding value of x.

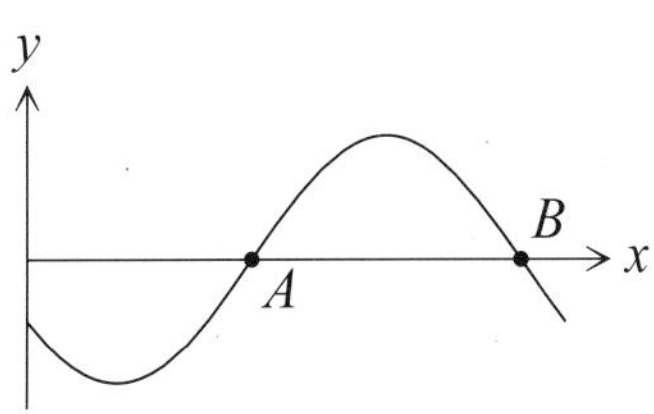

9 By considering the graph of each curve, complete a copy of the following table.

Curve equation	Maximum value	Least positive corresponding value of x	Minimum value	Least positive corresponding value of x
$y = 2\sin(x + 70)°$				
$y = 3\cos(x - 20)°$				
$y = 2\sin(x - 10)°$				
$y = 6\sin(x - 45)°$				
$y = 4\cos(x - 120)°$				
$y = 5\cos(x + 45)°$				

7.5 Graphs of the form $y = \sin(x + r)° + s$ or $y = \cos(x + r)° + s$

In this exercise you will learn how to:

- ❑ use graphs of the form $y = \sin(x + r)° + s$ or $y = \cos(x + r)° + s$
- ❑ find the equation from the graph
- ❑ find the point of intersection with the y-axis
- ❑ find the maximum and minimum values and corresponding values of x

1 The diagram shows the curve with equation $y = \sin(x + r)° + s$.
Write down the values of r and s.

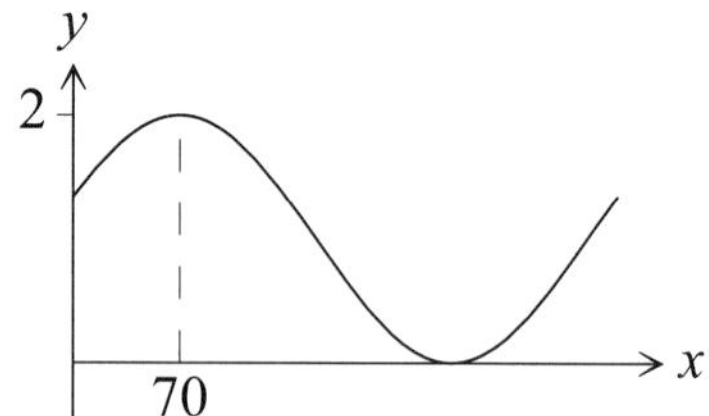

2 The diagram shows the curve with equation $y = \cos(x - b)° + c$.
Write down the values of b and c.

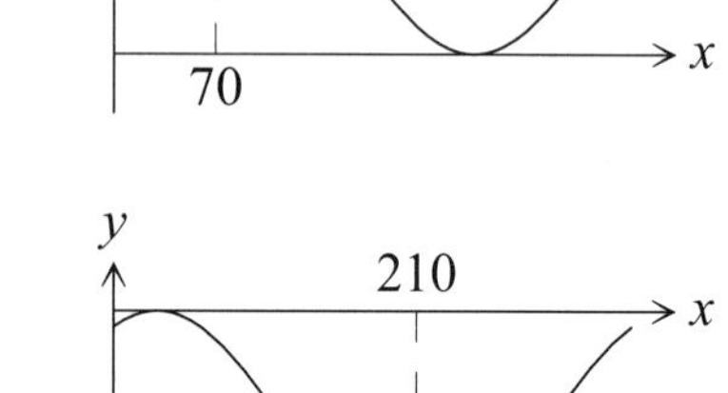

3 The diagram shows the curve with equation $y = \cos(t - r)° + s$.
Write down the values of r and s.

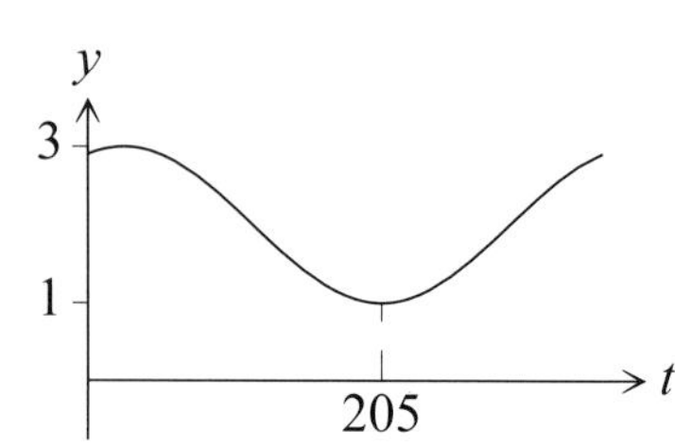

4 The diagram shows the curve with equation $v = \sin(t + b)° + c$.

Write down the values of b and c.

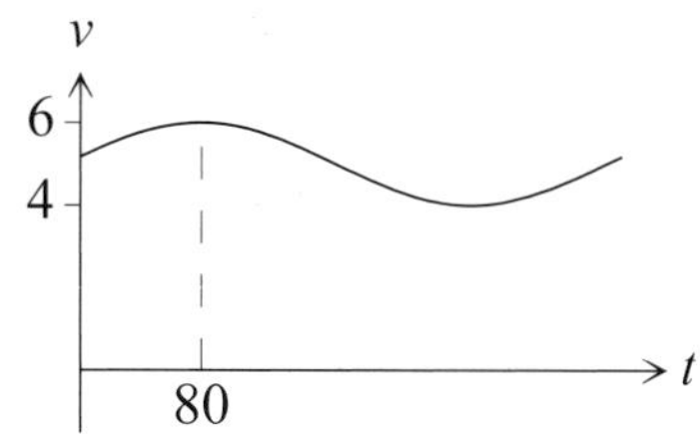

5 The diagram shows the curve with equation $y = \sin(x - r)° + s$.

Write down the values of r and s.

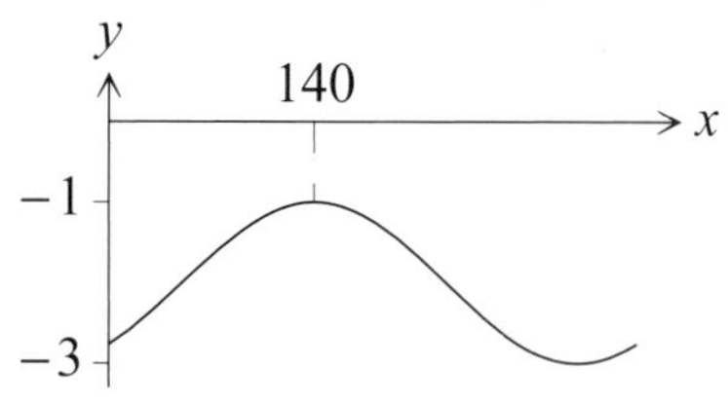

6 The diagram shows the curve with equation $y = \sin(x + 40)° - 1$. The points P and Q are maximum and minimum turning points.

(a) Write down the coordinates of P and Q.

The curve crosses the y-axis at A.

(b) Calculate the coordinates of A.

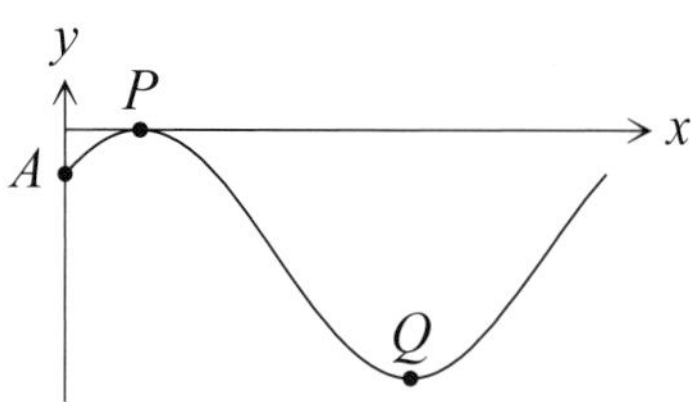

7 The diagram shows the curve with equation $y = \sin(t - 70)° + 1$. The points P and Q are maximum and minimum turning points.

(a) Write down the coordinates of P and Q.

The curve crosses the y-axis at A.

(b) Calculate the coordinates of A.

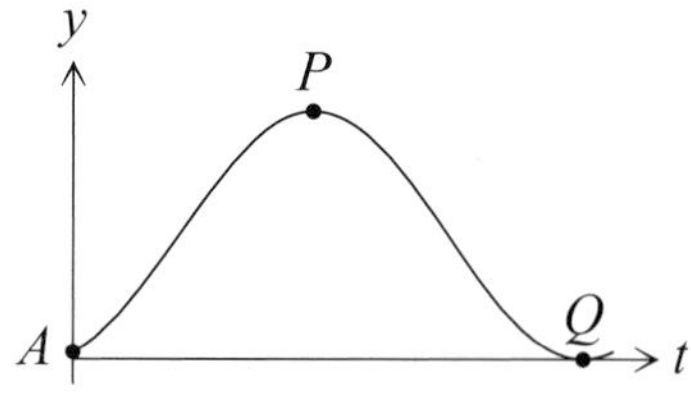

8 The diagram shows the curve with equation $x = \cos(t - 25)° + 3$. The points P and Q are maximum and minimum turning points.

(a) Write down the coordinates of P and Q.

The curve crosses the x-axis at A.

(b) Calculate the coordinates of A.

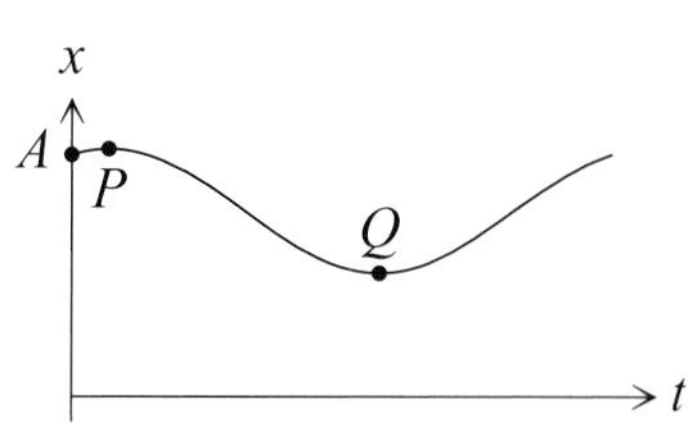

9 The diagram shows the curve with equation $y = \cos(x + 20)° + 2$. The points P and Q are maximum and minimum turning points.

(a) Write down the coordinates of P and Q.

The curve crosses the y-axis at T.

(b) Calculate the coordinates of T.

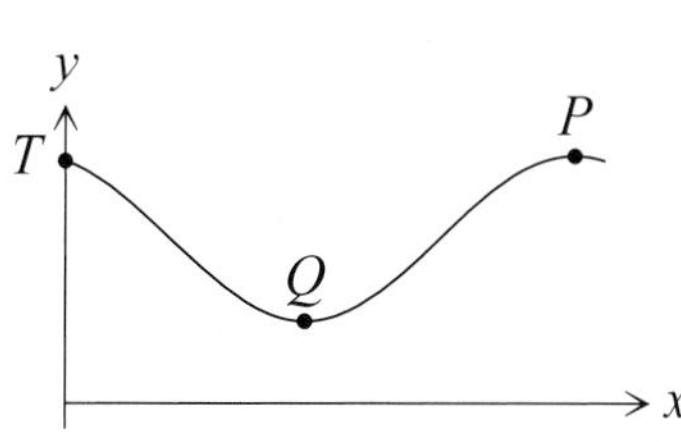

10 The diagram shows the curve with equation $y = f(x)$, where $f(x) \equiv \sin(x-40)° + 1$. The points P and Q are maximum and minimum turning points.

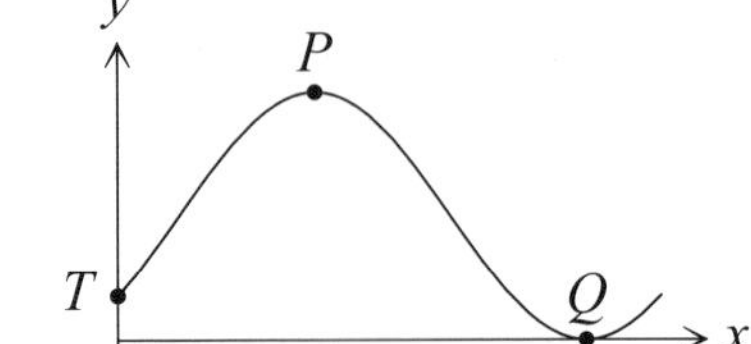

(a) Write down the coordinates of P and Q.

The curve crosses the y-axis at T.

(b) Calculate the coordinates of T.

11 The diagram shows the curve with equation $x = f(t)$, where $f(t) \equiv \cos(t-150)° - 3$. The curve crosses the x-axis at T.

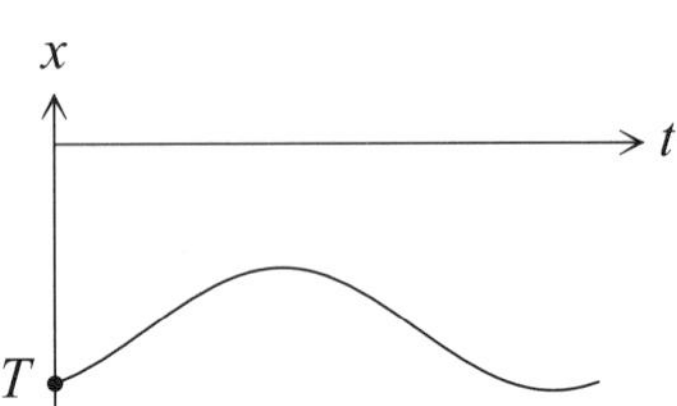

(a) Calculate the coordinates of T.

(b) State the maximum value of $f(t)$ and a corresponding value of t.

(c) State the minimum value of $f(t)$ and a corresponding value of t.

12 By considering the graph of each curve, complete a copy of the following table.

Curve equation	Maximum value	Least positive corresponding value of x	Minimum value	Least positive corresponding value of x
$y = \sin(x + 20)° + 4$				
$y = \cos(x - 25)° - 1$				
$y = \sin(x - 15)° + 3$				
$y = \cos(x + 70)° + 5$				
$y = \sin(x + 40)° - 1$				
$y = \cos(x - 60)° - 6$				

7.6 Graphs of the form $y = p\sin(x + r)° + s$ or $y = p\cos(x + r)° + s$

In this exercise you will learn how to:

- ❑ use graphs of the form $y = p\sin(x + r)° + s$ or $y = p\cos(x + r)° + s$
- ❑ find the equation from the graph
- ❑ find the maximum and minimum values and corresponding values of x
- ❑ find the point of intersection with the y-axis

❄ **1** The diagram shows the curve with equation $y = p\sin(x + r)° + s$.
Write down the values of p, r and s.

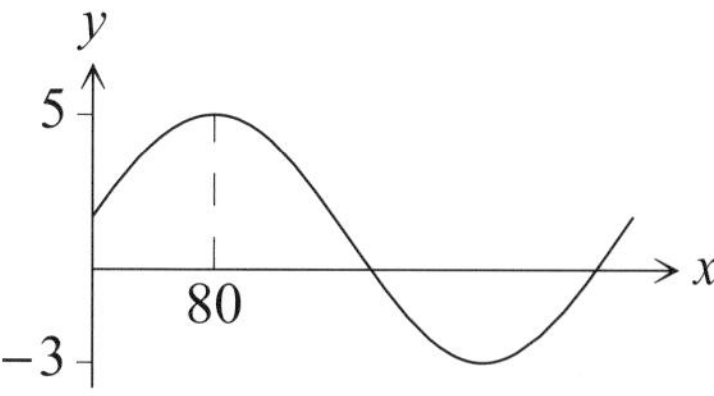

❄ **2** The diagram shows the curve with equation $y = a\cos(x + b)° + c$.
Write down the values of a, b and c.

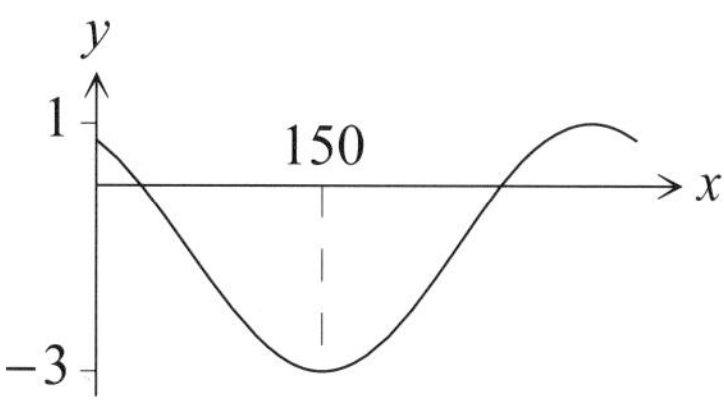

❄ **3** The diagram shows the curve with equation $y = p\cos(t + r)° + s$.
Write down the values of p, r and s.

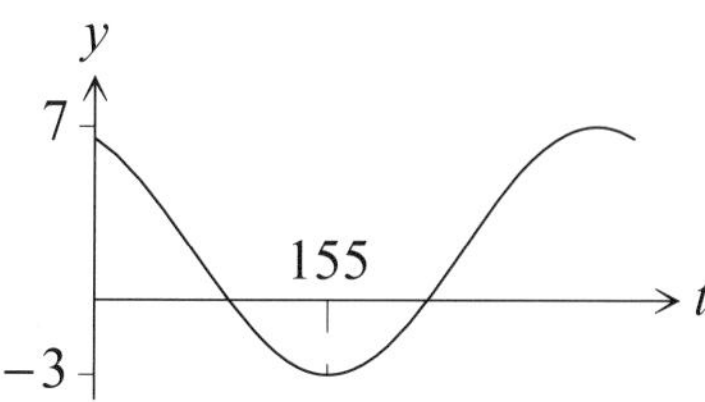

❄ **4** The diagram shows the curve with equation $x = a\sin(t - b)° + c$.
Write down the values of a, b and c.

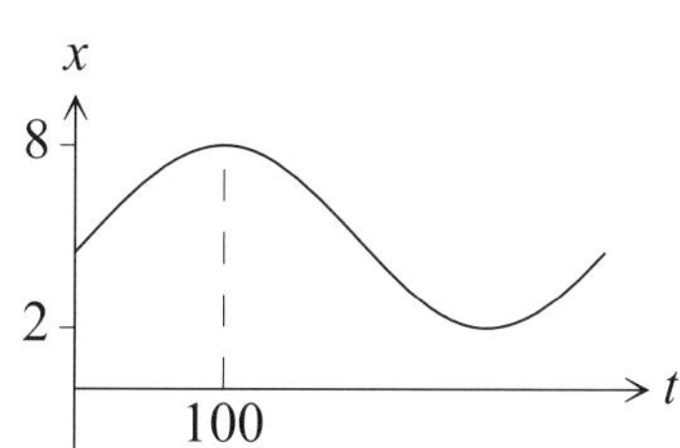

❄ **5** The diagram shows the curve with equation $y = p\sin(x - r)° + s$.
Write down the values of p, r and s.

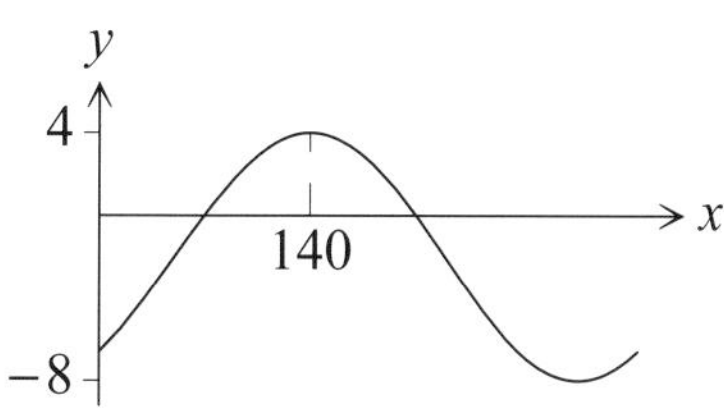

6 The diagram shows the curve with equation $x = f(t)$, where $f(t) \equiv 2\cos(t-150)° - 3$. The curve crosses the x-axis at T.

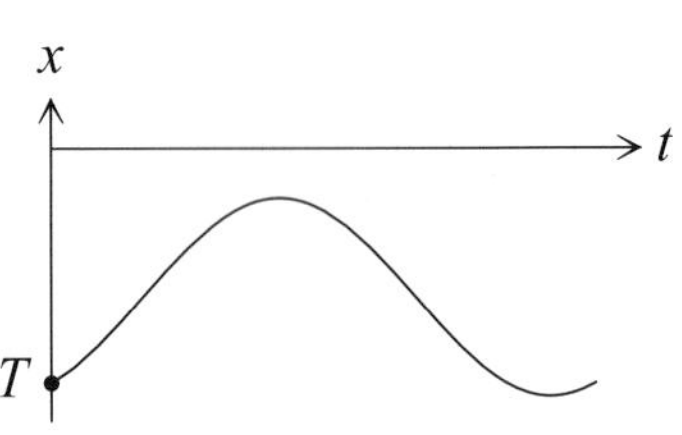

(a) Write down the coordinates of T.

(b) State the maximum value of $f(t)$ and a corresponding value of t.

(c) State the minimum value of $f(t)$ and a corresponding value of t.

7 By considering the graph of each curve, complete a copy of the following table.

Curve equation	Maximum value	Least positive corresponding value of x	Minimum value	Least positive corresponding value of x
$y = 2\sin(x+50)° + 1$				
$y = 5\cos(x-35)° - 3$				
$y = 4\sin(x-80)° + 4$				
$y = 3\cos(x+10)° + 4$				
$y = 7\sin(x+50)° - 5$				
$y = 2\cos(x-100)° - 4$				

8 Trigonometry

8.1 Basic trigonometric equations

In this exercise you will learn how to:

- ❑ use the four-quadrant diagram to find angles with a given sine, cosine or tangent
- ❑ rearrange an equation to find the sine, cosine or tangent of an angle
- ❑ find the points of intersection of a trigonometric graph and a straight line by solving an appropriate equation

1 For $0 \leq x < 360$, solve the equation:

(a) $\sin x° = 0.82$ (b) $\cos x° = -0.4$

(c) $\tan x° = -1.3$ (d) $4\cos x° = 1$

(e) $3\sin x° = -2$ (f) $5\tan x° = -1$

(g) $6\tan x° - 1 = 4$ (h) $5\cos x° + 2 = -2$

(i) $3 + \sin x° = 1 - 4\sin x°$ (j) $4(\sin x° + 2) = 10$

(k) $1 - 3\tan x° = 4$ (l) $\tan^2 x° = 3$

(m) $4\sin^2 x° = 3$ (n) $2\cos^2 x° - 1 = 0$

2 The diagram shows the graphs of $y = p\sin x°$ and $y = 2$.

(a) Write down the value of p.

The line and the curve intersect at A and B as shown in the diagram.

(b) Find the coordinates of A and B.

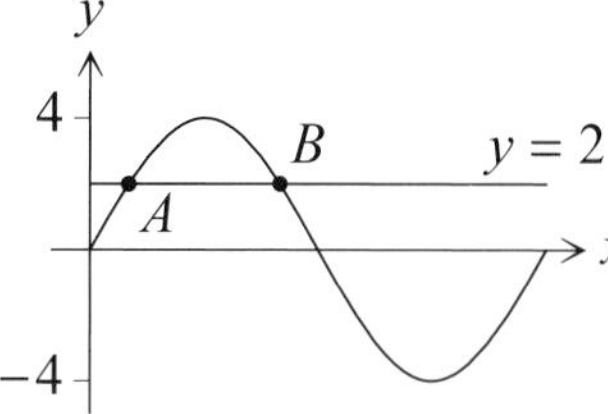

3 The diagram shows the graphs of $y = p\cos x°$ and $y = -1$.

(a) Write down the value of p.

The line and the curve intersect at A and B as shown in the diagram.

(b) Find the coordinates of A and B.

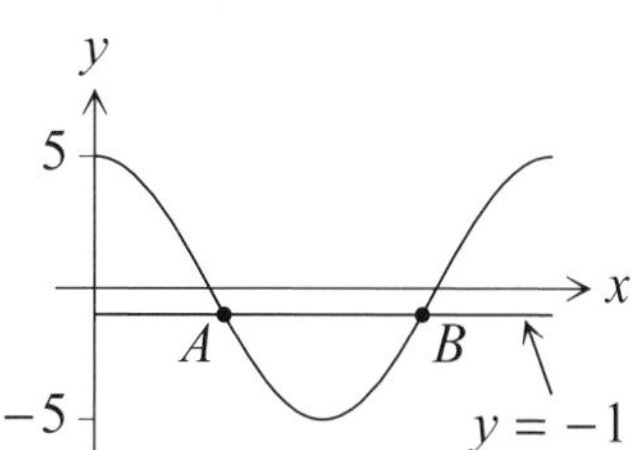

4 The diagram shows the graph of $y = a\sin t^\circ + b$.

(a) Write down the values of a and b.

The line with equation $y = 2$ intersects the curve at P and Q as shown in the diagram.

(b) Find the coordinates of P and Q.

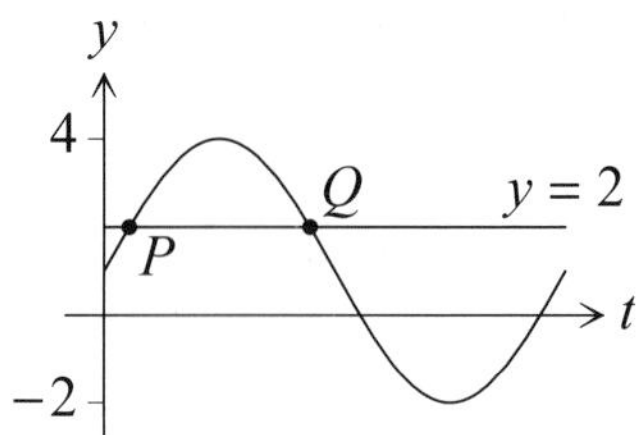

5 The diagram shows the graph of $x = p\cos t^\circ + q$.

(a) Write down the values of p and q

The curve crosses the t-axis at R and S as shown in the diagram.

(b) Find the coordinates of R and S.

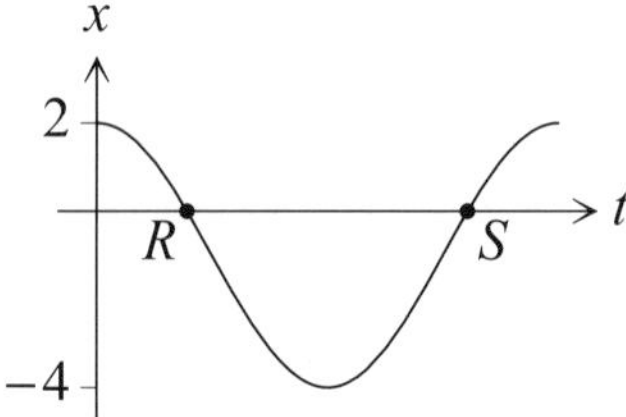

6 The curve with equation $y = 3\tan x^\circ + 2$ crosses the x-axis at G and H as shown in the diagram.

(a) Find the coordinates of G and H.

The line $y = 5$ intersects the curve at M and N.

(b) Find the coordinates of M and N.

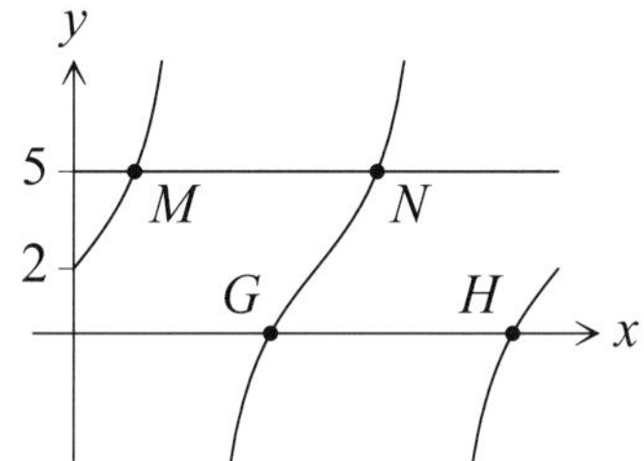

8.2 Harder trigonometric equations

In this exercise you will learn how to:

- ❏ use the four-quadrant diagram to find angles with a given sine, cosine or tangent, and hence solve an equation
- ❏ rearrange an equation to find the sine, cosine or tangent of an angle
- ❏ find the points of intersection of a trigonometric graph and a straight line by solving an appropriate equation

1 For $0 \le x < 360$, solve the equation:

(a) $\sin(x + 36)^\circ = 0.76$

(b) $\cos(x - 17.4)^\circ = 0.38$

(c) $\sin(x - 10)^\circ = -0.28$

(d) $\cos(x + 23)^\circ = -0.16$

(e) $3\sin(x + 20)^\circ - 2 = 0$

(f) $5\cos(x - 20)^\circ + 1 = 0$

(g) $1 + 2\cos(x + 50)^\circ = 0$

(h) $3 - 4\sin(x - 10)^\circ = 0$

2 For $0 \le x < 360$, solve the equation:

(a) $\sin(x + 80)^\circ = 0.6$

(b) $\cos(x - 40)^\circ = 0.8$

(c) $\cos(x + 70)^\circ = 0.5$

(d) $\sin(x - 60)^\circ = -0.4$

(e) $4\sin(x + 20)^\circ = 1$

(f) $6\cos(x - 65)^\circ = 5$

3 The diagram shows the curve with equation $y = a\cos(x + b)°$.

(a) Write down the values of a and b.

The line with equation $y = 3$ intersects the curve at A and B as shown in the diagram.

(b) Find the coordinates of A and B.

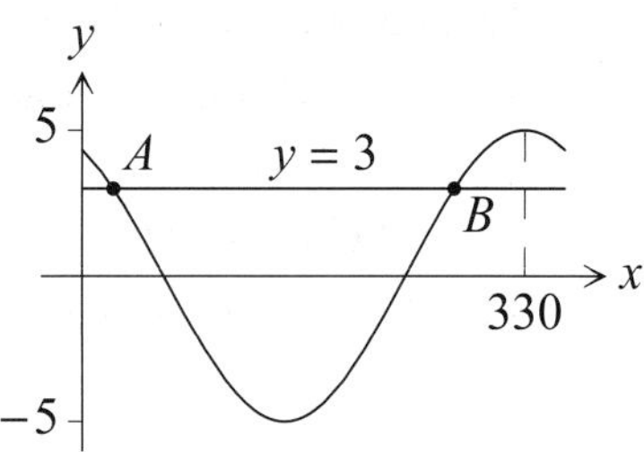

4 The diagram shows the curve with equation $y = p\sin(x - r)°$.

(a) Write down the values of p and r.

The line with equation $y = 1$ intersects the curve at M and N as shown in the diagram.

(b) Find the coordinates of M and N.

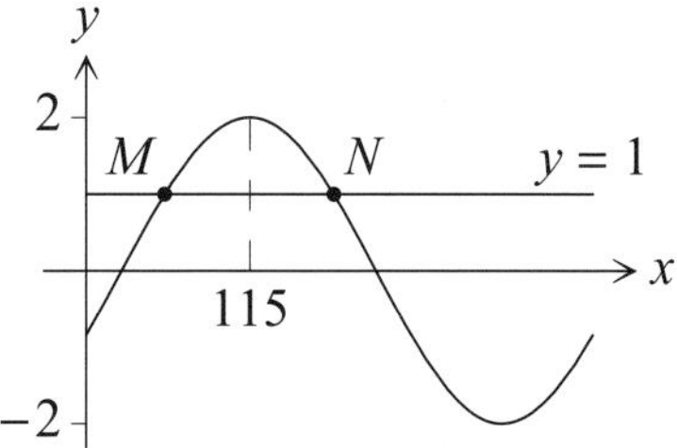

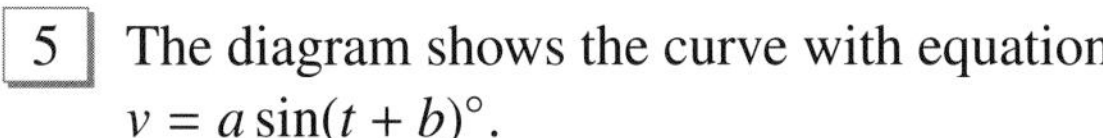

5 The diagram shows the curve with equation $v = a\sin(t + b)°$.

(a) Write down the values of a and b.

The line with equation $v = -2$ intersects the curve at R and S as shown in the diagram.

(b) Find the coordinates of R and S.

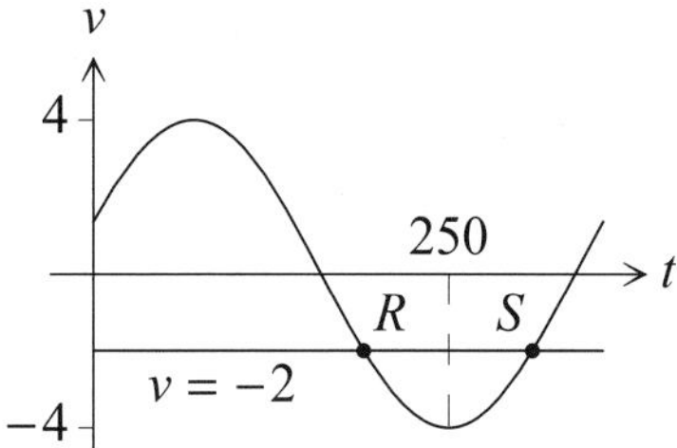

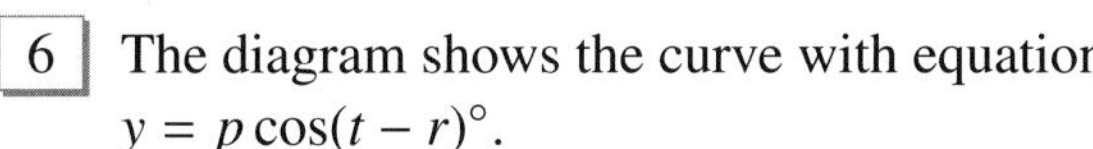

6 The diagram shows the curve with equation $y = p\cos(t - r)°$.

(a) Write down the values of p and r.

The line with equation $y = 6$ intersects the curve at A and B as shown in the diagram.

(b) Find the coordinates of A and B.

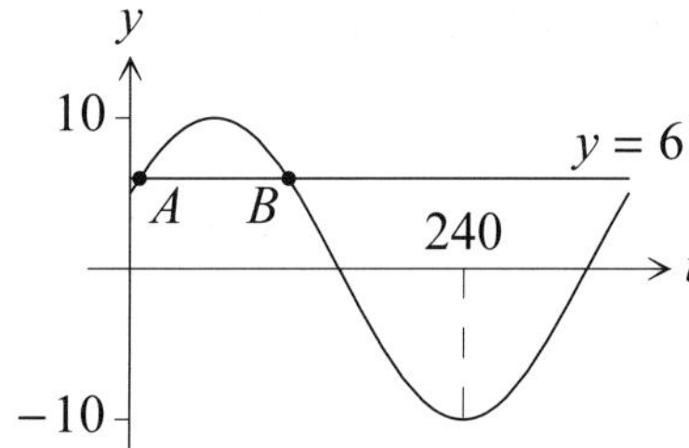

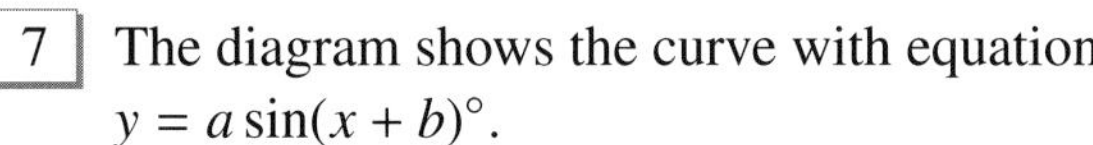

7 The diagram shows the curve with equation $y = a\sin(x + b)°$.

(a) Write down the values of a and b.

The line with equation $y = 1.5$ intersects the curve at C and D as shown in the diagram.

(b) Find the coordinates of C and D.

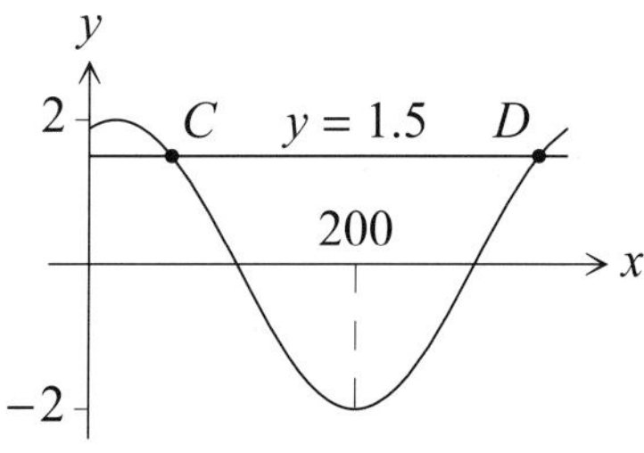

8.3 Angles related to 30°, 45° and 60°

In this exercise you will learn how to:

- use the exact values for the sine, cosine and tangent of 30°, 45° and 60° to find exact values for the sine, cosine and tangent of negative angles and angles greater than 90°
- use exact values to simplify expressions

Exact values are introduced in Exercise 1.7 on page 6.

This is a non-calculator exercise.

1 Find the exact value of:

(a) $\sin 120°$ (b) $\cos 240°$ (c) $\tan 150°$ (d) $\cos 330°$
(e) $\tan 225°$ (f) $\sin 225°$ (g) $\sin 300°$ (h) $\cos 315°$
(i) $\tan 300°$ (j) $\sin 135°$ (k) $\cos 120°$ (l) $\sin 210°$

2 Find the exact value of:

(a) $\sin 390°$ (b) $\tan 420°$ (c) $\cos -45°$ (d) $\cos -60°$
(e) $\sin 600°$ (f) $\cos -120°$ (g) $\sin 495°$ (h) $\tan 660°$
(i) $\tan 900°$

3 Prove that:

(a) $\sin^2 30° + \cos^2 30° = 1$ (b) $\sin^2 60° + \cos^2 60° = 1$
(c) $\sin^2 150° + \cos^2 150° = 1$ (d) $\sin^2 135° = 1 - \cos^2 135°$
(e) $\cos^2 300° = 1 - \sin^2 300°$

4 Prove that:

(a) $\dfrac{\sin 30°}{\cos 30°} = \tan 30°$ (b) $\dfrac{\sin 60°}{\cos 60°} = \tan 60°$
(c) $\dfrac{\sin 150°}{\cos 150°} = \tan 150°$ (d) $\dfrac{\sin 135°}{\cos 135°} = \tan 135°$

5 Prove that:

(a) $2 \sin 30° \cos 30° = \sin 60°$ (b) $2 \sin 315° \cos 315° = \sin 630°$
(c) $2 \sin 120° \cos 120° = \sin 240°$ (d) $2 \sin 150° \cos 150° = \sin 300°$

6 Prove that:

(a) $\sin 60° \cos 30° + \cos 60° \sin 30° = \sin 90°$
(b) $\sin 30° \cos 120° + \cos 30° \sin 120° = \sin 150°$
(c) $\cos 150° \cos 30° - \sin 150° \sin 30° = \cos 180°$
(d) $\cos 210° \cos 150° + \sin 210° \sin 150° = \cos 60°$

8.4 Equations involving 30°, 45°, 60° and related angles

In this exercise you will learn how to:

- ❏ use exact values for the sine, cosine and tangent of 30°, 45° and 60° to solve equations

Exact values are introduced in Exercise 1.7 on page 6.

This is a non-calculator exercise.

1 Solve for $0 \le x < 360$:

(a) $\sin x^\circ = \frac{\sqrt{3}}{2}$ (b) $\tan x^\circ = \sqrt{3}$

(c) $\cos x^\circ = -\frac{1}{\sqrt{2}}$ (d) $\cos x^\circ = -\frac{\sqrt{3}}{2}$

(e) $\sin x^\circ = \frac{1}{\sqrt{2}}$ (f) $\tan x^\circ = 1$

(g) $\sqrt{3}\tan x^\circ = 1$ (h) $2\cos x^\circ + 1 = 0$

(i) $2\sin x^\circ + \sqrt{3} = 0$

2 Solve for $0 \le t < 360$:

(a) $\sin(t + 30)^\circ = -\frac{1}{2}$ (b) $\cos(t - 10)^\circ = \frac{\sqrt{3}}{2}$

(c) $\tan(t + 30)^\circ = -\sqrt{3}$ (d) $\sqrt{2}\sin(t + 30)^\circ - 1 = 0$

(e) $2\sin(t - 20)^\circ - 1 = 0$ (f) $2\cos(t - 45)^\circ - 1 = 0$

❄ **3** Solve for $0 \le x < 360$:

(a) $2\sin^2 x^\circ + 3\sin x^\circ + 1 = 0$ (b) $2\cos^2 x^\circ - \cos x^\circ - 1 = 0$

(c) $\tan^2 x^\circ + \tan x^\circ = 0$ (d) $2\cos^2 x^\circ + \sqrt{3}\cos x^\circ = 0$

(e) $2\sin^2 x^\circ - 3\sin x^\circ + 1 = 0$ (f) $\tan x^\circ - \sqrt{3}\tan^2 x^\circ = 0$

8.5 Trigonometric ratios of the same angle

In this exercise you will learn how to:

- find the sine, cosine and tangent of an angle in a right-angled triangle, using Pythagoras' theorem where necessary
- calculate the value of other trigonometric ratios from the value of one ratio

See exercise 1.5 on page 4 for the simplification of surds.

This is a non-calculator exercise.

1 The diagram shows right-angled triangle ABC in which $AB = 4$ units and $BC = 3$ units.

(a) Calculate the length of AC.

(b) Write down the exact values of $\sin x°$, $\cos x°$ and $\tan x°$.

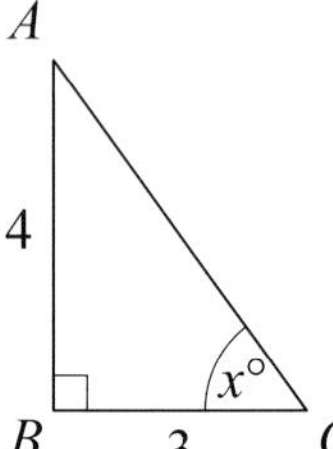

2 Use the information in the diagram to write down the exact values of $\sin x°$, $\cos x°$ and $\tan x°$.

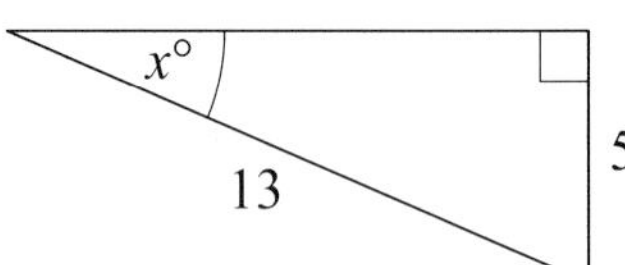

3 Use the information in the diagram to write down the exact values of $\sin t°$, $\cos t°$ and $\tan t°$.

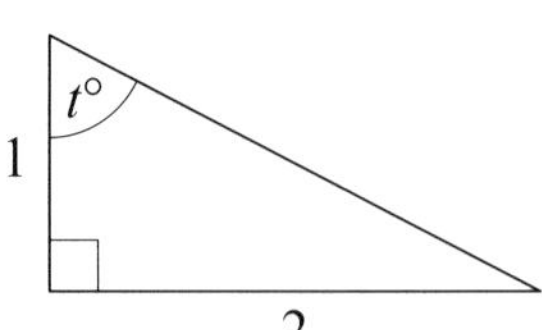

4 Use the information in the diagram to write down, in simplest form, the exact values of $\sin a°$, $\cos a°$ and $\tan a°$.

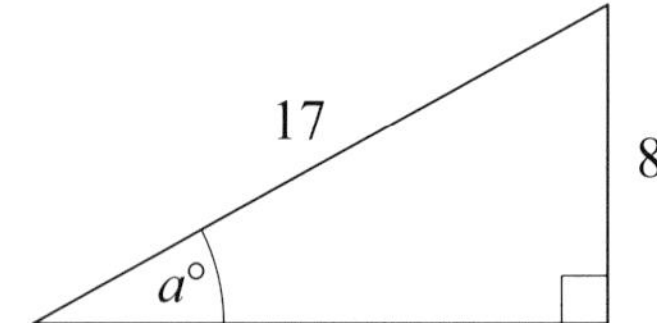

5 Given that $\sin A° = \frac{3}{5}$ and $0 < A < 90$, find the exact values of $\cos A°$ and $\tan A°$.

6 Given that $\tan X° = \frac{1}{3}$ and $0 < X < 90$, find the exact values of $\sin X°$ and $\cos X°$.

7 Given that $\cos Y° = \frac{1}{\sqrt{5}}$ and $0 < Y < 90$, find the exact values of $\sin Y°$ and $\tan Y°$.

8 Given that $\sin A° = \frac{1}{3}$ and $0 < A < 90$, find, in simplest form, the exact values of $\cos A°$ and $\tan A°$.

9 Given that $\cos X° = \frac{1}{\sqrt{10}}$ and $0 < X < 90$, find the exact values of $\sin X°$ and $\tan X°$.

10 Given that $\tan Z° = \frac{1}{7}$ and $0 < Z < 90$, find, in simplest form, the exact values of $\sin Z°$ and $\cos Z°$.

❄ **11** Given that $90 < A < 180$ and $\sin A° = \frac{3}{4}$, find the exact values of $\cos A°$ and $\tan A°$.

❄ **12** Given that $270 < P < 360$ and $\cos P° = \frac{40}{41}$, find, in simplest form, the exact values of $\sin P°$ and $\tan P°$.

13 Use the information in the diagram to write down the exact values of:

(a) $\sin x°$, $\cos x°$ and $\tan x°$

(b) $\sin y°$, $\cos y°$ and $\tan y°$

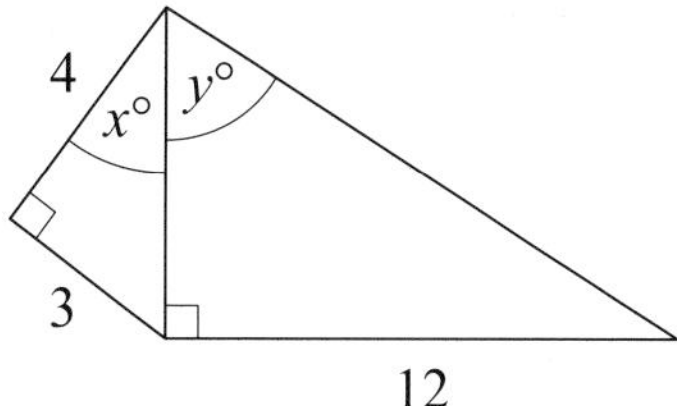

14 Use the information in the diagram to write down, in simplest form, the exact values of:

(a) $\sin p°$, $\cos p°$ and $\tan p°$

(b) $\sin q°$, $\cos q°$ and $\tan q°$

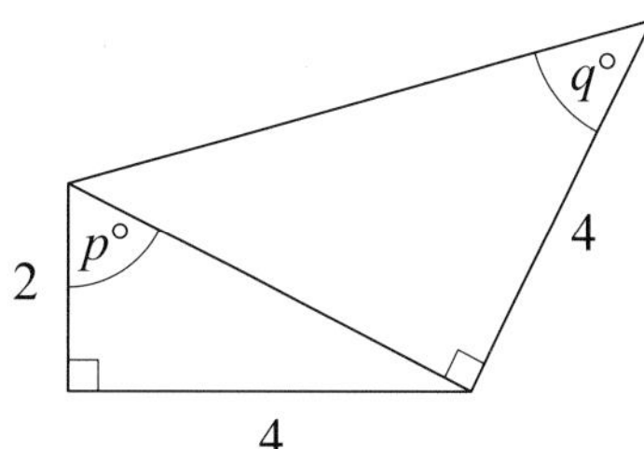

15 Use the information in the diagram to write down, in simplest form, the exact values of:

(a) $\sin z°$, $\cos z°$ and $\tan z°$

(b) $\sin t°$, $\cos t°$ and $\tan t°$

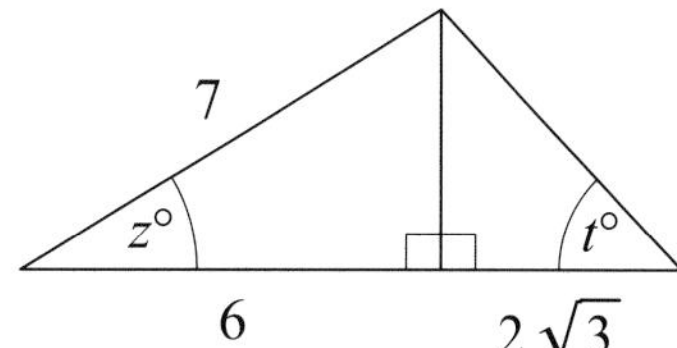

16 Use the information in the diagram to write down, in simplest form, the exact values of:

(a) $\sin \angle CBD$, $\cos \angle CBD$ and $\tan \angle CBD$

(b) $\sin \angle ABC$, $\cos \angle ABC$ and $\tan \angle ABC$

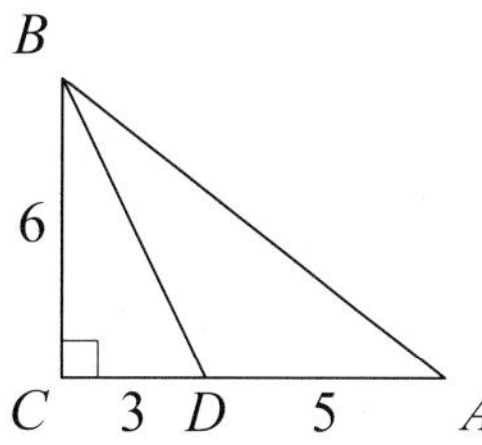

8.6 The identities $\sin^2 x + \cos^2 x \equiv 1$ and $\tan x \equiv \dfrac{\sin x}{\cos x}$

In this exercise you will learn how to:

- ❑ use the identities $\sin^2 x + \cos^2 x \equiv 1$ and $\tan x \equiv \dfrac{\sin x}{\cos x}$

1 Prove that $2\sin^2 A + 2\cos^2 A \equiv 2$.

2 Prove that $5\sin^2 A \equiv 5 - 5\cos^2 A$.

3 Prove that $(\sin X + \cos X)^2 \equiv 1 + 2\sin X \cos X$.

4 Prove that $(\sin x + \cos x)(\sin x - \cos x) \equiv 1 - 2\cos^2 x$.

5 Prove that $(\cos Y - \sin Y)^2 \equiv 1 - 2\sin Y \cos Y$.

6 Prove that $(2\sin x - \cos x)(\sin x + 2\cos x) \equiv 4\sin^2 x + 3\sin x \cos x - 2$.

7 Prove that $\tan A \cos A \equiv \sin A$.

8 Prove that $\dfrac{\tan X}{\sin X} \equiv \dfrac{1}{\cos X}$.

9 Prove that $\cos^3 x + \cos x \sin^2 x \equiv \cos x$.

10 Prove that $\sin^4 x + \sin^2 x \cos^2 x \equiv 1 - \cos^2 x$.

11 Prove that $\cos^4 A - \sin^4 A \equiv 2\cos^2 A - 1$.

12 Prove that $\dfrac{1 - \tan^2 A}{1 + \tan^2 A} \equiv \cos^2 A - \sin^2 A$.

8.7 Quadratic trigonometric equations

In this exercise you will learn how to:

- ❑ solve quadratic trigonometric equations
- ❑ solve a trigonometric equation by using the identity $\sin^2 x + \cos^2 x \equiv 1$ to form a quadratic equation in $\sin x$ or $\cos x$

Exercise 2.4 on page 10 shows how to solve quadratic equations of this type by making a substitution.

1 Solve for $0 \le x < 360$:

(a) $2\sin^2 x° - \sin x° = 0$ (b) $4\cos^2 x° - 3\cos x° = 0$

(c) $2\sin^2 x° + \sin x° - 1 = 0$ (d) $12\sin^2 x° - \sin x° - 1 = 0$

(e) $2\cos^2 x° - 11\cos x° + 5 = 0$ (f) $12\cos^2 x° - 11\cos x° + 2 = 0$

(g) $4\cos x° - 5\cos^2 x° = 0$ (h) $4\sin^2 x° - 1 = 0$

(i) $5\cos^2 x° + 11\cos x° = -2$ (j) $3\cos^2 x° = \cos x° + 2$

❄ 2 Solve for $0 \le t < 360$:

(a) $6\cos^2 t° + \sin t° - 5 = 0$ (b) $3\sin^2 t° + 2\cos t° - 3 = 0$

(c) $3\cos^2 t° - 5\sin t° - 1 = 0$ (d) $4\sin^2 t° = 7(1 - \cos t°)$

8.8 Further trigonometric graphs and equations

In this exercise you will learn how to:

- ❑ use graphs of the form $y = p\sin(x + r)^\circ + s$ or $y = p\cos(x + r)^\circ + s$
- ❑ find the maximum and minimum values and corresponding values of x
- ❑ find the points of intersection with the x-axis
- ❑ find the point of intersection with the y-axis

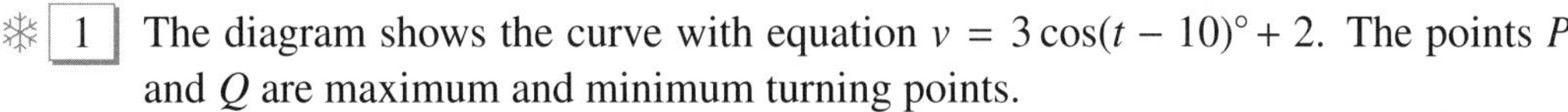

❄ **1** The diagram shows the curve with equation $v = 3\cos(t - 10)^\circ + 2$. The points P and Q are maximum and minimum turning points.

(a) Write down the coordinates of P and Q.

The curve crosses the t-axis at R and S.

(b) Calculate the coordinates of R and S.

The curve crosses the v-axis at A.

(c) Write down the coordinates of A.

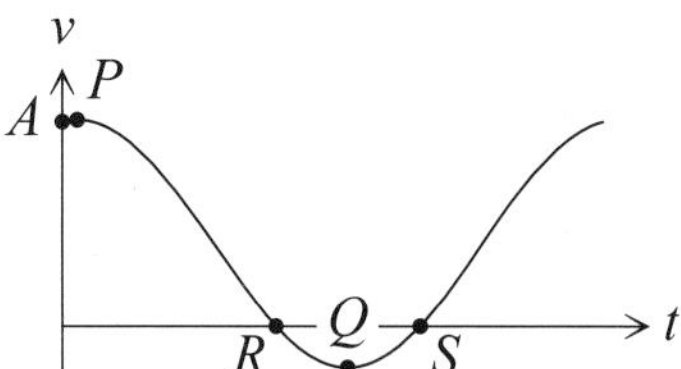

❄ **2** The diagram shows the curve with equation $y = 3\cos(x + 20)^\circ + 3$. The points P and Q are maximum and minimum turning points.

(a) Write down the coordinates of P and Q.

The curve crosses the y-axis at T.

(b) Write down the coordinates of T.

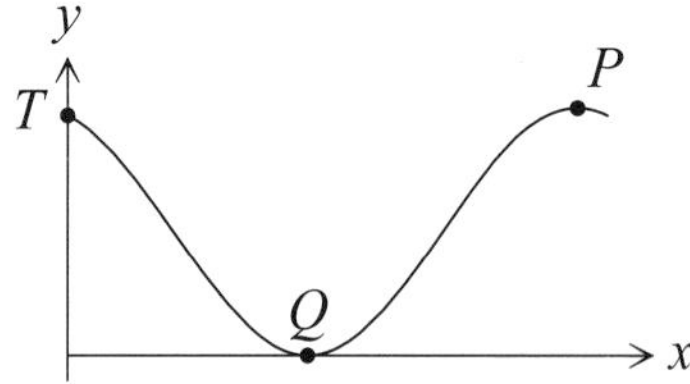

❄ **3** The diagram shows the curve with equation $y = f(x)$, where $f(x) \equiv 5\sin(x - 40)^\circ + 1$.

(a) State the maximum value of $f(x)$ and a corresponding value of x.

(b) State the minimum value of $f(x)$ and a corresponding value of x.

The curve crosses the y-axis at T.

(c) Write down the coordinates of T.

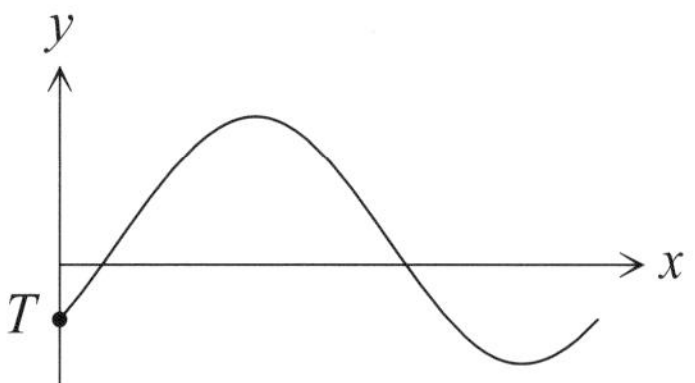

❄ **4** The diagram shows the curve with equation $y = 2\sin(x + 40)^\circ - 1$. The points P and Q are maximum and minimum turning points.

(a) Write down the coordinates of P and Q.

The curve crosses the x-axis at R and S.

(b) Calculate the coordinates of R and S.

The curve crosses the y-axis at A.

(c) Calculate the coordinates of A.

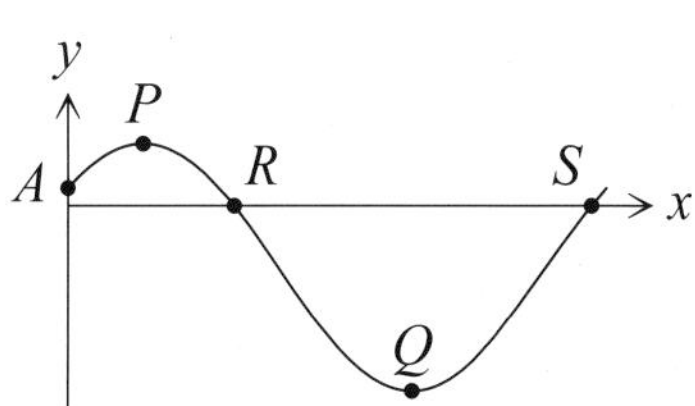

❄ 5 The diagram shows the curve with equation $y = 5\sin(t - 60)° + 1$. The points P and Q are maximum and minimum turning points.

(a) Write down the coordinates of P and Q.

The curve crosses the t-axis at R and S.

(b) Calculate the coordinates of R and S.

The curve crosses the y-axis at A.

(c) Calculate the coordinates of A.

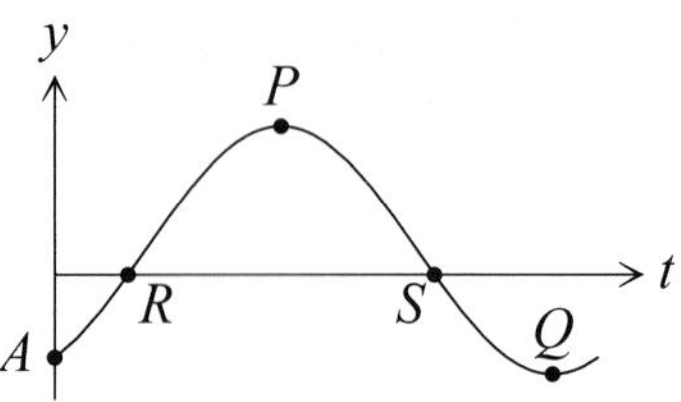

9 Algebra

9.1 Functional notation

In this exercise you will learn how to:

- ❑ use functional notation

1 The function f is defined by $f(x) = 5x + 7$.

(a) Find the value of:

i) $f(3)$ ii) $f(-2)$ iii) $f(0)$

(b) What value of x satisfies $f(x) = 27$?

2 The function f is defined by $f(x) = 3x - 1$.

(a) Find the value of:

i) $f(2)$ ii) $f(-5)$

(b) What value of m satisfies $f(m) = -10$?

3 The function f is defined by $f(x) = 2x^2 - 1$.

(a) Find the value of:

i) $f(5)$ ii) $f(-3)$ iii) $f(0)$

(b) What values of x satisfy $f(x) = 17$?

4 The function k is defined by $k(x) = 4^x$.

(a) Find the value of:

i) $k(3)$ ii) $k(0)$ iii) $k(-1)$ iv) $k\left(\frac{1}{2}\right)$

(b) What value of x satisfies $k(x) = 16$?

(c) What value of x satisfies $k(x) = \frac{1}{16}$?

5 The function h is defined by $h(t) = \cos t°$.

(a) Find the exact value of:

i) $h(30)$ ii) $h(45)$ iii) $h(60)$ iv) $h(180)$

(b) What is the smallest positive value of t satisfying $h(t) = 0$?

6 The function g is defined by $g(t) = 1 - 4t$.

(a) Find the value of:

i) $g(0)$ ii) $g(2)$ iii) $g(-3)$

(b) What value of t satisfies $g(t) = 21$?

(c) Find an expression for:

i) $g(x)$ ii) $g(a)$ iii) $g(p)$

7 The function f is defined by $f(x) = x^2 - 2$.

(a) Find the value of:

i) $f(5)$ ii) $f(-3)$

(b) Calculate the values of m satisfying $f(m) = 14$.

(c) Find an expression for:

i) $f(a)$ ii) $f(t)$ iii) $f(r)$

8 The function h is defined by $h(x) = x^2 + 2x$.

(a) Given that $h(t) = -1$, find the value of t.

(b) Given that $h(p) = 15$, find the possible values of p.

(c) Find an expression for:

i) $h(a)$ ii) $h(m)$

9 The function f is defined by $f(x) = 4x$.
Find an expression for:

(a) $f(t)$ (b) $f(2a)$ (c) $f(b + 1)$

10 The function k is defined by $k(x) = 3x - 2$.
Find an expression for:

(a) $k(m)$ (b) $k(2t)$ (c) $k(a - 1)$

11 The function g is defined by $g(x) = 2x^2 + 7$.
Find and simplify an expression for:

(a) $g(a)$ (b) $g(3t)$ (c) $g(m + 3)$

12 A function f is defined by $f(x) = x(x + 3)$.
Find an expression for:

(a) $f(t)$ (b) $f(2a)$ (c) $f(3m - 1)$

13 A function h is defined by $h(t) = \sin t°$.
Find an expression for:

(a) $h(x)$ (b) $h(2y)$ (c) $h(2m + 20)$

14 A function h is defined by $h(t) = t(4 - t)$.
Find and simplify an expression for:

(a) $h(x)$ (b) $h(x^2)$ (c) $h(x^3)$

15 A function g is defined by $g(x) = 3x - 1$.

(a) Find and simplify an expression for:

i) $g(a + 1)$ ii) $g(2 - a)$

(b) Find the value of a such that $g(a + 1) = g(2 - a) + 3$.

16 A function h is defined by $h(x) = 2x + 3$.

(a) Find and simplify an expression for:

i) $h(a + 3)$ ii) $h(2b)$

(b) Find the value of a such that $h(a + 3) = 5$.

(c) Find the value of b such that $h(2b) = 1$.

17 A function g is defined by $g(t) = 2t^2 - 3$.

(a) Find the values of a such that $g(a + 1) = 5$.

(b) Find the values of p such that $g(3p) = 15$.

18 The function h is defined by $h(x) = x(x - 3)$.
Find the values of p such that $h(p - 2) = 0$.

19 A function f is defined by $f(t) = 2t^2 - t$.

(a) Find the possible values of m such that $f(2m) = 10$.

(b) Find the possible values of a such that $f(a - 3) = 3$.

20 A function g is defined by $g(t) = \sin t°$.

(a) Find the exact value of:

i) $g(45)$ ii) $g(120)$ iii) $g(330)$

(b) Find the values of x such that $g(x) = \frac{1}{2}$ and $0 \leq x < 360$.

(c) Find the values of t such that $g(t + 20) = -\frac{1}{\sqrt{2}}$ and $0 \leq t < 360$.

9.2 Constructing expressions

In this exercise you will learn how to:

- ❑ construct an expression from given information
- ❑ use one expression in the construction of a second

1 A rectangle has breadth x cm and the length is 6 cm longer than the breadth. Write down an expression for the area of the rectangle in terms of x.

2 The perimeter of a rectangle is 56 cm. The length of the rectangle is l cm.

(a) Write down an expression for the breadth of the rectangle in terms of l.

(b) Find an expression for the area of the rectangle in terms of l.

3 The sum of two numbers is 34. One of the numbers is n. Write down an expression for the other number in terms of n.

4 The diagram shows a square of side s and a rectangle.
The area of the rectangle is three times that of the square.
Write down an expression, in terms of s, for the total area of the two shapes.

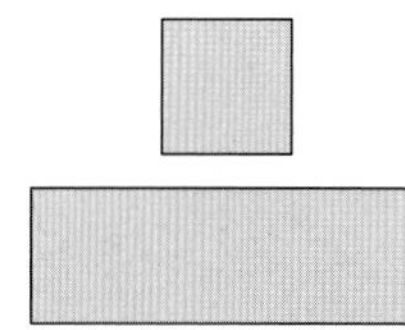

5 A 200 cm length of wire is used to form a skeletal cuboid with a square base of side s.

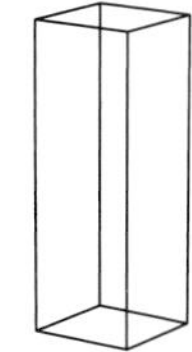

(a) Write down an expression for the height of the cuboid in terms of s.

(b) Write down an expression, in terms of s, for the volume of the cuboid.

6 A number p is 3 more than the number n.

(a) Write down an expression for p in terms of n.

The product of n, p and a third number is 89.

(b) Write down, in terms of n, an expression for the third number.

7 The diagram shows a solid cuboid with breadth b. The length of the cuboid is twice the breadth.

(a) Write down an expression for the length of the cuboid in terms of b.

(b) Write down an expression, in terms of b, for the area of the top face of the cuboid.

The volume of the cuboid is 10.

(c) Find an expression, in terms of b, for the height of the cuboid.

(d) Find an expression for the surface area of the cuboid in terms of b.

8 A piece of wire of length 60 cm is cut into two parts. One part is bent to form a square of side w cm and the other part is bent to form a rectangle of width w cm. Find an expression for the length of the rectangle in terms of w.

9 The diagram shows the curve with equation $y = 2 - x^2$ and the rectangle $PQRS$, where P, S are on the x-axis and Q, R are on the curve.

The point P has coordinates $(a, 0)$.

(a) Find an expression, in terms of a, for the height of the rectangle $PQRS$.

(b) Find an expression, in terms of a, for the area of the rectangle $PQRS$.

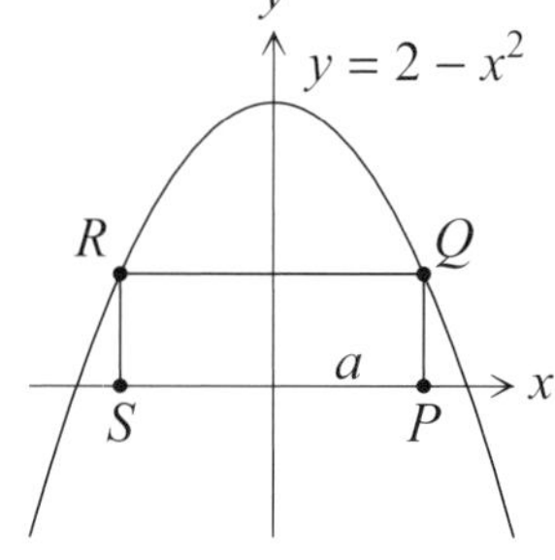

10 The diagram shows the point $P(x, 4 - x)$ on the line with equation $x + y = 4$.

Find an expression for the length of the line segment OP in terms of x.

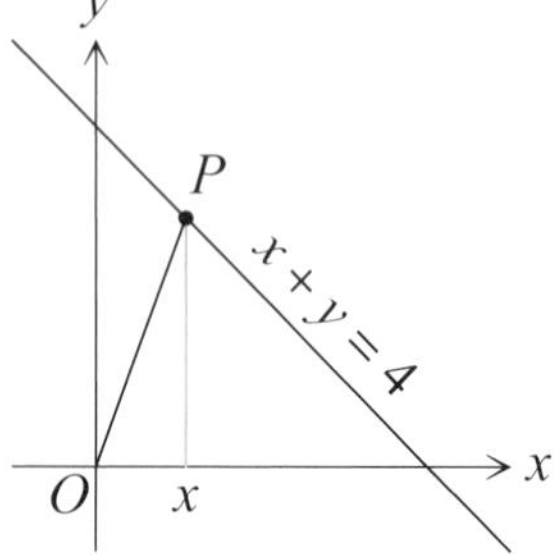

11 A rectangular sheet of paper measuring 30 cm × 24 cm has four squares cut from the corners, as shown. Each square has sides of length x cm. The resulting shape is then folded to form an open cuboid.

Write down expressions, in terms of x, for:

(a) the height of the box

(b) the length of the box

(c) the breadth of the box

(d) the volume of the box

(e) the surface area of the box

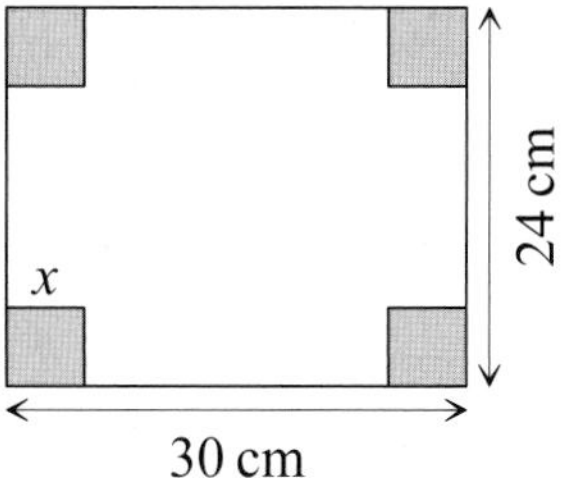

12 The diagram shows a closed box whose base length is three times its width w. Write down an expression, in terms of w, for:

(a) the length of the box.

(b) the area of the top face of the box

The box has a surface area of 34 square units. Find an expression, in terms of w, for:

(c) the height of the box

(d) the volume of the box.

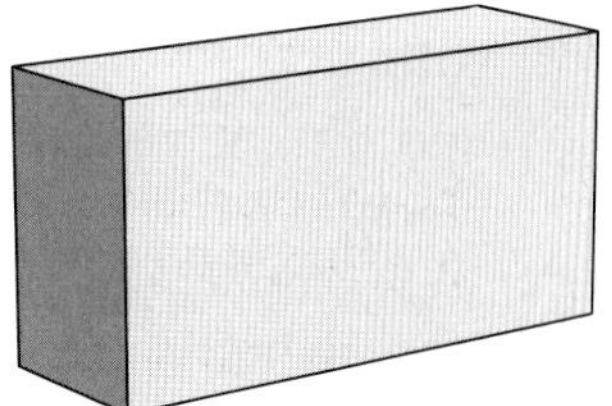

13 A car travelling at v km h^{-1} uses petrol at the rate of $7 + 0.02v^3$ litres per hour. The car travels 100 km at a steady speed of v km h^{-1}.

(a) Write down an expression for the time taken for the journey, in terms of v.

(b) Write down an expression, in terms of v, for the amount of petrol used on the journey.

9.3 Forming and solving equations

In this exercise you will learn how to:

- ❑ form and solve linear equations
- ❑ form and solve quadratic equations
- ❑ solve word problems

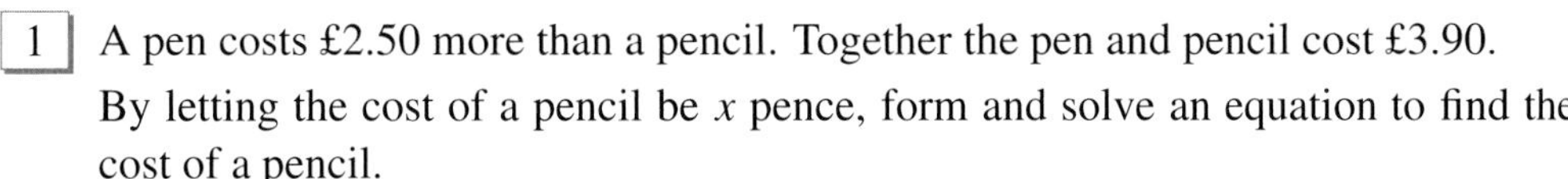

1 A pen costs £2.50 more than a pencil. Together the pen and pencil cost £3.90. By letting the cost of a pencil be x pence, form and solve an equation to find the cost of a pencil.

2 The perimeter of the shape shown on the right is 79 cm. All the indicated lengths are measured in centimetres.

Form and solve an equation to calculate the value of y.

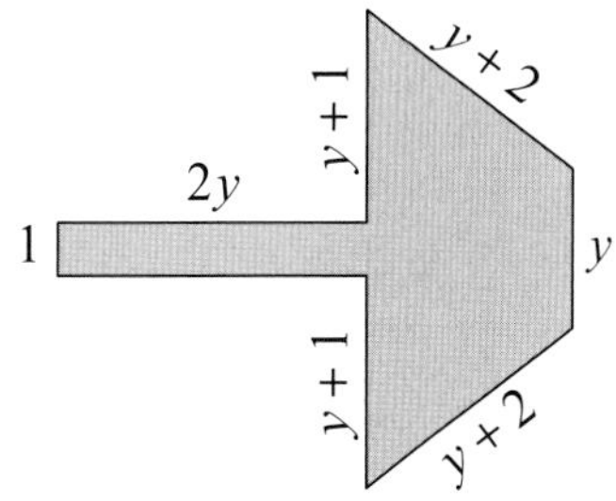

3 When $t = 2$ is substituted into the expression $t^3 - 4t^2 + 6t - a$ the answer is -3. Find the value of a.

4 Find the values of x, y and p so that each rectangle has the given area.

(a) Area = 60, sides $x - 2$ and $x + 5$

(b) Area = 72, sides $y + 1$ and $y + 7$

(c) Area = 36, sides p and $2p + 1$

5 A car tank was $\frac{1}{4}$ full. When 26 litres of petrol were added the tank was then 90% full. Form and solve an equation to calculate how much petrol needs to be added to fill the tank completely.

6 A metal rod 5 m long is cut three times so that each piece cut off is 10 cm longer than the one before. Form and solve an equation to find the lengths of the four pieces of rod.

7 The solid cuboid shown alongside has a volume of $324\ \text{cm}^3$.

Calculate the value of a.

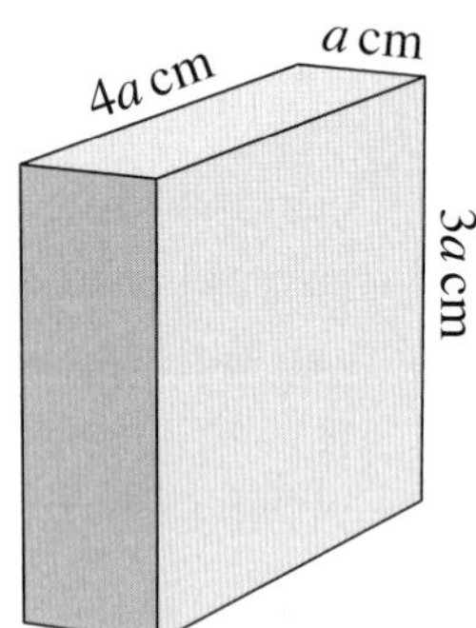

8 The volume, in cm^3, of the solid cuboid shown on the right is numerically equal to the surface area, in cm^2.

Calculate the value of b.

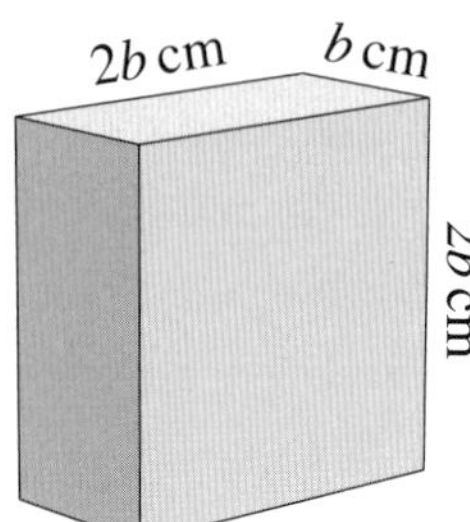

❄ 9 The diagram shows a rectangular-based pyramid. The base has dimensions $2l$ units and $4l$ units, and all the slant lengths are $3l$ units.

(a) Find an expression in l for the perpendicular height of the pyramid.

The volume of the pyramid is 144 cubic units.

(b) Calculate the value of l.

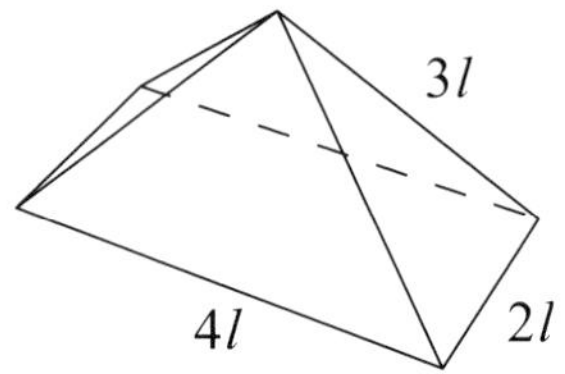

❄ 10 The sum of two positive integers is 8. The sum of the squares of the two integers is 34. Form and solve a quadratic equation to find the integers.

❄ 11 The area of the symmetrical shape shown alongside is 48.
Find the length of the perimeter of the shape.

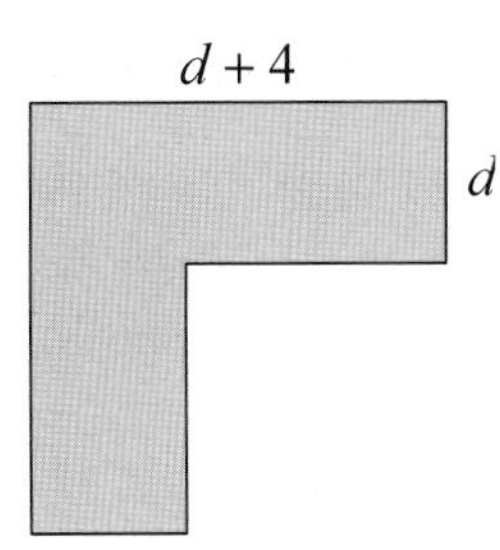

❄ 12 The length of a rectangular lawn is 7 metres more than the width. The lawn is surrounded by a gravel path, 2 metres wide. The total area of the lawn and path is $144\,\text{m}^2$. Find the dimensions of the lawn.

❄ 13 A cuboid has dimensions w cm, $(w + 4)$ cm and $(w + 5)$ cm. The surface area of the cuboid is $472\,\text{cm}^2$. Calculate the volume of the cuboid.

❄ 14 The triangle shown in the diagram is right-angled.
Find the value of h.

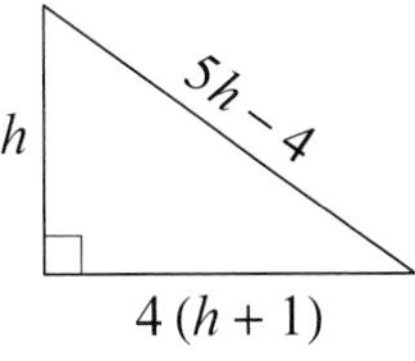

❄ 15 Adding an integer to twice its square gives a total of 21. Find the integer.

❄ 16 Adding an integer to its reciprocal gives $\frac{5}{2}$. Find the integer.

❄ 17 A closed metal cube has sides of length l cm. The cube is hollow, with a shell 1 cm thick, and the volume of metal used to form the cube is $296\,\text{cm}^3$. Calculate the value of l.

9.4 Surds and indices

In this exercise you will learn how to:

- multiply, divide and simplify expressions involving surds and indices
- rewrite an expression involving surds into one involving indices
- rewrite a fractional expression as a sum of separate terms, by dividing each term in the numerator by the denominator

Surds and indices are introduced in Exercises 1.5 and 1.6 on pages 4 and 5.

1 Expand and simplify, giving the answer in terms of powers and square roots:

(a) $x\left(\sqrt{x}+1\right)$ (b) $\sqrt{x}\left(\sqrt{x}+3\right)$ (c) $x^2\left(\sqrt{x}+3x\right)$

(d) $\left(\sqrt{x}+1\right)^2$ (e) $\left(\sqrt{x}+1\right)\left(\sqrt{x}-1\right)$ (f) $x\sqrt{x}\left(2\sqrt{x}+x\right)$

(g) $\left(x\sqrt{x}+5\right)\left(x\sqrt{x}-2\right)$ (h) $x\left(\frac{2}{x}+1\right)$ (i) $\left(\frac{1}{x}-2\right)\left(\frac{3}{x}+5\right)$

(j) $\left(x-\frac{2}{x}\right)\left(3x+\frac{1}{x}\right)$ (k) $\left(1-\frac{2}{\sqrt{x}}\right)\left(1+\frac{3}{\sqrt{x}}\right)$ (l) $\left(\sqrt{x}-\frac{4}{\sqrt{x}}\right)^2$

2 Write as a sum of separate terms, giving the answer in terms of powers and square roots:

(a) $\frac{x^2+2x}{\sqrt{x}}$ (b) $\frac{x^3+x^2-\sqrt{x}}{\sqrt{x}}$ (c) $\frac{5x^2-3x-2}{\sqrt{x}}$

(d) $\frac{5\sqrt{x}-8x}{x\sqrt{x}}$ (e) $\frac{3\sqrt{x}+x\sqrt{x}}{2\sqrt{x}}$ (f) $\frac{5x+3x^2}{2x\sqrt{x}}$

3 Simplify, giving the answer in index form:

(a) $\frac{a^{\frac{1}{2}}\times a^{\frac{5}{2}}}{a^2}$ (b) $\frac{b^{\frac{5}{2}}\times b^{-\frac{1}{2}}}{b}$ (c) $\frac{6x^{\frac{3}{2}}}{2x^{\frac{1}{2}}}$

(d) $\frac{a^{\frac{1}{4}}\times a^{\frac{7}{4}}}{a^2}$ (e) $\frac{p^{\frac{5}{2}}\times p^{\frac{3}{2}}}{p^{-1}}$ (f) $\frac{4a^{\frac{3}{4}}\times a^{\frac{5}{4}}}{12a}$

(g) $a^2\left(2a^{-\frac{1}{2}}+a\right)$ (h) $b^{\frac{1}{2}}\left(2b^{-\frac{1}{2}}+b^{\frac{1}{2}}\right)$ (i) $x\left(5x^{\frac{1}{2}}-x^{\frac{5}{2}}\right)$

(j) $u\left(u^{-\frac{1}{2}}+3u\right)$ (k) $a^2\left(a^{-\frac{3}{2}}+a^{-2}\right)$ (l) $p^{-1}\left(p^{-\frac{1}{2}}+3p^{\frac{3}{2}}\right)$

(m) $\frac{y+2}{y^{\frac{1}{2}}}$ (n) $\frac{s^2+3s}{s^{\frac{3}{2}}}$ (o) $\frac{2t^{\frac{1}{2}}+t^3}{t^{\frac{1}{2}}}$

4 Write as an expression in index form:

(a) $\frac{1}{x^2}$ (b) $\frac{2}{x}$ (c) $\frac{1}{3x^2}$ (d) $\frac{2}{5x}$ (e) $\sqrt{x}$ (f) $x\sqrt{x}$

(g) $5x\sqrt{x}$ (h) $\frac{x^2}{\sqrt{x}}$ (i) $\frac{\sqrt{x}}{2x}$ (j) $4\sqrt[3]{x}$ (k) $\frac{2x}{\sqrt[3]{x^2}}$ (l) $\frac{5\sqrt[3]{x}}{3x}$

❄ **5** Expand and simplify, giving the answer in index form:

(a) $x\left(4\sqrt{x}+1\right)$ (b) $\sqrt{x}\left(2\sqrt{x}-5\right)$ (c) $7x^2\left(\sqrt{x}+4x\right)$

(d) $\left(\sqrt{x}+10\right)^2$ (e) $\left(\sqrt[3]{a}+1\right)\left(\sqrt[3]{a}-1\right)$ (f) $\sqrt{p}\left(p\sqrt{p}-2\right)$

(g) $\left(\sqrt{t}+3\right)\left(t\sqrt{t}-1\right)$ (h) $\left(\sqrt[3]{a}+2\right)\left(\sqrt[3]{a}-3\right)$

❄ **6** Write as a sum of separate terms:

(a) $\dfrac{x^3-4x^2+5x}{x}$ (b) $\dfrac{3c^3-c^2+c}{c^2}$ (c) $\dfrac{2z+3}{z^4}$

(d) $\dfrac{5a^4-6a^2+1}{2a^2}$ (e) $\dfrac{(2p-5)^2}{p}$ (f) $\dfrac{\left(m^2-2\right)^2}{m^2}$

❄ **7** Write as a sum of separate terms, giving the answer in index form:

(a) $\dfrac{x^2-4x}{\sqrt{x}}$ (b) $\dfrac{s^3+5s^2-\sqrt{s}}{\sqrt{s}}$ (c) $\dfrac{x^2+2x}{\sqrt{x}}$

(d) $\dfrac{3\sqrt{t}-4t}{t\sqrt{t}}$ (e) $\dfrac{6\sqrt{x}+x\sqrt{x}}{2\sqrt{x}}$ (f) $\dfrac{a+4a^2}{2a\sqrt{a}}$

(g) $\dfrac{y^2+2y-7}{\sqrt[3]{y}}$

Answers

Exercise 1.1 page 1

1. (a) $7x + 2$
   (b) $7 - p$
   (c) $5m + 6$
   (d) $9q + 6$
   (e) $4y - 10$
   (f) $5p^2 + 5p$
   (g) $2x^2 - 6x$
   (h) $-2t - 2t^2$
   (i) $7 - 3n$
   (j) $2x^2 + 2x$
2. (a) $3x^2 + 7x + 2$
   (b) $4p^2 - p - 3$
   (c) $6x^2 + 11x - 2$
   (d) $6x^2 - 7x + 2$
   (e) $4q^2 + 4q + 1$
   (f) $9m^2 - 12m + 4$
   (g) $3x^2 - 6x + 3$
   (h) $4p^2 + 16p + 16$
   (i) $2x^2 - 7x + 7$
   (j) $6x - 3$
   (k) $5y^2 - 9y - 5$
   (l) $8 - 2x - 2x^2$
3. (a) $x^3 + x^2 + 2x + 2$
   (b) $y^3 - 4y^2 - 3y + 12$
   (c) $z^3 + 4z^2 + 3z - 2$
   (d) $t^3 - 8t^2 + 17t - 6$
   (e) $w^3 + w^2 + 7w - 9$
   (f) $m^4 + 5m^2 + 4$
   (g) $n^4 + 4n^2 - 12$
   (h) $a^3 + 12a^2 + 48a + 64$
   (i) $b^3 - 15b^2 + 75b - 125$
   (j) $8c^3 + 12c^2 + 6c + 1$

Exercise 1.2 page 2

1. (a) $\frac{3}{2}$
   (b) 8
   (c) -3
   (d) -3.5
   (e) 10
   (f) -3
2. (a) 9
   (b) -6
   (c) 6
   (d) 9
   (e) 5
   (f) $\frac{1}{12}$

Exercise 1.3 page 2

1. (a) $x = 1, y = 5$
   (b) $x = 2, y = -3$
   (c) $a = 3, b = -3$
   (d) $c = 7, d = 4$
   (e) $m = 8, n = 3$
   (f) $p = -1, q = -3$
   (g) $s = 1, t = 1$
2. (a) $x = -7, y = 4$
   (b) $u = 3, v = 2$
   (c) $a = 7, b = -2$
   (d) $p = -3, q = -4$
3. (a) $x = 6, y = -2$
   (b) $x = 4, y = 1$
   (c) $x = -2, y = 3$
   (d) $a = 3, b = -4$
   (e) $x = 0, y = 3$
   (f) $u = 4, v = -1$
   (g) $p = 5, q = 0$
   (h) $a = 3, b = -3$
   (i) $x = 2, y = 1$
   (j) $x = 4, y = 1$

Exercise 1.4 page 3

1. (a) $4 + \dfrac{4}{x} + \dfrac{1}{x^2}$
   (b) $p^2 - 2 + \dfrac{1}{p^2}$
   (c) $k^4 + 2k + \dfrac{1}{k^2}$
   (d) $x^2 - \dfrac{25}{x^2}$
   (e) $2t^2 - 3 - \dfrac{2}{t^2}$
   (f) $2a + 13 + \dfrac{15}{a}$
2. (a) $\dfrac{x + 1}{3x - 1}$
   (b) $\dfrac{2r - 3}{4r + 1}$
   (c) $\dfrac{1}{a^2 - 5}$
   (d) $\dfrac{y + 3}{y - 2}$
   (e) $\dfrac{2 - p}{4 + 9p}$

Exercise 1.5 page 4

1. (a) $2\sqrt{2}$
   (b) $2\sqrt{3}$
   (c) $3\sqrt{2}$
   (d) $2\sqrt{6}$
   (e) $3\sqrt{3}$
   (f) $4\sqrt{2}$
   (g) $4\sqrt{3}$
   (h) $5\sqrt{3}$
   (i) $7\sqrt{2}$
   (j) $\dfrac{1}{8\sqrt{2}}$
   (k) $\dfrac{2\sqrt{2}}{7}$
   (l) $\dfrac{3\sqrt{2}}{5\sqrt{5}}$

(m) $\dfrac{7\sqrt{3}}{5\sqrt{2}}$
(n) $\dfrac{10}{11}$

2. (a) $2 - \sqrt{2}$
(b) $3\sqrt{5} - 5$
(c) $12 - 5\sqrt{3}$
(d) $7\sqrt{2} - 21$
(e) $-1 + 2\sqrt{2}$
(f) $7 - 2\sqrt{5}$
(g) $7 - 2\sqrt{2}$
(h) $7 + 4\sqrt{5}$
(i) 13
(j) -1

3. (a) $\sqrt{2}$
(b) $2\sqrt{5}$
(c) $2\sqrt{3}$
(d) $3\sqrt{7}$
(e) $4\sqrt{3}$
(f) $9\sqrt{2}$
(g) $\sqrt{2} + 1$
(h) $3 + \sqrt{5}$
(i) $5 + \sqrt{2}$
(j) $1 + 2\sqrt{7}$
(k) $\dfrac{5\sqrt{3}}{3} + \sqrt{2}$
(l) $\dfrac{1}{5} + \dfrac{2\sqrt{2}}{5}$

Exercise 1.6 *page 5*

1. (a) 2
(b) 5
(c) 20
(d) 3
(e) 16
(f) 27
(g) 49
(h) 125
(i) 8
(j) $\frac{1}{6}$
(k) $\frac{1}{5}$
(l) $\frac{1}{2}$
(m) $\frac{1}{8}$
(n) $\frac{1}{25}$
(o) $\frac{1}{4}$
(p) $\frac{4}{9}$
(q) $\frac{8}{7}$
(r) $\frac{125}{216}$

2. (a) x^3
(b) y^6
(c) a^6
(d) z^{-1}
(e) b^{-10}
(f) t^6

3. (a) a^5
(b) $2b^4$
(c) 7
(d) $2p^{-1}$
(e) $3c^{-2}$
(f) $8r^{-1}$
(g) d^3
(h) $3s^{11}$
(i) $4g^3$
(j) $12t^2$
(k) $3w^5$
(l) $24a^2$
(m) $10p^{-5}$
(n) 6
(o) 24

Exercise 1.7 *page 6*

1. (a) 1 unit
(b) $\sqrt{2}$ units
(c) 45°
(d) $\frac{1}{\sqrt{2}}, \frac{1}{\sqrt{2}}, 1$

2. (a) 2 units, 2 units
(b) 1 unit
(c) $\sqrt{3}$ units
(d) 60°; 30°
(e) $\frac{1}{2}, \frac{\sqrt{3}}{2}, \frac{1}{\sqrt{3}}$
(f) $\frac{\sqrt{3}}{2}, \frac{1}{2}, \sqrt{3}$

3.

	30°	45°	60°
sin	$\frac{1}{2}$	$\frac{1}{\sqrt{2}}$	$\frac{\sqrt{3}}{2}$
cos	$\frac{\sqrt{3}}{2}$	$\frac{1}{\sqrt{2}}$	$\frac{1}{2}$
tan	$\frac{1}{\sqrt{3}}$	1	$\sqrt{3}$

4. (a) $6\sqrt{3}$
(b) 60
(c) $6\sqrt{2}$
(d) 45
(e) 8
(f) $5\sqrt{3}$
(g) 30
(h) $\frac{5\sqrt{3}}{3}$
(i) $2\sqrt{2}$

5. (a) $12\,\text{cm}^2$
(b) $3\,\text{cm}^2$
(c) $7\sqrt{3}\,\text{cm}^2$
(d) $\left(\sqrt{3} + 1\right)\text{cm}^2$

Exercise 2.1 *page 8*

1. (a) 2
(b) -3
(c) ± 1
(d) ± 2
(e) -4

2. (a) 3
(b) ± 25
(c) $\pm\frac{1}{2}$
(d) -6

3. (a) ± 3
(b) ± 7
(c) -2
(d) $\pm\frac{7}{2}$
(e) $\frac{2}{5}$

Exercise 2.2 *page 8*

1. (a) -2 or 3
(b) 1 or 5

(c) -4 or -2
(d) 0 or 5
(e) -3 or 9
(f) 2 or 7
(g) 0 or 6
(h) -8 (twice)
(i) -5 or 2
(j) -6 or 6
(k) -9 or -3
(l) -8 or 9

2. (a) -7 or 1
(b) 3 or 7
(c) -1 or 5
(d) -6 or -2
(e) -9 or 2
(f) 1 or 5
(g) -3 or -2
(h) -1 or 4
(i) -4 or 0

3. (a) 2 or 3
(b) -3 or 4
(c) -1 or 5
(d) -3 or -1
(e) -5 or 12
(f) 7 or 10

Exercise 2.3 *page 9*

1. (a) $\frac{1}{2}$ or 1
(b) $\frac{1}{5}$ or 1
(c) $\frac{1}{7}$ or $\frac{1}{3}$
(d) $-\frac{1}{2}$ (twice)
(e) $-\frac{1}{2}$ or 1
(f) -1 or $\frac{1}{3}$
(g) $-\frac{1}{2}$ or $\frac{1}{7}$
(h) $-\frac{1}{2}$ or $-\frac{1}{5}$
(i) $-\frac{1}{6}$ or $\frac{1}{2}$
(j) $-\frac{1}{4}$ or $\frac{1}{6}$
(k) $-\frac{1}{6}$ or $-\frac{1}{5}$
(l) $-\frac{1}{5}$ or $\frac{1}{12}$

2. (a) $\frac{1}{2}$ or 3
(b) -1 or $-\frac{2}{3}$
(c) $\frac{1}{5}$ or 2
(d) $-\frac{7}{3}$ or 1
(e) $-\frac{1}{5}$ or 7
(f) $-\frac{11}{2}$ or 1
(g) $\frac{1}{7}$ or 5
(h) $-\frac{5}{3}$ or 1
(i) -5 or $-\frac{1}{2}$
(j) $\frac{3}{2}$ or 5
(k) -7 or $\frac{2}{3}$
(l) $-\frac{3}{5}$ or 4
(m) $-\frac{7}{3}$ or 9
(n) $-\frac{3}{2}$ or 3
(o) $-\frac{3}{5}$ (twice)
(p) $-\frac{5}{2}$ or $\frac{2}{3}$
(q) $-\frac{4}{3}$ or $\frac{7}{2}$
(r) $-\frac{5}{2}$ or $-\frac{2}{5}$

3. (a) $-\frac{1}{3}$ or $\frac{1}{5}$
(b) $-\frac{1}{2}$ or $-\frac{1}{5}$
(c) $-\frac{2}{3}$ or $\frac{1}{7}$
(d) $-\frac{3}{2}$ or 1
(e) $\frac{1}{5}$ or $\frac{1}{3}$
(f) $\frac{1}{2}$ or 3

Exercise 2.4 *page 10*

1. (a) $\cos x = 0$ or -1
(b) $\sin x = \pm\frac{1}{2}$
(c) $\cos t = 0$ or $\frac{2}{5}$
(d) $\sin t = -1$ or $\frac{1}{6}$

2. (a) ± 1 or ± 3
(b) -2 or 1
(c) -5 or 11
(d) 25 or 36
(e) 1 or 64

Exercise 2.5 *page 10*

1. (a) -5 or 1
(b) -6 or 14
(c) -10 or 0
(d) $-\frac{15}{2}$ or $\frac{3}{2}$
(e) $\frac{1}{3}$ or $\frac{5}{3}$
(f) $-\frac{7}{4}$ or $-\frac{1}{4}$
(g) -2 or -1
(h) -1 or $\frac{1}{5}$
(i) $-\frac{3}{4}$ or $\frac{1}{12}$

2. (a) $-3 \pm \sqrt{5}$
(b) $1 \pm \sqrt{2}$
(c) $7 \pm \sqrt{5}$
(d) $-2 \pm \sqrt{6}$
(e) $\dfrac{1 \pm \sqrt{3}}{2}$
(f) $\dfrac{5 \pm \sqrt{7}}{2}$

3. (a) -5
(b) 1 or 9
(c) 5
(d) $-\frac{3}{2}$ or 1
(e) 3
(f) -1

Exercise 2.6 *page 11*

1. (a) -5, -3 or 2
(b) -3 (twice) or 7
(c) -2, $-\frac{1}{2}$ or 10
(d) -3, -1 or 0
(e) -4 (twice) or 2
(f) 0 (twice) or 8
(g) 0
(h) 0 or $\pm\sqrt{3}$

2. (a) -1, 0 or 4
(b) 0 or -5 (twice)
(c) -2, -3 or 0
(d) -3, 0 or 3
(e) -3, 0 or 4
(f) 0

3. (a) -1, 0 or 2
(b) -1 (twice) or 0

Exercise 3.1 *page 12*

1. (a) 3
(b) 5

(c) -2
(d) $\frac{1}{3}$
(e) $-\frac{3}{5}$
(f) 0

2. (a) 3
(b) -2
(c) 2
(d) 1
(e) $\frac{1}{3}$
(f) $-\frac{4}{5}$
(g) $-\frac{2}{3}$

3. (a) $y = 2x + 4$
(b) $y = -x + 2$
(c) $y = 3x - 2$
(d) $y = -2x + 7$
(e) $3y = 2x + 18$
(f) $x + 2y = 8$

4. (a) $y = x + 3$
(b) $y = 2x - 9$
(c) $2y = x + 6$
(d) $y = -4x + 3$
(e) $x + 5y = 0$
(f) $3y = 2x + 3$
(g) $4x + 3y = 0$

5. (a) B
(b) D
(c) C
(d) A

6. (a) $(-2, 0)$ and $(0, 4)$
(b) $(4, 0)$ and $(0, 12)$
(c) $\left(3\frac{1}{3}, 0\right)$ and $(0, -10)$
(d) $(5, 0)$ and $(0, 5)$
(e) $(10, 0)$ and $(0, 6)$
(f) $(4, 0)$ and $(0, -1)$
(g) $(3, 0)$ and $(0, 6)$
(h) $\left(2\frac{1}{2}, 0\right)$ and $\left(0, -1\frac{2}{3}\right)$
(i) $(-15, 0)$ and $(0, -5)$
(j) $\left(1\frac{1}{2}, 0\right)$ and $(0, -9)$

7. (a) $3y = 2x + 15$
(b) $9y = 9x + 1$
(c) $15y = 12x - 5$
(d) $2x + 5y = 30$
(e) $x + 2y + 8 = 0$
(f) $4 + 12y = 3x$

8. (a) $x - y - 4 = 0$
(b) $x - 2y + 5 = 0$
(c) $3x + 4y - 6 = 0$
(d) $2x - 3y - 3 = 0$
(e) $3x + 5y - 10 = 0$
(f) $5x - 6y = 0$

Exercise 3.2 *page 13*

1. (a) $y = 3$
(b) $y = 4$
(c) $x = 2$
(d) $y = 1$
(e) $y = 4$

2. $y = 4$

3. (a) $x = -3, y = 8$
(b) $y = -2x + 2;$ $y = 2x$

4. (a) $(-2, 5)$
(b) $(-4, 5), (-2, 2)$

5. (a) $x = 9, y = 1;$ $x = 10, y = 3$
(b) $x = 13, y = 1;$ $x = 20, y = 3$

6. $y = x + 2$

Exercise 3.3 *page 14*

1. (a) $y = 4x + 1$
(b) $y = 2x - 2$
(c) $x + y = 3$
(d) $3x + 2y + 12 = 0$
(e) $y = 6x$

2. $y = 2x - 8$

3. $y = -5 - x$

4. $2x + 5y = 13$

5. $y = -5x - 3,$ $x + 2y = 3$

6. (a) $x + 3y = 9$
(b) $x + 3y + 6 = 0$

Exercise 3.4 *page 15*

1. (a) $(8, 6)$
(b) $(-2, 1)$
(c) $\left(4, \frac{3}{2}\right)$

2. $(4, 1)$

3. $(12, -5)$

5. $(4a, 2b)$

6. (a) 5
(b) 13
(c) $5\sqrt{2}$
(d) $3\sqrt{2}$

7. 5 or -3

8. $(0, 1)$ or $(-6, 1)$

Exercise 3.5 *page 16*

2. (a) P and R

4. (a) 7
(b) 22
(c) -3
(d) -5
(e) 8

5. (a) Yes
(b) No
(c) No
(d) Yes

Exercise 3.6 *page 17*

1. (a) 5
(b) -7
(c) -0.5
(d) 0
(e) 0.3
(f) -0.6

2. (a) 63.4
(b) 71.6

(c) 104.0
(d) 116.6
(e) 135
(f) 63.4

3. (a) 45°
(b) 104°
(c) 33.7°
(d) 143.1°

4. (a) 45°
(b) 18.4°
(c) 63.4°
(d) 63.4°

5. (a) $y = x - 1$
(b) $y = 0.5x + 4$
(c) $y = -x + 2$
(d) $y = 2x - 1$
(e) $y = -5x - 10$
(f) $y = 0.2x + 2$

7. (a) $y = \frac{1}{\sqrt{3}}x + 4$
(b) $y = \sqrt{3}(x + 2)$
(c) $y = -\sqrt{3}x + 3$
(d) $y = -\sqrt{3}(x - 3)$
(e) $y = -\sqrt{3}x$
(f) $y = \frac{1}{\sqrt{3}}(x + 2)$

8. (a) 45°
(b) 71.6°
(c) 116.6°

9. (a) 123.7°
(b) 18.4°
(c) 153.5°
(d) 90°

Exercise 3.7 *page 20*

1. (a) $(-1, 12)$
(b) 5

2. (a) $(4, -1)$
(b) $2\sqrt{2}$

3. $(0, 2)$

4. A inside, B on the circle, C outside, D outside, E inside

5. $(2, 2)$, $(-2, 2)$, $(2, -2)$, $(-2, -2)$

6. $(7, 7)$, 7

7. $2\sqrt{2}$

Exercise 3.8 *page 21*

1. $(6, 6)$, $(6, -6)$, $(-6, -2)$, $(-2, 2)$

2. $(40, 30)$, $(85, 15)$, $(55, 35)$

3. (a) 2 units, 2 units, 1 unit
(b) $(2, 4)$, $(14, 4)$, $(8, 9)$

4. (a) 10 units
(b) 3 units

5. 1 unit

7. $\sqrt{5}$ units

Exercise 4.1 *page 23*

1. (a)

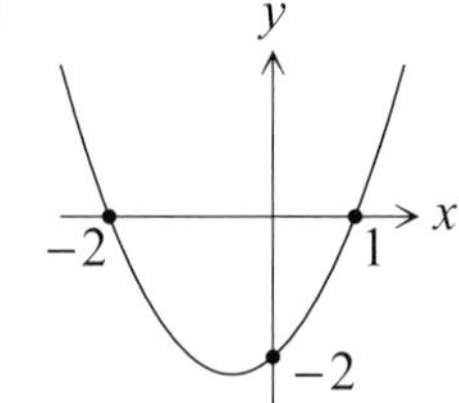

(b)

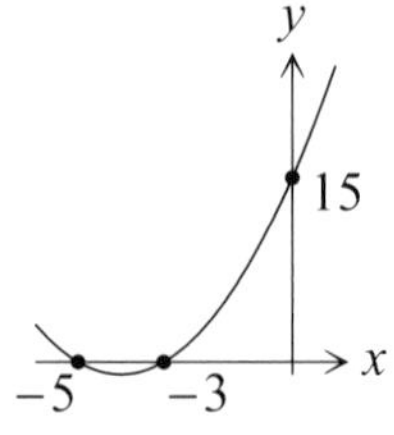

(c)

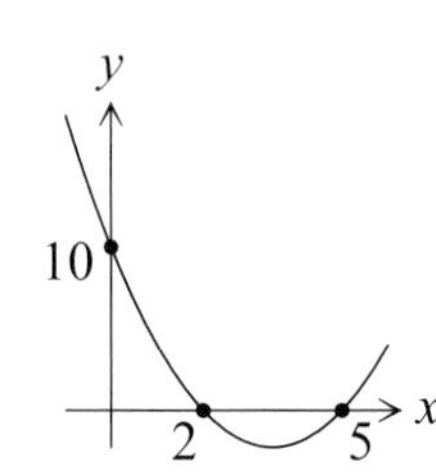

(d)

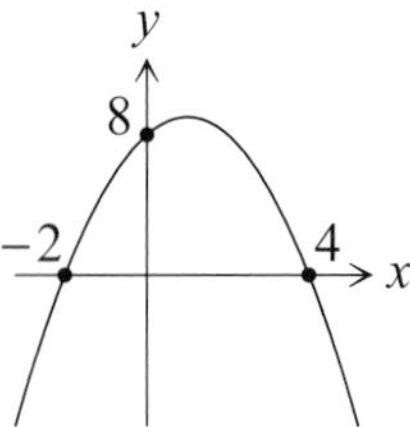

(e)

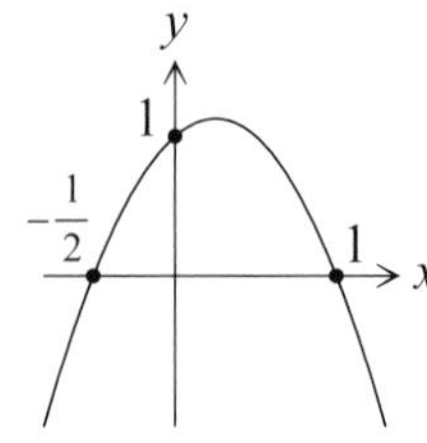

(f)

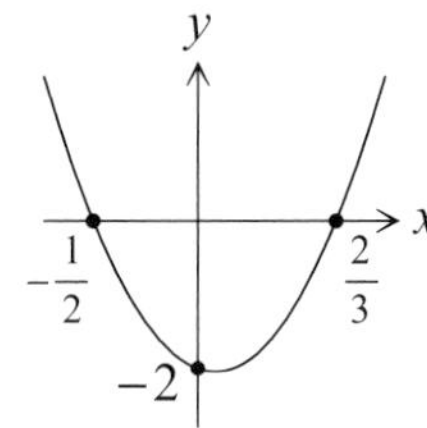

(g)

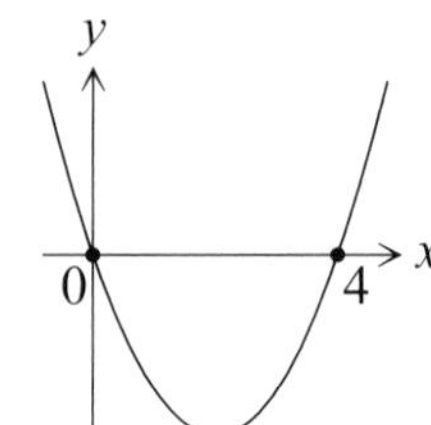

(h)

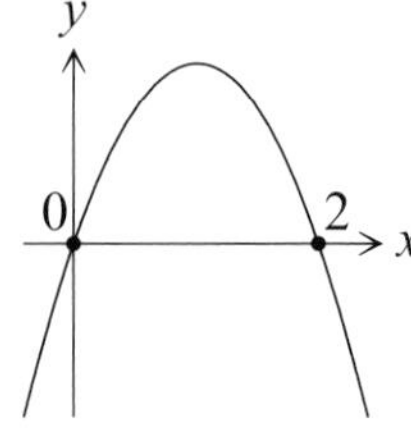

(i)

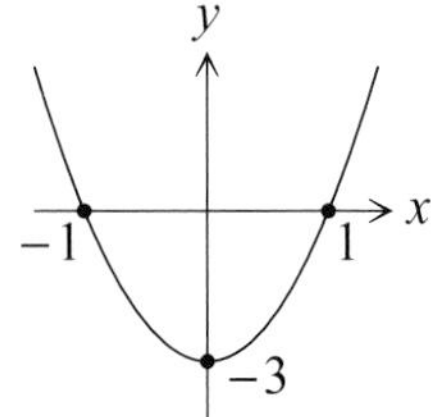

(j)

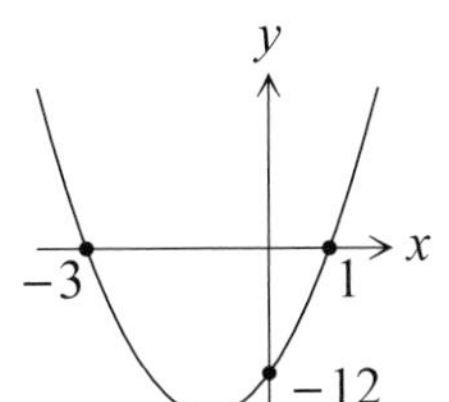

(k)

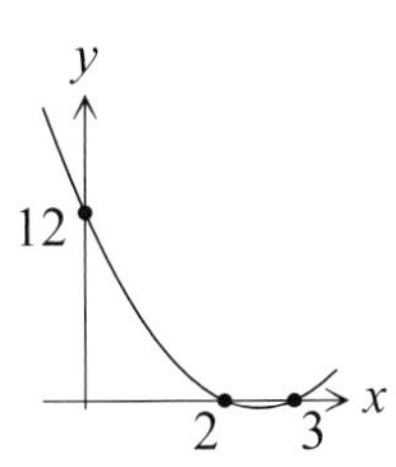

(l)

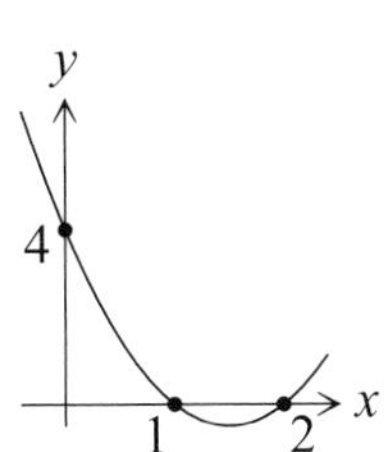

2. (a)

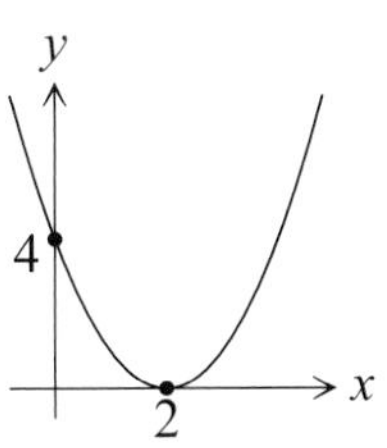

(b)

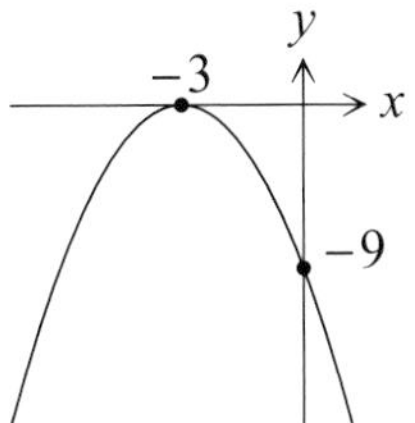

(c)

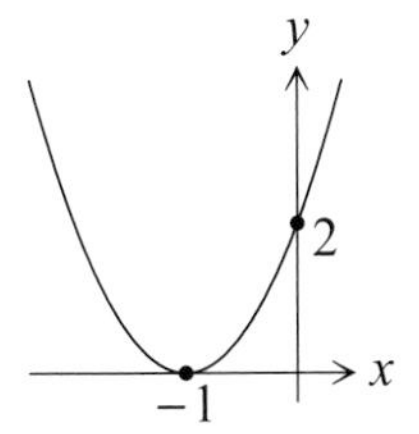

(d)

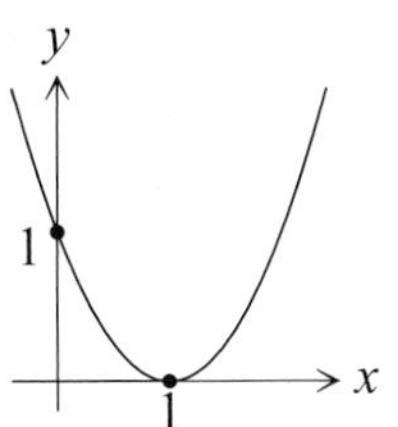

(e)

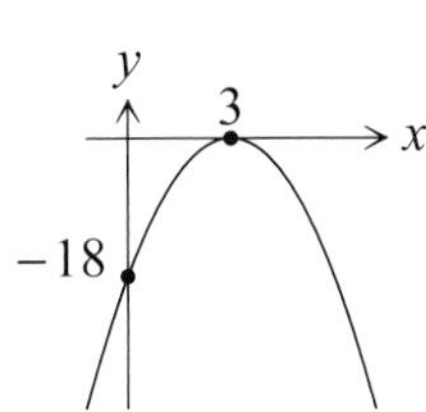

(f)

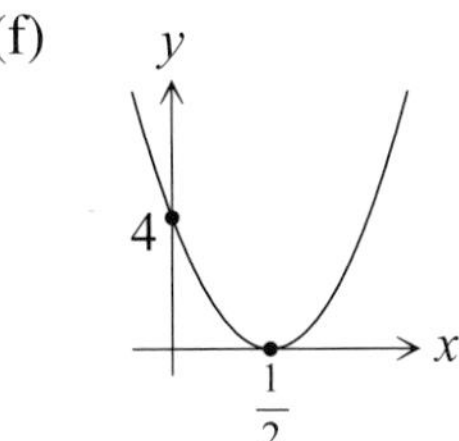

3. (a)

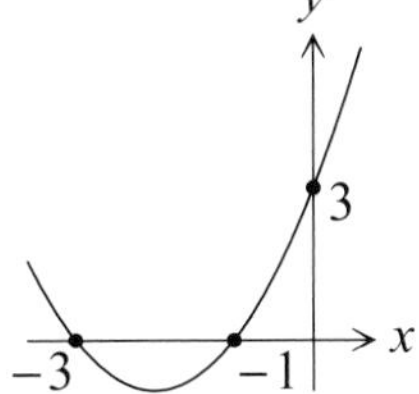

(b)

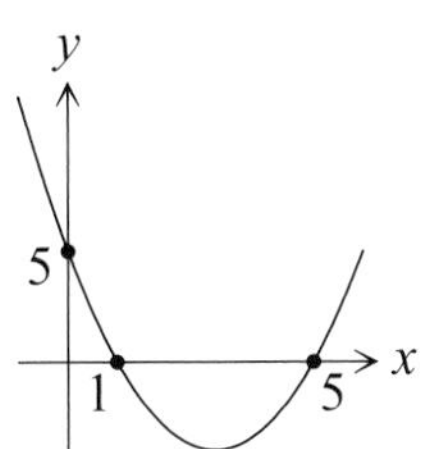

(c)

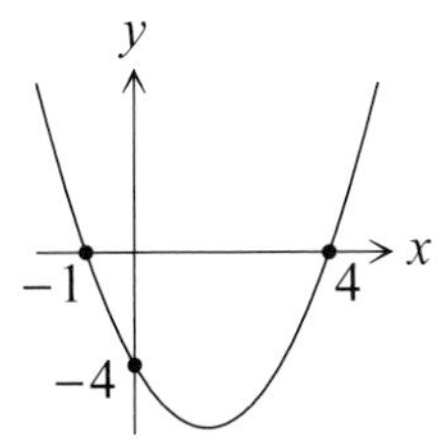

(d)

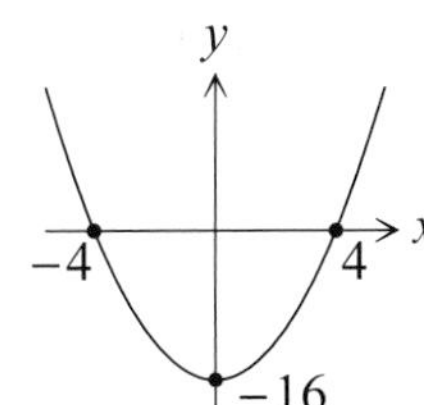

(e)

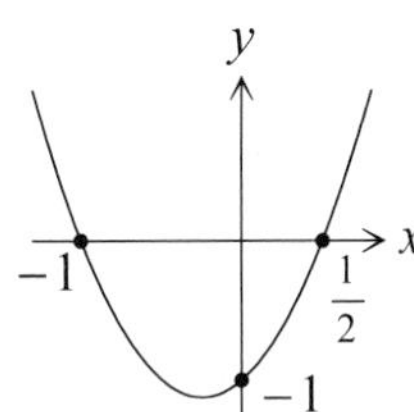

(f)

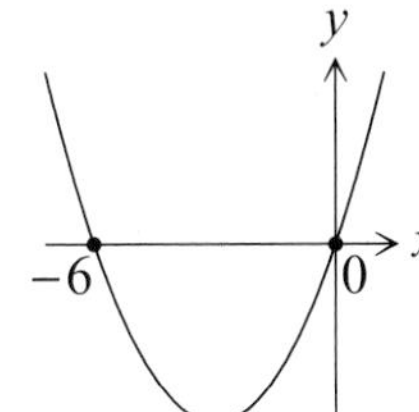

(g)

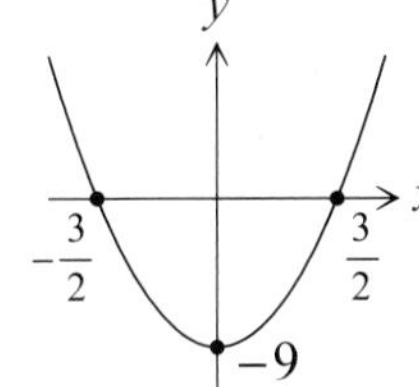

(h)

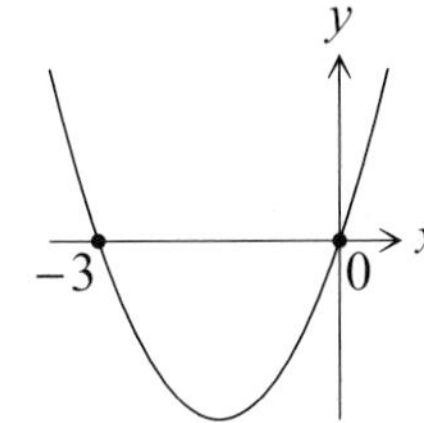

(i)

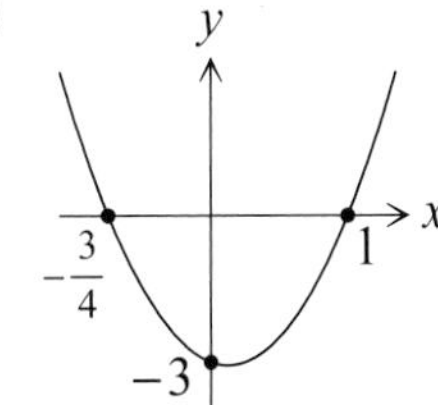

(j)

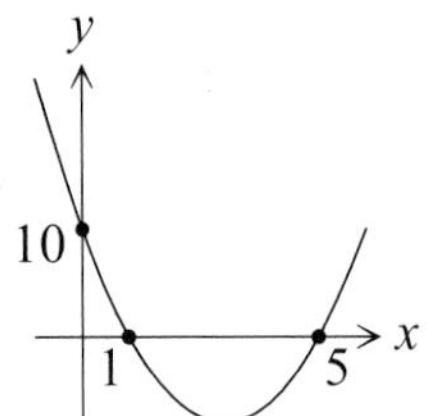

(k)

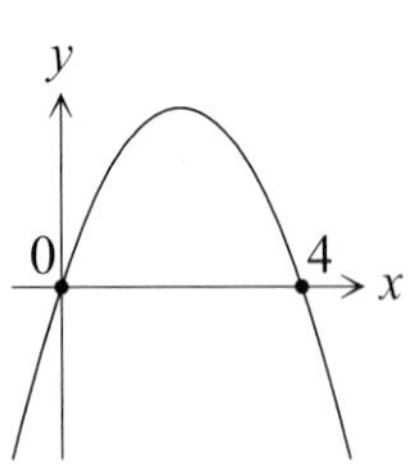

(l)

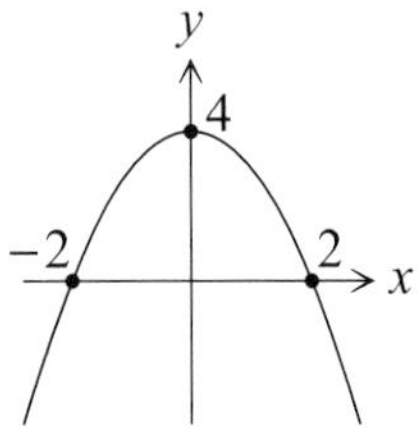

(m)

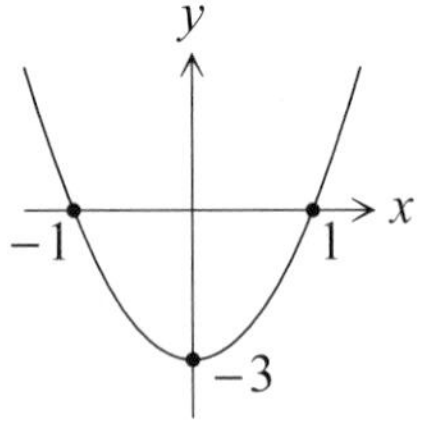

(n)

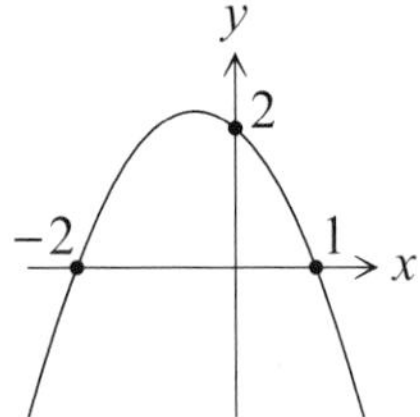

(o)

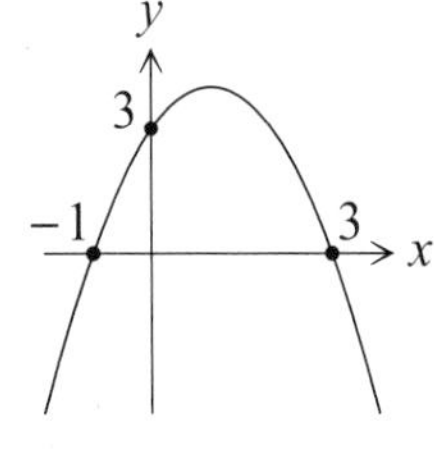

(p)

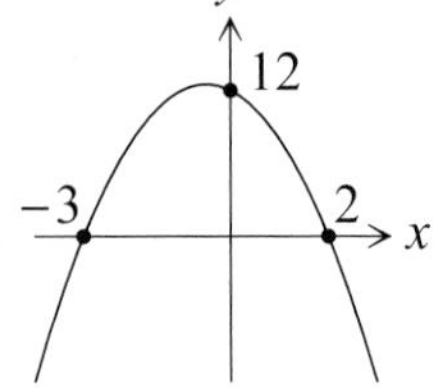

4. (a)

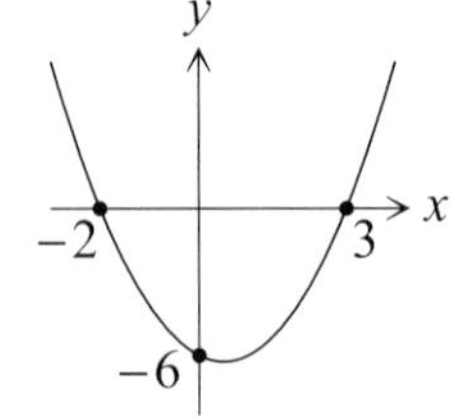

(b) 6

(c) −4 or 5

5. (a)

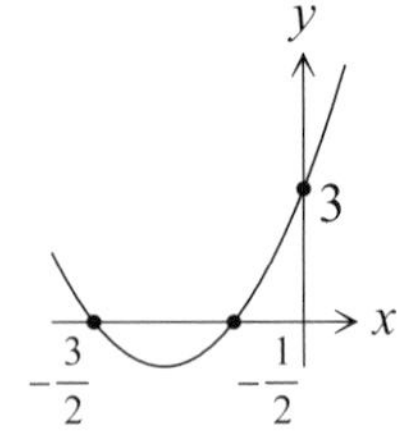

(b) 63

(c) −4 or 2

6. (a)

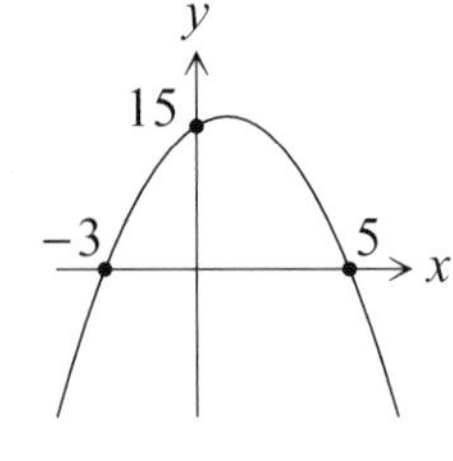

(b) −9

(c) −1 or 3

Exercise 4.2 *page 24*

1. (a)

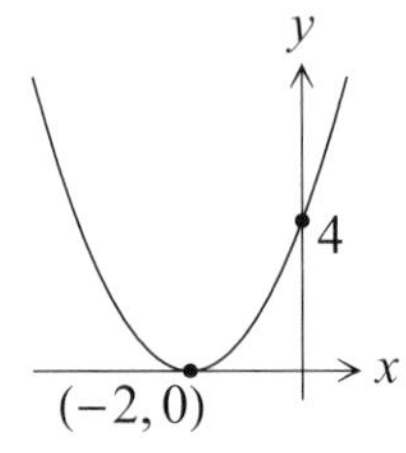

(b)

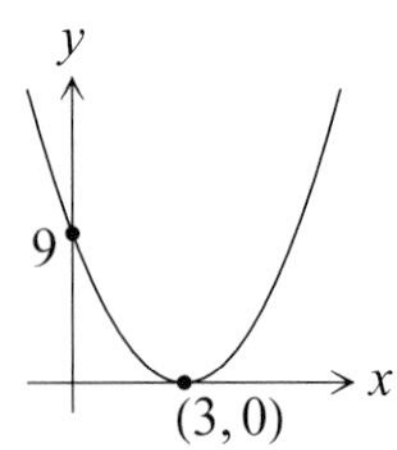

(c)

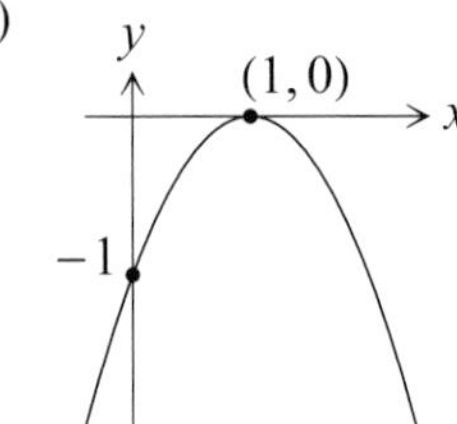

(d)

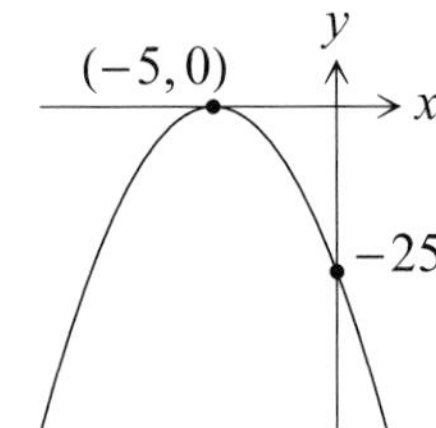

(e)

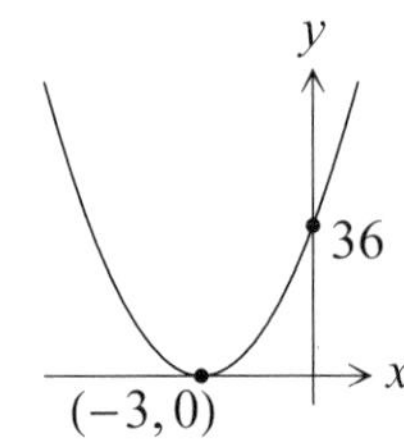

(f)

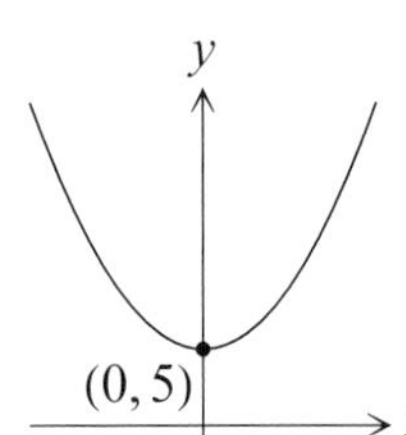

(g)

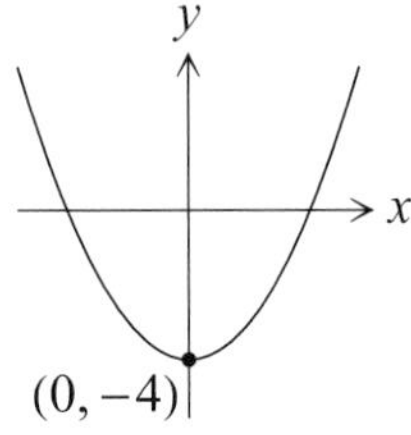

(h)

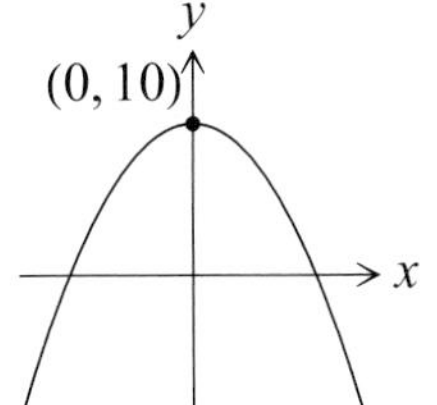

(i)

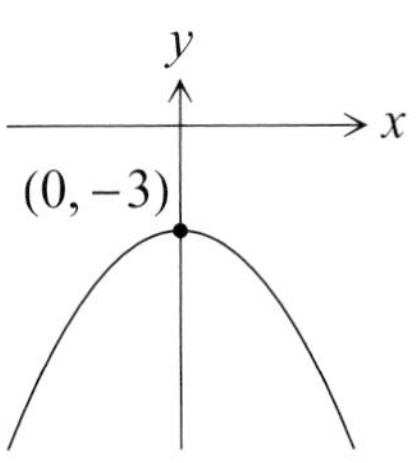

2. (a)

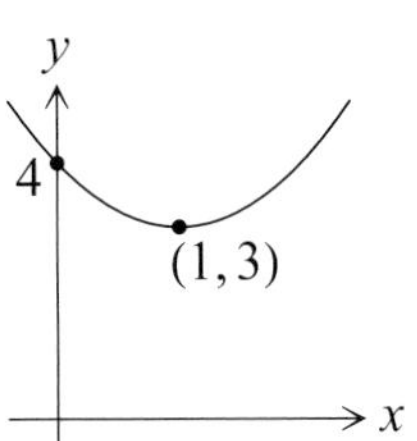

(b)

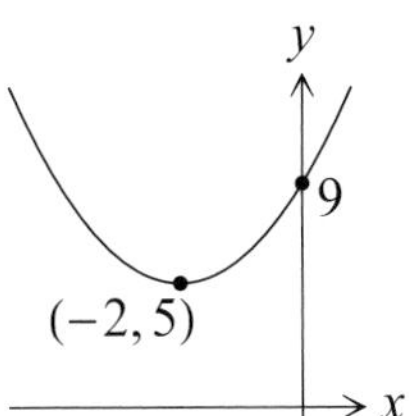

(c)

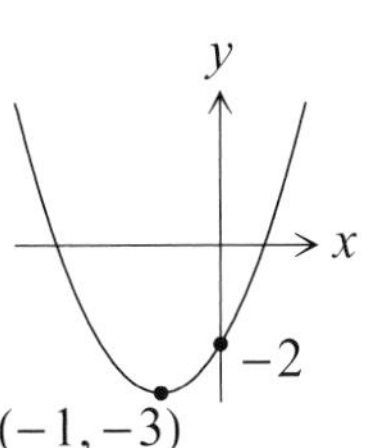

(d)

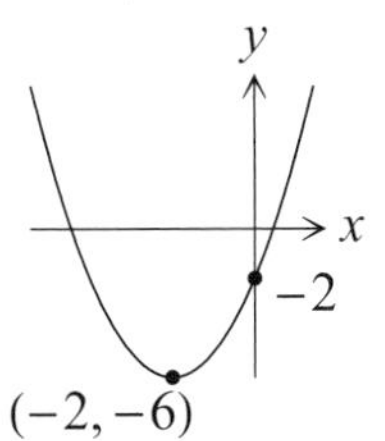

(e)

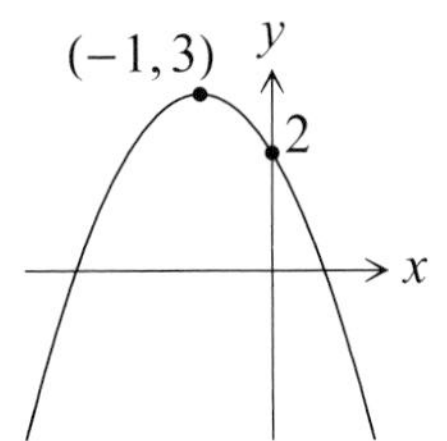

(f)

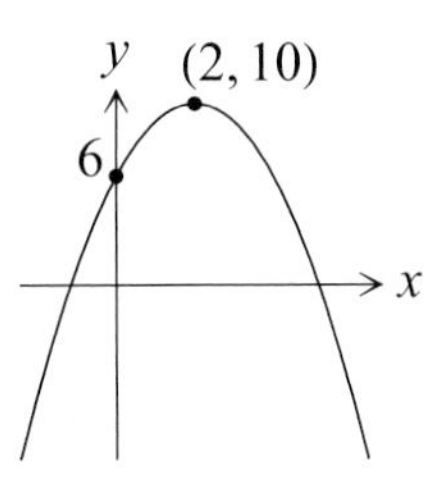

(g)

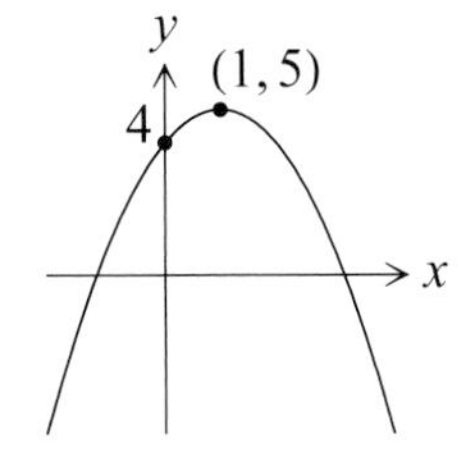

(h)

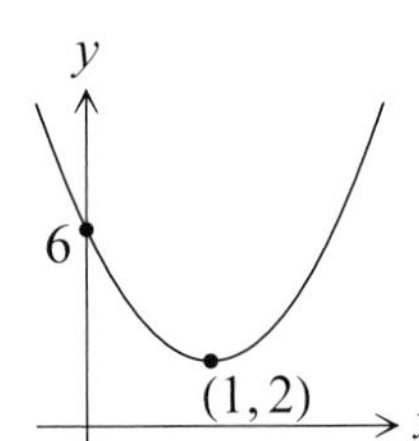

(i)

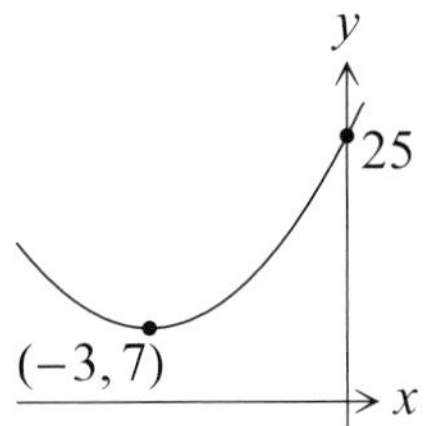

(j)

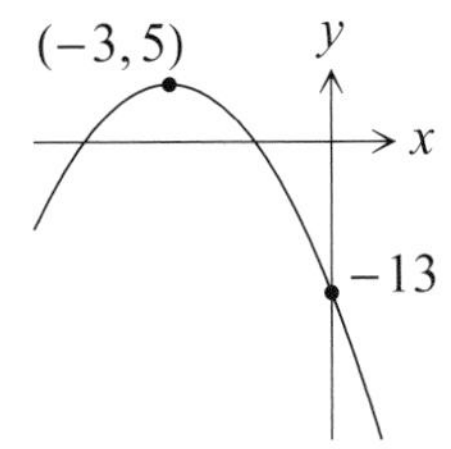

(k)

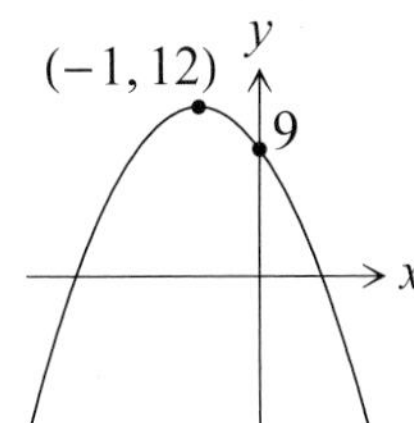

(l)

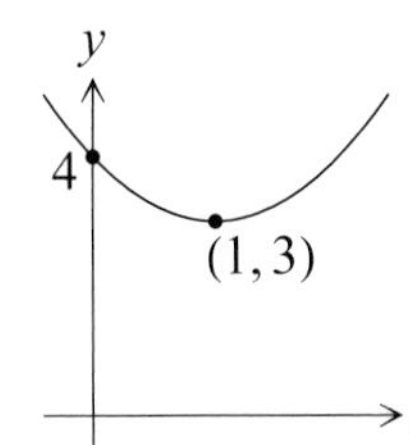

3. (a)

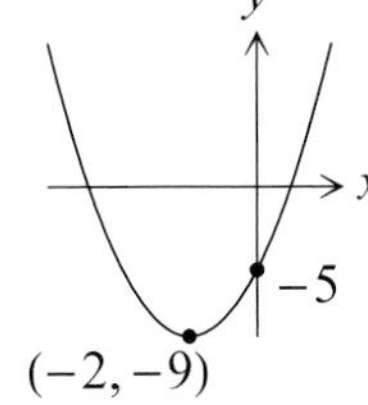

(b) $(-5, 0)$, $(1, 0)$

4. (a)

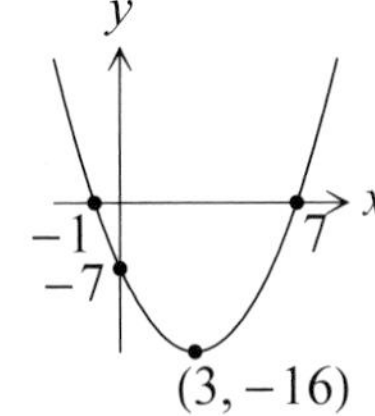

(b)

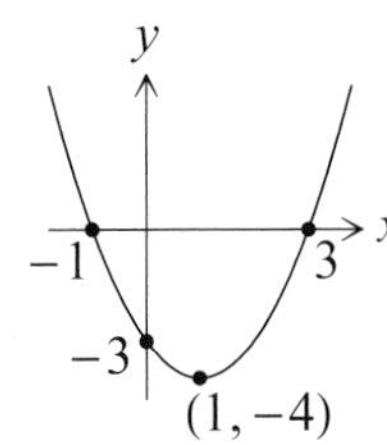

(c)

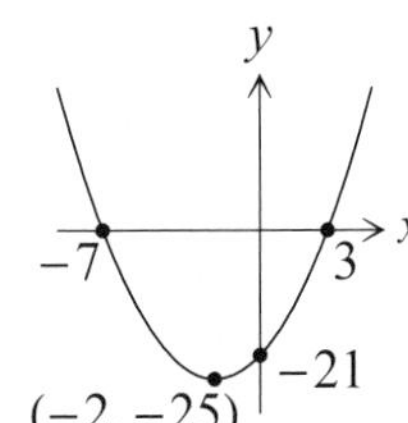

(d)

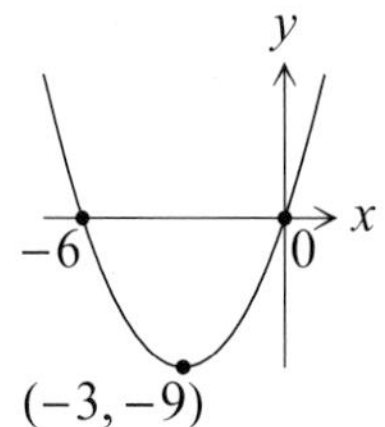

(e)

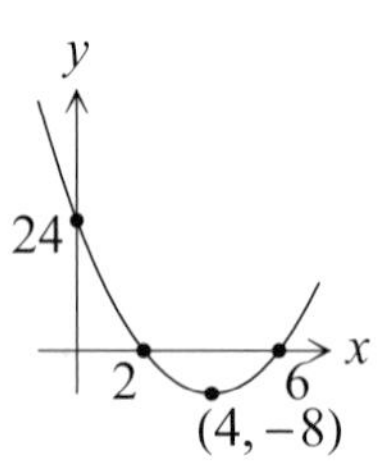

(f)

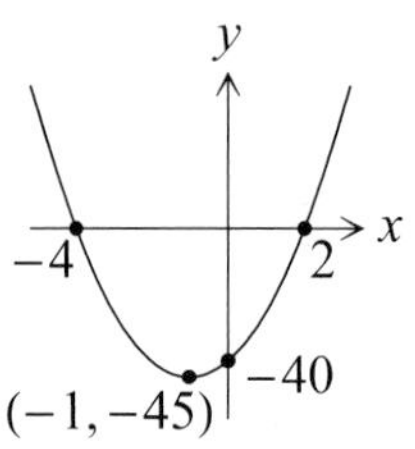

(g)

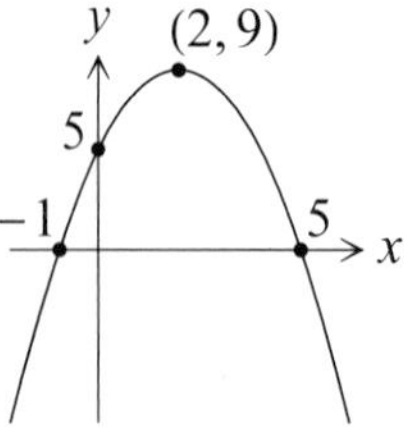

(h)

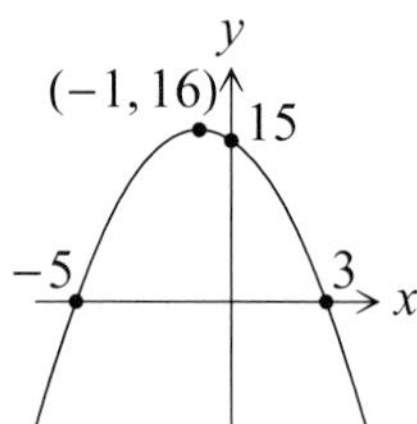

(i)

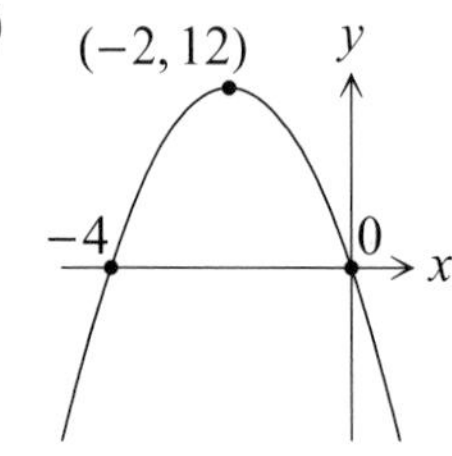

5. (a)

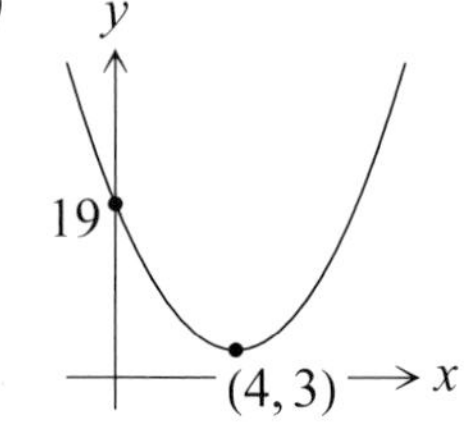

(b) 12

(c) 1 or 7

6. (a)

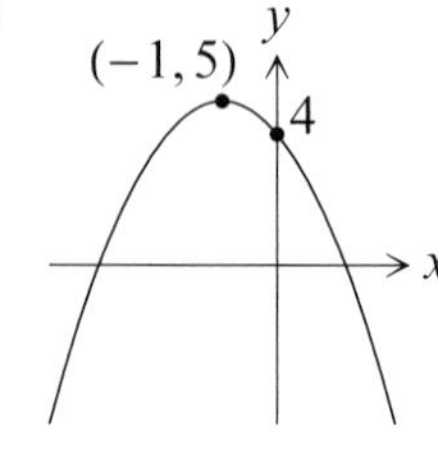

(b) 1

(c) −5 or 3

7. (a)

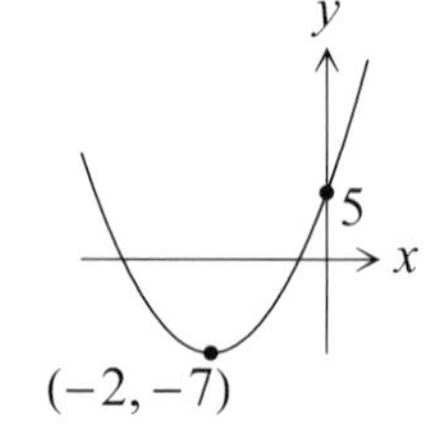

(b) −4

(c) −5 or 1

8. (a)

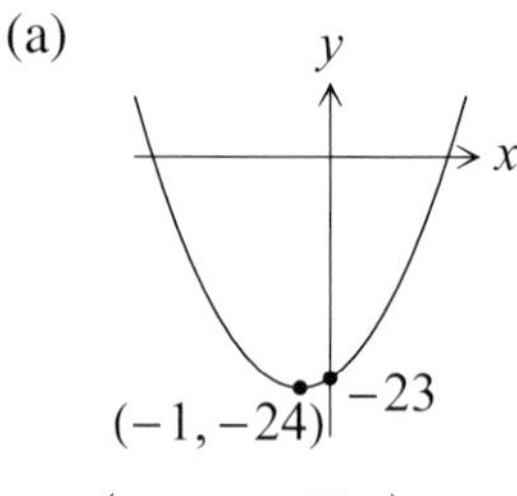

(b) $\left(-1-2\sqrt{6},0\right)$, $\left(-1+2\sqrt{6},0\right)$

9. (a)

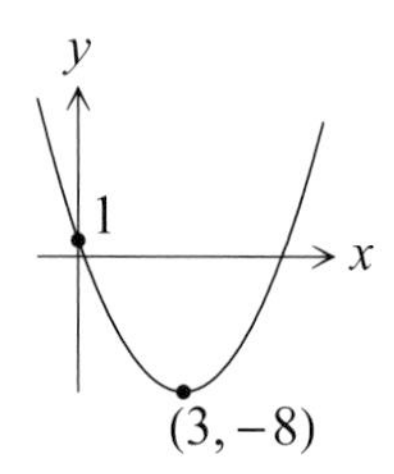

(b) $\left(3-2\sqrt{2},0\right)$, $\left(3+2\sqrt{2},0\right)$

10. (a)

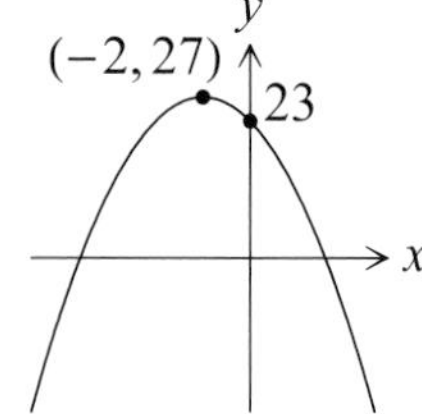

(b) $\left(-2-3\sqrt{3},0\right)$, $\left(-2+3\sqrt{3},0\right)$

11. (a)

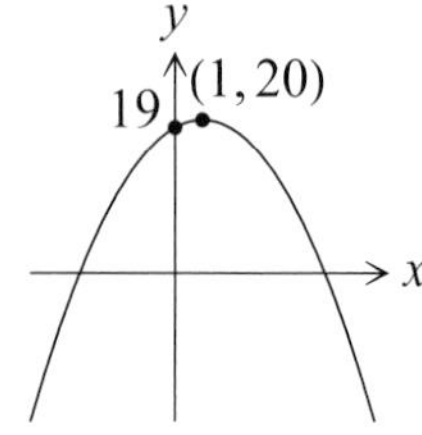

(b) $\left(1-2\sqrt{5},0\right)$, $\left(1+2\sqrt{5},0\right)$

Exercise 4.3 *page 26*

1. (a)

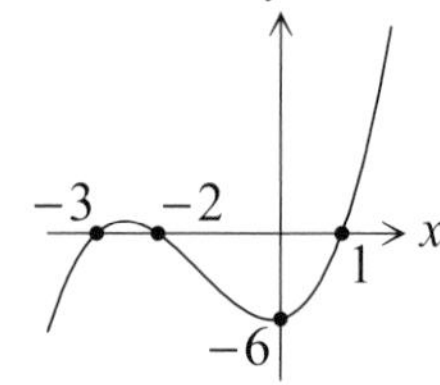

(b)

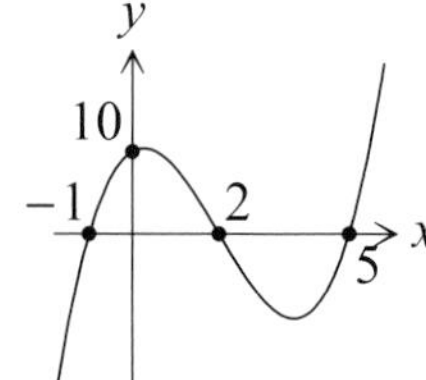

(c)

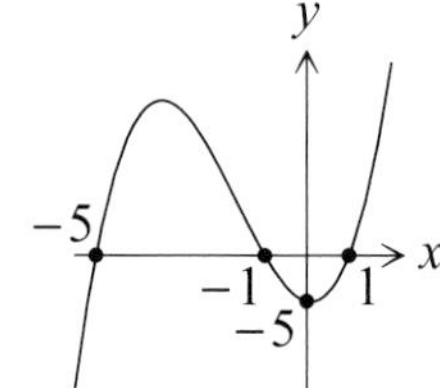

(d)

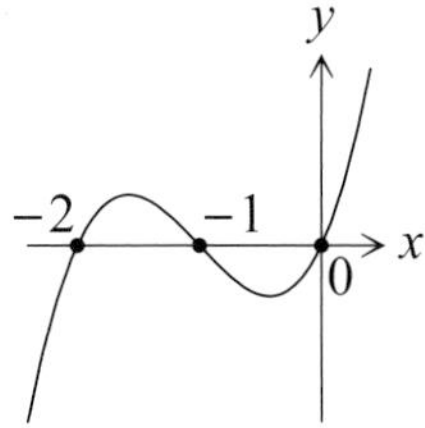

(e)

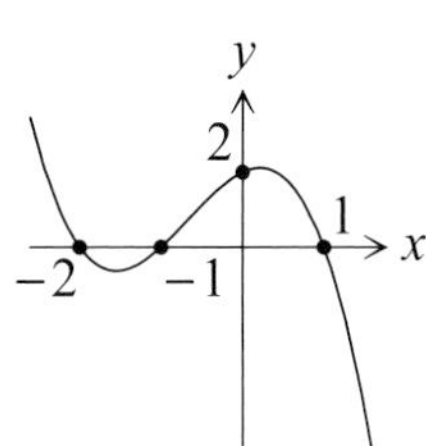

(f)

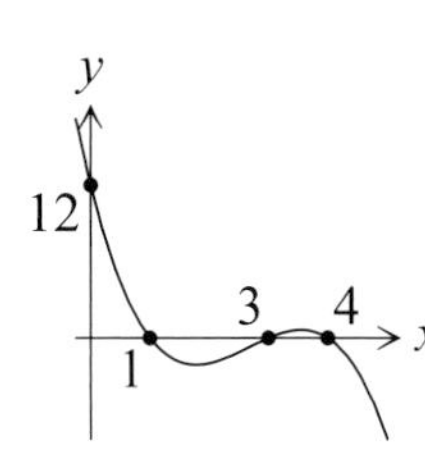

(g)

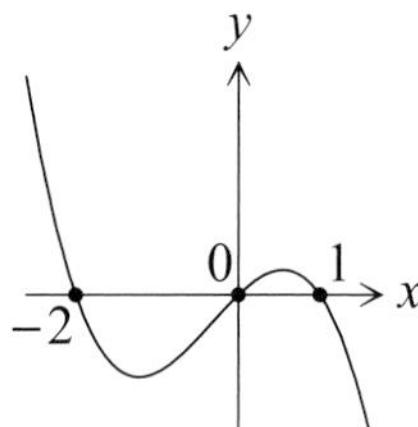

2. (a)

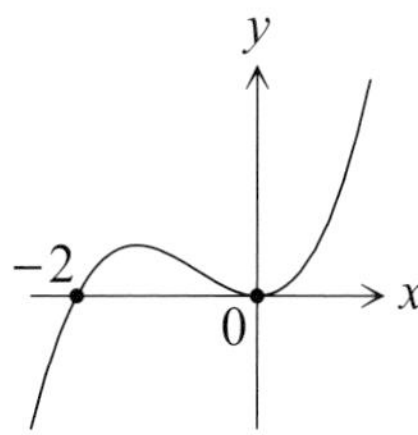

(b)

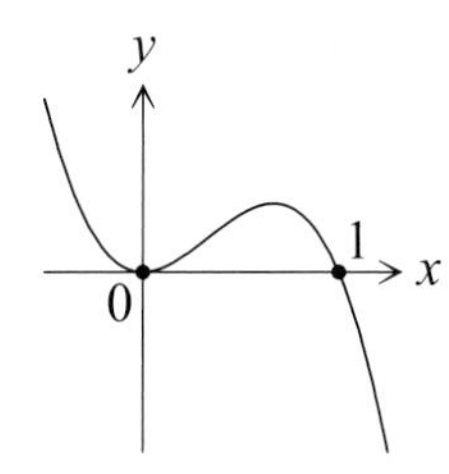

(c)

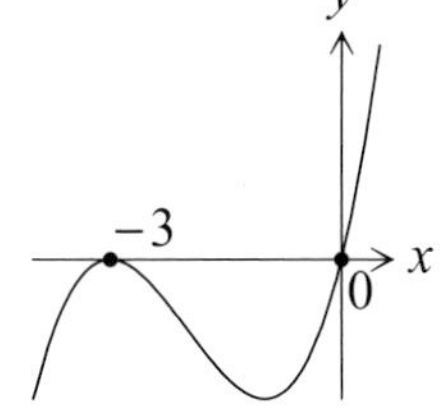

(d)

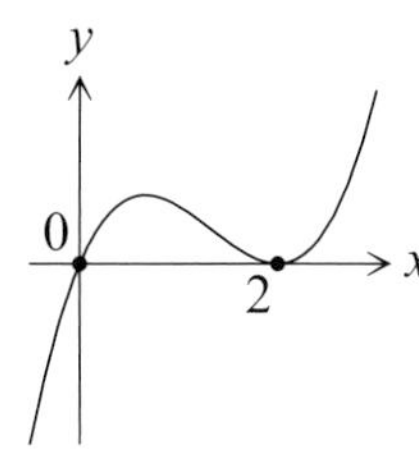

(e)

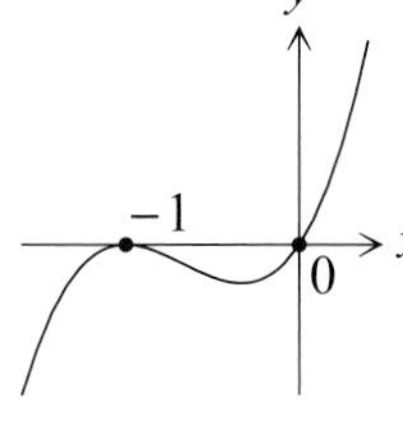

(f)

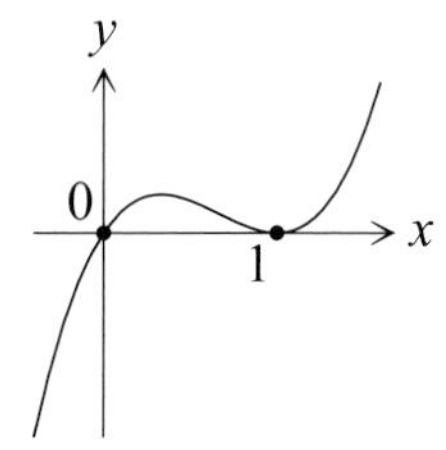

3. (a) $x(x+1)(x-2)$

(b)

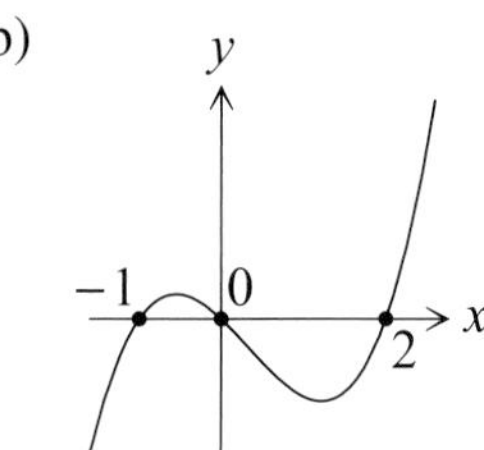

4. (a) $x(3x-1)(x+1)$

(b)

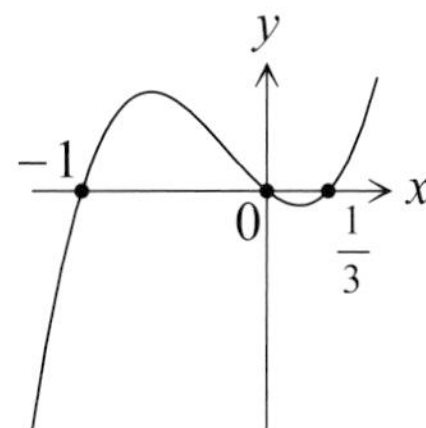

5. (a) $x^2(4-x)$

(b)

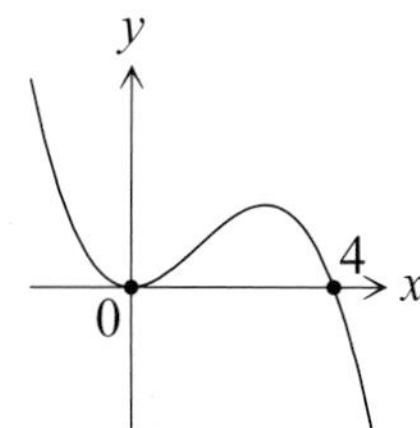

6. (a) $x(x+2)^2$

(b)

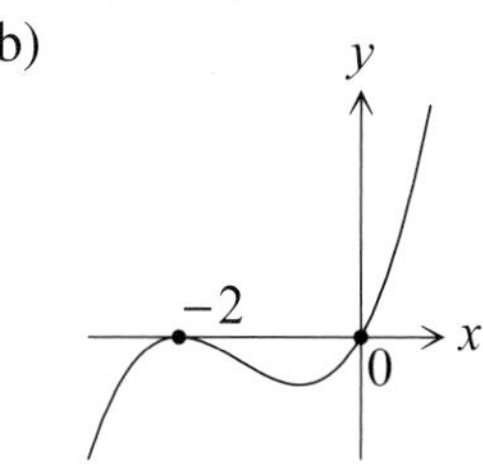

Exercise 5.1 *page 28*

1. (a) $y = 3x^2$
(b) $y = 6x^2$
(c) $y = 4x^2$
(d) $y = -5x^2$
(e) $y = -6x^2$
(f) $y = 7x^2$
(g) $y = 8x^2$
(h) $y = -2x^2$
(i) $y = 4x^2$
(j) $y = -3x^2$
(k) $y = \frac{3}{2}x^2$
(l) $y = -\frac{4}{3}x^2$

2. (a) $y = 8x^2 + 3$
(b) $y = 7x^2 - 1$
(c) $y = -2x^2 + 4$
(d) $y = x^2 - 3$
(e) $y = 2x^2 + 5$
(f) $y = -3x^2 + 4$
(g) $y = 5x^2 + 8$
(h) $y = x^2 + 2$
(i) $y = -4x^2 - 50$
(j) $y = -x^2 + 6$
(k) $y = \frac{5}{2}x^2 - 4$
(l) $y = -\frac{4}{3}x^2 + 11$

3. 3, −1

4. −2, 17

Exercise 5.2 *page 30*

1. (a) $y = 3(x-1)(x-4)$
(b) $y = 2(x-2)(x-6)$
(c) $y = -(x-3)(x-5)$
(d) $y = -4(x-1)(x-3)$
(e) $y = \frac{1}{2}(x-2)(x-4)$
(f) $y = -\frac{3}{2}(x-3)(x-8)$
(g) $y = 2(x+1)(x-4)$
(h) $y = -3(x+2)(x-5)$
(i) $y = 5(x+2)(x+5)$
(j) $y = -\frac{1}{4}(x+3)(x+8)$
(k) $y = 3(x-5)^2$
(l) $y = -\frac{1}{3}(x+6)^2$

2. (a) $y = x(x-5)$
(b) $y = -(x-2)(x-3)$
(c) $y = (x+1)(x-6)$
(d) $y = -(x+3)(x-2)$
(e) $y = (x+1)(x+2)$
(f) $y = -x(x+4)$
(g) $y = -2(x+2)(x+3)$
(h) $y = 3x(x-5)$
(i) $y = 4(x-1)(x-2)$
(j) $y = -5(x-3)(x-5)$
(k) $y = -2x(x+2)$
(l) $y = 4(x+5)(x-6)$

3. -2

4. 6

Exercise 5.3 *page 32*

1. (a) $(4, 2)$, minimum
(b) $(2, -5)$, minimum
(c) $(3, -8)$, maximum
(d) $(5, 7)$, maximum
(e) $(-2, 9)$, minimum
(f) $(-6, -4)$, minimum
(g) $(-11, 6)$, maximum
(h) $(-7, -1)$, maximum

2. (a) $(3, 9)$, minimum
(b) $(4, -6)$, minimum
(c) $(7, 11)$, maximum
(d) $(1, -3)$, maximum
(e) $(-1, 8)$, minimum
(f) $(-5, -7)$, minimum
(g) $(-8, 6)$, maximum
(h) $(-3, -13)$, maximum

Exercise 5.4 *page 32*

1. (a) $y = (x-1)^2 + 6$
(b) $y = -(x-3)^2 + 7$
(c) $y = (x+2)^2 + 4$
(d) $y = -(x+1)^2 + 6$
(e) $y = (x+3)^2 - 7$
(f) $y = -(x-5)^2 - 15$
(g) $y = -x^2 + 2$
(h) $y = (x-2)^2 - 4$
(i) $y = -(x+2)^2 - 3$

2. (a) $(5, 6)$
(b) 3

3. (a) $y = 2(x-1)^2 + 3$
(b) $y = -3(x-2)^2 + 4$
(c) $y = 5(x+2)^2 + 20$
(d) $y = -3(x+1)^2 + 12$
(e) $y = 7(x+2)^2 - 7$
(f) $y = -2(x-4)^2 - 24$
(g) $y = 4(x-3)^2 - 4$
(h) $y = -\frac{1}{2}(x+2)^2 - 5$
(i) $y = -\frac{3}{2}(x-4)^2 + 8$

Exercise 5.5 *page 34*

1. (a) $y = 2(x-2)(x-5)$
(b) $y = 4(x-1)^2 + 5$
(c) $y = -3(x+1)^2 - 7$
(d) $y = -(x+2)(x-5)$
(e) $y = 2 - (x-2)^2$
(f) $y = 3(x+6)^2 - 48$
(g) $y = 2(x+3)(x+5)$
(h) $y = -5(x-1)(x-4)$
(i) $y = 2(x+8)^2$
(j) $y = -(2x+3)(x+3)$
(k) $y = 1 - \frac{1}{4}(x-8)^2$
(l) $y = 3(x+1)(2x-1)$

2. (a) $y = x^2 - 11x + 28$
(b) $y = 3x^2 + 6x + 5$
(c) $y = -2x^2 + 8x - 15$
(d) $y = -4x^2 + 10x + 24$
(e) $y = -7x^2 + 49x - 70$
(f) $y = 2x^2 + 12x - 6$

Exercise 5.6 *page 35*

1. (a) 1, 5
(b) $x = 3$
(c) -4
(d) $y = (x-3)^2 - 4$

2. (a) 2, 8
(b) $x = 5$
(c) 9
(d) $y = -(x-5)^2 + 9$

3. (a) 2, 6, 5
(b) $x = 4$
(c) -20
(d) $y = 5(x-4)^2 - 20$

4. (a) 3, 9, -3
(b) $x = 6$
(c) 27
(d) $y = -3(x-6)^2 + 27$

5. (a) -6, 4
(b) $x = -1$
(c) $(-1, -25)$
(d) $y = (x+1)^2 - 25$

6. (a) -3, -1
(b) $x = -2$
(c) $(-2, 1)$
(d) $y = -(x+2)^2 + 1$

7. (a) -2, 4, -6
(b) $x = 1$
(c) $(1, 54)$
(d) $y = -6(x-1)^2 + 54$

8. (a) -6, -2, 3
(b) $x = -4$
(c) $(-4, -12)$

(d) $y = 3(x+4)^2 - 12$

9. (a) $y = -2(x+7)(x-3)$
(b) $y = -2(x+2)^2 + 50$

10. (a) $y = 4(x+1)x - 5)$
(b) $y = 4(x-2)^2 - 36$

11. (a) $y = (x-3)(x-5)$
(b) $x = 4$
(c) $(4, -1)$
(d) $y = (x-4)^2 - 1$

12. (a) $y = (x+2)(x+10)$
(b) $x = -6$
(c) $(-6, -16)$
(d) $y = (x+6)^2 - 16$

Exercise 5.7 *page 38*

1. (a) $y = (x-1)(x-2)(x-3)$
(b) $y = -(x-1)(x-4)(x-5)$
(c) $y = -(x+1)(x-2)(x-3)$
(d) $y = (x+3)(x+2)(x-2)$
(e) $y = x(x+4)(x+2)$
(f) $y = -(x+4)(x+3)(x+1)$
(g) $y = (x+3)^2(x-5)$
(h) $y = (x-2)^2(x-5)$
(i) $y = -x^2(x+5)$

2. (a) $y = 2(x-1)(x-2)(x-3)$
(b) $y = -3(x-1)(x-3)(x-5)$
(c) $y = -2(x+2)(x-2)(x-3)$
(d) $y = -(x+3)(x+2)(x-3)$
(e) $y = 5(x+4)(x+2)(x+1)$
(f) $y = (x+4)(x+3)(x+1)$
(g) $y = 2(x+5)^2(x+2)$
(h) $y = -3(x+2)^2(x-1)$
(i) $y = \frac{5}{2}(x+2)(x+1)(x-1)$

3. (a) $y = (x+4)(x+3)(x-1)$
(b) $y = -2(x-1)(x-3)(x-6)$
(c) $y = 3(x-1)(x-2)(x-3)$
(d) $y = 4(x+5)(x+3)(x-2)$
(e) $y = 5x^2(x+2)$
(f) $y = -\frac{1}{2}x(x+9)^2$

Exercise 6.1 *page 40*

1. $(5, 11)$
2. $(1, 3)$
3. $(-2, 9)$
4. $(4, -2)$
5. $(5, 3)$
6. $(4, 7)$
7. $(4, 3)$
8. $(-2, -4)$
9. $(-5, -1)$
10. $(7, -2)$
11. $(-4, 2)$
12. $(4, 0)$
13. (a) $x = 4$
(b) $y = -3$
(c) $(4, 9), (-2, -3)$
14. (a) $y = 2x + 5$
(b) $y = -3x + 15$
(c) $(2, 9)$
15. $(-1, 2), (5, 2), (3, 8)$
16. (a) $(6, 11)$
(b) $y = -4x + 5$
(c) $(1, 1)$
(d) $y = 2x + 5$
(e) $(5, 15)$

Exercise 6.2 *page 43*

1. $(-4, 8), (4, 8)$
2. $(-3, 4), (3, 4)$
3. (a) $y = 8$
(b) $(-1, 8), (5, 8)$
4. (a) $y = 3$
(b) $(0, 3), (2, 3)$
5. (a) $y = -4$
(b) $(-3, -4)$
6. $(-3, 14), (5, 6)$
7. $(-2, -7), (5, 0)$
8. $\left(-\frac{1}{2}, \frac{1}{2}\right), (1, 2)$
9. $(1, -3)$
10. $(3, 12), (5, 20)$
11. $(-1, -2), (8, 25)$
12. $(-3, -2), \left(\frac{3}{2}, \frac{5}{2}\right)$
13. (a) $y = (x-2)(x-3)$
(b) $y = -2x + 10$
(c) $(-1, 12), (4, 2)$
14. (a) $y = (x-3)^2 + 1$
(b) $y = x$
(c) $(2, 2), (5, 5)$

Exercise 6.3 *page 46*

1. $(-2, 4), (2, 4)$
2. $(-3, 27), (3, 27)$
3. $(-5, -25), (5, -25)$
4. $(0, 0), (2, 4)$
5. $(-2, 8), (2, 8)$
6. $(0, 0), (4, -16)$
7. $(-1, 5), (3, 5)$
8. $(3, 3), (5, 3)$
9. $(-1, 5), (2, 8)$
10. $(1, 0), (4, 3)$
11. $(0, 3), (5, -2)$

12. (1, 9), (4, 0)

Exercise 6.4 *page 49*

1. (−1, 0), (0, 0), (1, 1)

2. $\left(-\frac{1}{2}, -\frac{1}{2}\right)$, (0, 0), $\left(\frac{1}{2}, \frac{1}{2}\right)$

3. (0, 0), (1, 3), (5, 15)

4. (0, 0), (1, 4), (4, 16)

5. (−2, 5), (0, 3), (2, 1)

6. (−5, −7), (0, −2)

7. (−3, 5), (0, 2), (2, 0)

8. $\left(-\frac{1}{2}, \frac{9}{2}\right)$, (0, 4), (2, 2)

9. $\left(-\frac{3}{2}, -\frac{5}{2}\right)$, (0, −1), (1, 0)

Exercise 7.1 *page 51*

1. (a) (90, 1)
(b) (270, −1)
(c) 90
(d) 270
(e) 0, 180, 360

2. (a) (0, 1), (360, 1)
(b) (180, −1)
(c) 0, 360
(d) 180
(e) 90,270

3. (a) 90, 450
(b) 270, 630
(c) 0, 180, 360, 540, 720

4. (a) 0
(b) −180, 180
(c) −90, 90

5. (a) −270, 90
(b) 180, 540
(c) 0, 180, 360, 540, 720, 900, 1080
(d) −270, −90, 90, 270
(e) −90
(f) 0, 360, 720, 1080
(g) 0, 180, 360

Exercise 7.2 *page 52*

1. 3, 2

2. 5, 3

3. 4, 2

4. 2, $\frac{1}{2}$

5. (a) (90, 0), (180, 0)
(b) (45, 4), (135, −4)

6. (a) (45, 0), (135, 0)
(b) (90, −3)

7. (a) (60, 0), (120, 0)
(b) 5 when $t = 30$
(c) −5 when $t = 90$

8. (a) (30, 0), (90, 0)
(b) 10 when $x = 120$
(c) −10 when $x = 60$

9.

7	30	−7	90
8	180	−8	90
2	22.5	−2	67.5
6	120	−6	60
7	45	−7	135
7	90	−7	45

Exercise 7.3 *page 54*

1. 2, 1

2. 3, −1

3. 2, 2

4. 3, 5

5. 3, −2

6. (a) (0, −1)
(b) (90, 1), (270, −3)

7. (a) (0, 1)
(b) (90, 4), (270, −2)

8. (a) (0, 5)
(b) (180, 1)

9. (a) (0, 6)
(b) (180, −4)

10. (a) (0, 3)
(b) 4 when $x = 90$
(c) 2 when $x = 270$

11. (a) (0, 2)
(b) 2 when $t = 360$
(c) −8 when $t = 180$

12.

5	90	−1	270
1	360	−9	180
6	90	−2	270
3	360	1	180
−1	90	−3	270
0	360	−6	180

Exercise 7.4 *page 56*

1. 3, 30

2. 5, 40

3. 2, 50

4. 4, 100

5. (a) (20, 0), (200, 0)
(b) (110, 4), (290, −4)

6. (a) (20, 0), (200, 0)
(b) (110, −3)

7. (a) (60, 0), (240, 0)
(b) 5 when $t = 150$
(c) −5 when $t = 330$

8. (a) (150, 0), (330, 0)
(b) 10 when $x = 240$
(c) −10 when $x = 60$

9.

2	20	−2	200
3	20	−3	200
2	100	−2	280
6	135	−6	315
4	120	−4	300
5	315	−5	135

Exercise 7.5 *page 58*

1. 20, 1

2. 30, −1

3. 25, 2

4. 10, 5

5. 50, −2

6. (a) (50, 0), (230, −2)
(b) (0, −0.36)

7. (a) (160, 2), (340, 0)
(b) (0, 0.06)

8. (a) (25, 4), (205, 2)
(b) (0, 3.9)

9. (a) (340, 3), (160, 1)
(b) (0, 2.9)

10. (a) (130, 2), (310, 0)
(b) (0, 0.36)

11. (a) (0, −3.9)
(b) −2 when $t = 150$
(c) −4 when $t = 330$

12.

5	70	3	250
0	25	−2	205
4	105	2	285
6	290	4	110
0	50	−2	230
−5	60	−7	240

Exercise 7.6 *page 61*

1. 4, 10, 1

2. 2, 30, −1

3. 5, 25, 2

4. 3, 10, 5

5. 6, 50, −2

6. (a) (0, −4.7)
(b) −1 when $t = 150$
(c) −5 when $t = 330$

7.

3	40	−1	220
2	35	−8	215
8	170	0	350
7	350	1	170
2	40	−12	220
−2	100	−6	280

Exercise 8.1 *page 63*

1. (a) 55.1, 124.9
(b) 113.6, 246.4
(c) 127.6, 307.6
(d) 75.5, 284.5
(e) 221.8, 318.2
(f) 168.7, 348.7
(g) 39.8, 219.8
(h) 143.1, 216.9
(i) 203.6, 336.4
(j) 30, 150
(k) 135, 315
(l) 60, 120, 240, 300
(m) 60, 120, 240, 300
(n) 45, 135, 225, 315

2. (a) 4
(b) (30, 2), (150, 2)

3. (a) 5
(b) (101.5, −1), (258.5, −1)

4. (a) 3, 1
(b) (19.5, 2), (160.5, 2)

5. (a) 3, −1
(b) (70.5, 0), (289.5, 0)

6. (a) (146.3, 0), (326.3, 0)
(b) (45, 5), (225, 5)

Exercise 8.2 *page 64*

1. (a) 13.5, 94.5
(b) 85.1, 309.7
(c) 206.3, 353.7
(d) 76.2, 237.8
(e) 21.8, 118.2
(f) 121.5, 278.5
(g) 70, 190
(h) 58.6, 141.4

2. (a) 63.1, 316.9
(b) 3.1, 76.9
(c) 230, 350
(d) 36.4, 263.6
(e) 145.5, 354.5
(f) 31.4, 98.6

3. (a) 5, 30
(b) (23.1, 3), (276.9, 3)

4. (a) 2, 25
(b) (55, 1), (175, 1)

5. (a) 4, 20
(b) (190, −2), (310, −2)

6. (a) 10, 60
(b) (6.9, 6), (113.1, 6)

7. (a) 2, 70
(b) (61.4, 1.5), (338.6, 1.5)

Exercise 8.3 *page 66*

1. (a) $\frac{\sqrt{3}}{2}$
(b) $-\frac{1}{2}$
(c) $-\frac{1}{\sqrt{3}}$
(d) $\frac{\sqrt{3}}{2}$
(e) 1
(f) $-\frac{1}{\sqrt{2}}$
(g) $-\frac{\sqrt{3}}{2}$
(h) $\frac{1}{\sqrt{2}}$
(i) $-\sqrt{3}$
(j) $\frac{1}{\sqrt{2}}$
(k) $-\frac{1}{2}$
(l) $-\frac{1}{2}$

2. (a) $\frac{1}{2}$
(b) $\sqrt{3}$
(c) $\frac{1}{\sqrt{2}}$
(d) $\frac{1}{2}$
(e) $-\frac{\sqrt{3}}{2}$
(f) $-\frac{1}{2}$
(g) $\frac{1}{\sqrt{2}}$
(h) $-\sqrt{3}$
(i) 0

Exercise 8.4 *page 67*

1. (a) 60, 120
(b) 60, 240
(c) 135, 225
(d) 150, 210
(e) 45, 135
(f) 45, 225
(g) 30, 210
(h) 120, 240
(i) 240, 300

2. (a) 180, 300
(b) 40, 340
(c) 90, 270
(d) 15, 105
(e) 50, 170
(f) 105, 345

3. (a) 210, 270, 330
(b) 0, 120, 240
(c) 0, 135, 180, 315
(d) 90, 150, 210, 270
(e) 30, 90, 150
(f) 0, 30, 180, 210

Exercise 8.5 *page 68*

1. (a) 5 units
(b) $\frac{4}{5}, \frac{3}{5}, \frac{4}{3}$

2. $\frac{5}{13}, \frac{12}{13}, \frac{5}{12}$

3. $\frac{2}{\sqrt{5}}, \frac{1}{\sqrt{5}}, 2$

4. $\frac{8}{17}, \frac{15}{17}, \frac{8}{15}$

5. $\frac{4}{5}, \frac{3}{4}$

6. $\frac{1}{\sqrt{10}}, \frac{3}{\sqrt{10}}$

7. $\frac{2}{\sqrt{5}}, 2$

8. $\frac{2\sqrt{2}}{3}, \frac{1}{2\sqrt{2}}$

9. $\frac{3}{\sqrt{10}}, 3$

10. $\frac{1}{5\sqrt{2}}, \frac{7}{5\sqrt{2}}$

11. $-\frac{\sqrt{7}}{4}, -\frac{3}{\sqrt{7}}$

12. $-\frac{9}{41}, -\frac{9}{40}$

13. (a) $\frac{3}{5}, \frac{4}{5}, \frac{3}{4}$
(b) $\frac{12}{13}, \frac{5}{13}, \frac{12}{5}$

14. (a) $\frac{2}{\sqrt{5}}, \frac{1}{\sqrt{5}}, 2$
(b) $\frac{\sqrt{5}}{3}, \frac{2}{3}, \frac{\sqrt{5}}{2}$

15. (a) $\frac{\sqrt{13}}{7}, \frac{6}{7}, \frac{\sqrt{13}}{6}$
(b) $\frac{\sqrt{13}}{5}, \frac{2\sqrt{3}}{5}, \frac{\sqrt{13}}{2\sqrt{3}}$

16. (a) $\frac{1}{\sqrt{5}}, \frac{2}{\sqrt{5}}, \frac{1}{2}$
(b) $\frac{4}{5}, \frac{3}{5}, \frac{4}{3}$

Exercise 8.7 *page 70*

1. (a) 0, 30, 150, 180
(b) 41.4, 90, 270, 318.6
(c) 30, 150, 270
(d) 19.5, 160.5, 194.5, 345.5
(e) 60, 300
(f) 48.2, 75.5, 284.5, 311.8
(g) 36.9, 90, 270, 323.1
(h) 30, 150, 210, 330
(i) 101.5, 258.5
(j) 0, 131.8, 228.2

2. (a) 30, 150, 199.5, 340.5
(b) 48.2, 90, 270, 311.8
(c) 19.5, 160.5
(d) 0, 41.4, 318.6

Exercise 8.8 *page 71*

1. (a) (10, 5), (190, −1)
(b) (141.8, 0), (238.2, 0)
(c) (0, 4.95)

2. (a) (340, 6), (160, 0)
(b) (0, 5.8)

3. (a) 6 when $x = 130$
(b) −4 when $x = 310$
(c) (0, −2.2)

4. (a) (50, 1), (230, −3)
(b) (110, 0), (350, 0)
(c) (0, 0.29)

5. (a) (150, 6), (330, −4)
(b) (251.5, 0), (48.5, 0)
(c) (0, −3.3)

Exercise 9.1 *page 73*

1. (a) 22, −3, 7
(b) 4

2. (a) 5, −16
(b) −3

3. (a) 49, 17, −1
(b) −3 or 3

4. (a) 64, 1, $\frac{1}{4}$, 2
(b) 2
(c) −2

5. (a) $\frac{\sqrt{3}}{2}, \frac{1}{\sqrt{2}}, \frac{1}{2}, -1$
(b) 90

6. (a) 1, −7, 13
(b) −5
(c) $1 - 4x$, $1 - 4a$, $1 - 4p$

7. (a) 23, 7
(b) −4 or 4
(c) $a^2 - 2$, $t^2 - 2$, $r^2 - 2$

8. (a) −1
(b) −5 or 3
(c) $a^2 + 2a$, $m^2 + 2m$

9. (a) $4t$
(b) $8a$
(c) $4(b + 1)$

10. (a) $3m - 2$
(b) $6t - 2$
(c) $3a - 5$

11. (a) $2a^2 + 7$
(b) $18t^2 + 7$
(c) $2m^2 + 12m + 25$

12. (a) $t(t+3)$
(b) $2a(2a+3)$
(c) $(3m-1)(3m+2)$

13. (a) $\sin x°$
(b) $\sin 2y°$
(c) $\sin(2m+20)°$

14. (a) $x(4-x)$
(b) $x^2\left(4-x^2\right)$
(c) $x^3\left(4-x^3\right)$

15. (a) $3a+2,\ 5-3a$
(b) 1

16. (a) $2a+9,\ 4b+3$
(b) -2
(c) $-\frac{1}{2}$

17. (a) -3 or 1
(b) -1 or 1

18. 2 or 5

19. (a) -1 or $\frac{5}{4}$
(b) 2 or $\frac{9}{2}$

20. (a) $\frac{1}{\sqrt{2}}, \frac{\sqrt{3}}{2}, -\frac{1}{2}$
(b) 30, 150
(c) 205,295

Exercise 9.2 *page 75*

1. $x(x+6)\,\text{cm}^2$

2. (a) $(28-l)$ cm
(b) $l(28-l)\,\text{cm}^2$

3. $34-n$

4. $4s^2$

5. (a) $50-2s$
(b) $s^2(50-2s)$

6. (a) $p=n+3$
(b) $\dfrac{89}{n(n+3)}$

7. (a) $2b$
(b) $2b^2$
(c) $\dfrac{5}{b^2}$
(d) $4b^2+\dfrac{30}{b}$

8. $(30-3w)$ cm

9. (a) $2-a^2$
(b) $2a(2-a^2)$

10. $\sqrt{2(x^2-4x+8)}$

11. (a) x cm
(b) $(30-2x)$ cm
(c) $(24-2x)$ cm
(d) $4x(12-x)(15-x)\,\text{cm}^3$
(e) $4\left(180-x^2\right)\text{cm}^2$

12. (a) $3w$
(b) $3w^2$
(c) $\dfrac{17-3w^2}{4w}$
(d) $\frac{3}{4}w\left(17-3w^2\right)$

13. (a) $\dfrac{100}{v}$ hours
(b) $\left(2v^2+\dfrac{700}{v}\right)$ litres

Exercise 9.3 *page 77*

1. 70 p

2. 8

3. 7

4. (a) 7
(b) 5
(c) 4

5. 4 litres

6. 110 cm, 120 cm, 130 cm, 140 cm

7. 3

8. 4

9. (a) $2l$ units
(b) 3

10. 3 and 5

11. 32

12. 5 m by 12 m

13. $660\,\text{cm}^3$

14. 9

15. 3

16. 2

17. 8

Exercise 9.4 *page 80*

1. (a) $x\sqrt{x}+x$
(b) $x+3\sqrt{x}$
(c) $x^2\sqrt{x}+3x^3$
(d) $x+2\sqrt{x}+1$
(e) $x-1$
(f) $2x^2+x^2\sqrt{x}$
(g) $x^3+3x\sqrt{x}-10$
(h) $2+x$
(i) $\dfrac{3}{x^2}-\dfrac{1}{x}-10$
(j) $3x^2-5-\dfrac{2}{x^2}$
(k) $1+\dfrac{1}{\sqrt{x}}-\dfrac{6}{x}$
(l) $x-8+\dfrac{16}{x}$

2. (a) $x\sqrt{x}+2\sqrt{x}$
(b) $x^2\sqrt{x}+x\sqrt{x}-1$
(c) $5x\sqrt{x}-3\sqrt{x}-\dfrac{2}{\sqrt{x}}$
(d) $\dfrac{5}{x}-\dfrac{8}{\sqrt{x}}$
(e) $\dfrac{3}{2}+\dfrac{x}{2}$
(f) $\dfrac{5}{2\sqrt{x}}+\dfrac{3\sqrt{x}}{2}$

3. (a) a
(b) b
(c) $3x$
(d) 1
(e) p^5
(f) $\frac{1}{3}a$
(g) $2a^{\frac{3}{2}}+a^3$
(h) $2+b$
(i) $5x^{\frac{3}{2}}-x^{\frac{7}{2}}$
(j) $u^{\frac{1}{2}}+3u^2$

(k) $a^{\frac{1}{2}} + 1$
(l) $p^{-\frac{3}{2}} + 3p^{\frac{1}{2}}$
(m) $y^{\frac{1}{2}} + 2y^{-\frac{1}{2}}$
(n) $s^{\frac{1}{2}} + 3s^{-\frac{1}{2}}$
(o) $2 + t^{\frac{5}{2}}$

4. (a) x^{-2}
(b) $2x^{-1}$
(c) $\frac{1}{3}x^{-2}$
(d) $\frac{2}{5}x^{-1}$
(e) $x^{\frac{1}{2}}$
(f) $x^{\frac{3}{2}}$
(g) $5x^{\frac{3}{2}}$
(h) $x^{\frac{3}{2}}$
(i) $\frac{1}{2}x^{-\frac{1}{2}}$
(j) $4x^{\frac{1}{3}}$
(k) $2x^{\frac{1}{3}}$
(l) $\frac{5}{3}x^{-\frac{2}{3}}$

5. (a) $4x^{\frac{3}{2}} + x$
(b) $2x - 5x^{\frac{1}{2}}$
(c) $7x^{\frac{5}{2}} + 28x^3$
(d) $x + 20x^{\frac{1}{2}} + 100$
(e) $a^{\frac{2}{3}} - 1$
(f) $p^2 - 2p^{\frac{1}{2}}$
(g) $t^2 + 3t^{\frac{3}{2}} - t^{\frac{1}{2}} - 3$
(h) $a^{\frac{2}{3}} - a^{\frac{1}{3}} - 6$

6. (a) $x^2 - 4x + 5$
(b) $3c - 1 + \dfrac{1}{c}$
(c) $\dfrac{2}{z^3} + \dfrac{3}{z^4}$
(d) $\dfrac{5a^2}{2} - 3 + \dfrac{1}{2a^2}$
(e) $4p - 20 + \dfrac{25}{p}$
(f) $m^2 - 4 + \dfrac{4}{m^2}$

7. (a) $x^{\frac{3}{2}} - 4x^{\frac{1}{2}}$
(b) $s^{\frac{5}{2}} + 5s^{\frac{3}{2}} - 1$
(c) $x^{\frac{3}{2}} + 2x^{\frac{1}{2}}$
(d) $3t^{-1} - 4t^{-\frac{1}{2}}$
(e) $3 + \frac{1}{2}x$
(f) $\frac{1}{2}a^{-\frac{1}{2}} + 2a^{\frac{1}{2}}$
(g) $y^{\frac{5}{3}} + 2y^{\frac{2}{3}} - 7y^{-\frac{1}{3}}$

Index